CONTENTS

12 TRANSPORT AND COMPARTMENTALIZATION

An important aspect of this chapter is to understand how proteins are transported between different subcellular compartments. Several of the movies in the *Movie Gallery* section entitled 'Intracellular compartments and trafficking' illustrate these processes very vividly, and the text directs you to them where appropriate. Choose a suitable time, when you are using your computer to view the movies, and relate what you see to the underlying molecular actions and cellular processes described in the text. The chapter opens with a section on the cytoskeleton, a subject that was introduced in S204, Book 3 *The Core of Life,* Vol. II, Section 7.2.

12.1 The cytoskeleton

The cytoskeleton is of fundamental importance to a cell, and we suggested in Chapter 1 that the development of different elements of the cytoskeleton were key steps in the evolution of eukaryotic cells. The cytoskeleton controls cell shape and allows cell movement; it is required for many aspects of intracellular trafficking of vesicles and organelles, and it is involved in cell division. Because of these diverse functions, it is difficult to know where to place it in this course. We discuss the cytoskeleton here, because of its important role in facilitating the movement of vesicles between compartments, but a basic understanding of how the cytoskeleton works is equally important for cell division (Chapter 8) and cell migration (Chapter 16).

☐ What are the three principal elements of the cytoskeleton? What proteins are they made from? Do all cells have all three elements?

⬤ Microtubules are made from tubulin and microfilaments from actin. These are present in all eukaryotic cells. Intermediate filaments are widely distributed, being found in many, but not all, cells of multicellular organisms.

12.1.1 Microtubules and microfilaments

The elements of the cytoskeleton each have their own distribution within the cell. Microtubules extend from the **microtubule organizing centre (MTOC)**, which in animal cells is the centrosome, usually located close to the nucleus. The centrosome consists of two centrioles, short cylinders of microtubules arranged at 90° to each other, which are embedded in a matrix of protein (Figure 12.1). The filamentous network of microtubules extends throughout the cell and has an important role in determining cell shape. As we shall see later, microtubules have plus and minus ends and they tend to extend and shrink from the plus end. The MTOC stabilizes the minus ends of microtubules.

Figure 12.1
Microtubules originate from the microtubule organizing centre, which stabilizes their minus ends.

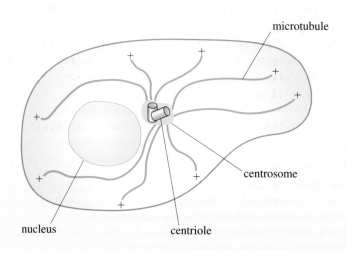

The microfilament network formed from polymerized or fibrous actin (**F-actin**) extends throughout the cytoplasm, but its organization, the length of the filaments and their degree of branching depend very much on the type of cell, its shape, and how it is interacting with the extracellular matrix. The great majority of cell adhesion molecules, which allow a cell to bind to the extracellular matrix, interact inside the cell with microfilaments – usually via adaptor proteins. Indeed, one can view the microfilament network as an *intra*cellular matrix, which links to the *extra*cellular matrix by adhesion molecules. Reorganization of the microfilament network can take place both locally (affecting only part of the cell) and globally (across the whole cell). In particular, cells that are moving rearrange their entire cytoskeleton as the cell becomes polarized, with engagement of microfilaments required for movement of the cell, and microtubules involved in moving the organelles. We shall look into this in much more detail in Chapter 16.

Microfilaments are formed from pools of actin monomers, which associate non-covalently and can grow or shrink or remain stable, and do so continuously. Microtubules are formed from units consisting of a dimer of α-tubulin and β-tubulin. Direct observation of cells shows that microtubules in particular are highly dynamic structures and microfilaments somewhat less so. The dynamic rearrangement of the cytoskeleton requires energy from GTP in the case of microtubules and ATP for microfilaments. Proteins other than actin and tubulin associated with the microtubules and microfilaments are critically important, and determine their overall stability and whether they will grow or shrink. In the case of microfilaments, the proteins can also determine to what extent the network will branch.

12.1.2 Polymerization and depolymerization of actin

Actin is a highly conserved protein. Most organisms have several genes encoding actin; in humans there are six principal isoforms, four of which are found in different types of muscle and the other two (β and γ) in all non-muscle cells. The β and γ cytoskeletal forms differ by just four amino acid residues at the N-terminus. The high level of conservation is probably partly due to the structural requirements of microfilament formation and partly related to the fact that actin interacts with dozens of other highly conserved molecules, so its scope for variation is limited.

The term 'isoform' describes variants of a protein. These may be produced by different genes, or by differential splicing of the mRNA, or be generated by post-translational modifications.

Microfilaments are formed by the polymerization of actin monomers by the formation of multiple non-covalent bonds between adjacent molecules. The monomers form **protofilaments,** strings of monomers linked end-to-end, which align with and wind around another string to form the filament. The helix twists once every 37 nm, and each monomer has the same orientation within the helix (i.e. it is a parallel double helix – see Figure 3.21a).

○ What is the advantage of having non-covalent bonds linking the elements of the protofilaments?

● The advantage of assembling the protofilaments non-covalently is that they can be disassembled and reassembled relatively quickly by loss or addition of monomers to the ends. This allows greater flexibility to the cell than would be provided by a fixed (covalently linked) network.

In solution, filament assembly starts when an actin dimer forms spontaneously. As additional monomers bind to the assembling filament it becomes increasingly stable. This process is called **nucleation** and in solution it is relatively slow. In a cell, however, actin monomers will normally add on to an already formed filament. Alternatively, nucleation can start from sites at the plasma membrane, and attachment of microfilaments to the plasma membrane is important in maintaining cell shape and permitting movement.

The rate of assembly of an actin filament depends on the concentration of the monomers. Once a critical threshold concentration has been exceeded, assembly of the polymeric form is favoured. However, actin monomers add on to one end of a filament much faster than to the other end, and these are referred to as the **plus end** and **minus end** of the filament, respectively. The difference in the rate of growth is due to a difference in the conformational changes that occur to the subunits when they attach to the plus or minus ends of the filament. The converse is also true: when the concentration of monomers falls below a threshold, the filament tends to depolymerize, but it also depolymerizes more rapidly from the plus end. Be careful not to think of the plus end as the place where monomers are always added and the minus end as the place where they are always removed. It is better to think of the plus end as the more active end and the minus end as the less active end. Given the appropriate conditions, filaments do tend to grow from the plus end and shrink from the minus end, but this is not necessarily the case.

So far, we have thought of actin assembly just as an equilibrium reaction, which is dependent on the concentrations of actin monomers and actin polymers. However, actin is an ATPase. Normally, free actin has bound ATP (Figure 12.2). In polymerized actin the ATP is slowly hydrolysed to ADP, so the longer an actin molecule has been in a filament, the more likely it is to be converted into actin-ADP.

Consider the plus end of a microfilament. As it grows, new actin-ATP molecules are added to the plus end faster than the ATP is hydrolysed to ADP, and consequently the tip of the filament contains a cap of actin-ATP molecules, called an ATP cap (or T form). At the minus end, the rate of ATP hydrolysis exceeds the rate at which actin-ATP monomers

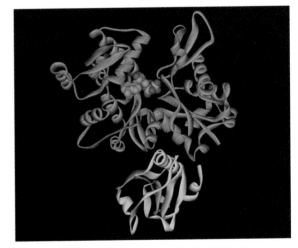

Figure 12.2 Actin (red) normally has ATP (shown as a space-filling model) located in its active site. The molecule shown in blue is gelsolin, which ruptures actin filaments (see later).

are added, and the microfilament consists mainly of actin containing ADP (or the D form). Hydrolysis of ATP to ADP changes the conformation of actin, causing the critical concentration for D actin to be higher than that for T actin.

☐ Consider the situation in which monomeric actin is present at a concentration below the critical concentration of D actin (at the minus end) but above the critical concentration of T actin (at the plus end). Will the plus end grow or shrink? Similarly, will the minus end grow or shrink?

⬤ Because the actin monomer concentration exceeds the critical concentration of T actin, the plus end will grow. However, because the actin monomer concentration is below the critical concentration of D actin, the minus end will shrink.

Because of this, when the actin monomer concentration is between the critical concentrations of T actin and D actin, actin filaments appear to move forwards at their plus end and retract at their minus end. This phenomenon is called **treadmilling**. It requires the presence of ATP, and a similar effect is seen with microtubules. Notice, however, that although the filament appears to move, the individual monomers do not (Figure 12.3).

The basic behaviour of actin is greatly modified by actin-binding proteins. In particular, **capping proteins** attach to the plus end of filaments and prevent addition or loss of further actin monomers. In practice, at any one time, most of the microfilaments in a cell are capped. Capping proteins can also protect the minus end of microfilaments. In muscle cells, where actin fibres are extremely stable, the plus ends of the filaments are capped by CapZ and the minus ends are capped by tropomodulin.

☐ If an actin filament is capped at the plus end and the concentration of actin-ATP is high (above the threshold for polymerization) what will happen to the filament?

⬤ It will grow slowly from its minus end. The plus end is capped, so nothing happens there. The level of actin-ATP is high so the fibre will grow, but because it is at the minus end (low activity), it will do so only slowly.

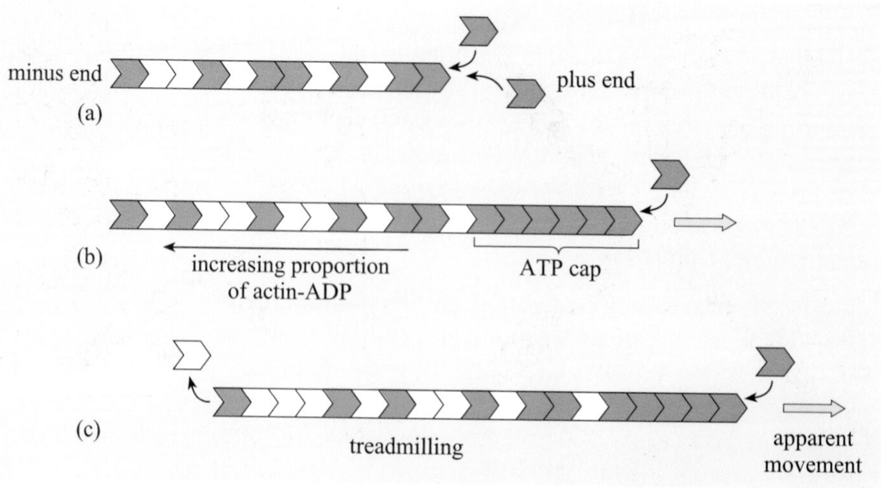

Figure 12.3

Actin polymerization and depolymerization. (a) Actin-ATP monomers (red) join to the plus end of an actin filament. (b) As more monomers join the filament an actin cap is formed in which all the monomers have linked ATP. Behind the cap there is a progressive increase in the proportion of actin-ADP towards the minus end of the filament. (c) At the critical actin concentration the rate of addition of actin-ATP, which predominantly occurs at the plus end, is balanced by loss of monomers (mostly actin-ADP) at the minus end. The filament thus appears to move to the right, even though individual actin monomers remain stationary.

Other proteins can attach to the sides of filaments and promote rupture of the filaments, stabilization of the filaments, bundling of filaments, or branching by the nucleation of new filaments. An example of a filament-cleaving molecule, gelsolin, is shown in Figure 12.2. It is thought that gelsolin takes advantage of random thermally induced flexions of the microfilament, to insert itself between two actin molecules, thus causing the filament to rupture. Gelsolin binds to the plus end of the actin monomer, so that it also acts as a capping protein.

Molecules that cross-link microfilaments into bundles are very important in maintaining the structure of the microfilament network. Different molecules do this in different ways, so creating different types of structure. For example, α-actinin cross-links bundles of filaments in an antiparallel fashion, forming bundles that are relatively open. This enables cellular myosin to intercalate and engage with the actin, forming a **stress fibre**. A quite different type of cross-link is made by filamin, which links the filaments in loose three-dimensional bundles to form a gel-like array. Within a cell, the microfilament network will be organized in different ways in different parts of the cell. Some examples of cross-linking are shown in Figure 12.4. We shall look further at the roles of actin-binding proteins in Chapter 16, when we consider their role in cell movement.

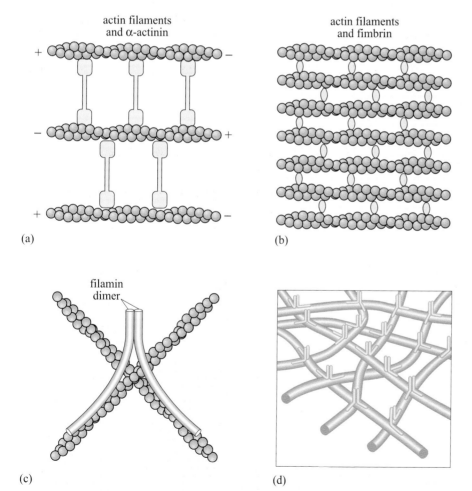

(a)

(b)

(c)

(d)

Figure 12.4
Different types of actin cross-linking. (a) α-Actinin cross-links actin filaments in open antiparallel bundles that allow access to myosin II (see Box 12.1 for myosin nomenclature). This linkage is found in stress fibres. (b) Tight cross-links of parallel filaments, made by fimbrin, produce tight arrays of filaments, such as those found in microvilli. (c) and (d) Filamin dimers produce flexible cross-links that allows the formation of actin gels, which are typically found beneath the plasma membrane and are required for the formation of lamellipodia (see Chapter 16).

actin filaments
and α-actinin

actin filaments
and fimbrin

filamin
dimer

Box 12.1 Myosins

Myosin was originally identified as a component of skeletal muscle, which interacted with actin fibres to generate muscle contraction. Subsequently, this myosin was found to be just one of a large family of molecules present in all eukaryotic cells, including plants, all of which have motor functions and ATPase activity. Skeletal muscle myosin has a long tail and two heads, which contain the catalytic sites, and the basic units become bundled together in fibres. This protein is also found widely in animal cells, and has since been called myosin II – two-headed. The designation was prompted by the discovery of a single-headed myosin in *Acanthamoeba*. Since then numerous single-headed and double-headed cytoplasmic myosins have been discovered. Some are confined to animals, some to plants and some to particular protoctists, but the majority of them are found in all eukaryotes, which indicates that the myosin family of molecules evolved before the divergence of these kingdoms.

12.1.3 Polymerization and depolymerization of tubulin

Polymerization of microtubules is similar in concept to microfilament polymerization, but different in almost every detail. The basic subunit of the microtubule is the tubulin heterodimer, consisting of an α-tubulin and a β-tubulin monomer, which are firmly associated with each other. These assemble end-to-end to form filaments. The overall assembly consists of a ring of 13 such filaments arranged into a microtubule with a plus and a minus end (Figures 12.5 and 12.6). The minus ends of the tubules are stabilized and nucleated within the MTOC by γ-tubulin, which effectively acts as a capping protein. The plus ends of the microtubules are stabilized by other capping molecules or by attachment to organelles.

Both α- and β-tubulin units bind to GTP and act as GTPases. In the presence of GTP and Mg^{2+} ions, polymerization is favoured and the tubules extend from the plus end of the tubule, forming a **GTP cap**. GTP is progressively hydrolysed by the tubulin, and tubulin-GDP dissociates more readily from the tubule than tubulin-GTP. These characteristics lead to the behaviour known as **dynamic instability**. This is the observation that microtubules grow slowly from the plus end and then tend to shrink back suddenly, which can be explained in terms of the reactions above.

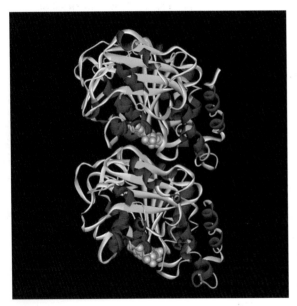

Figure 12.5 A molecular model of the tubulin heterodimer. The α-chain (top) and β-chain (bottom) are structurally very similar, and both bind to one molecule of GTP, shown as a space-filling model in purple; α helix is shown in red, β sheet in blue, and regions lacking secondary structure in green.

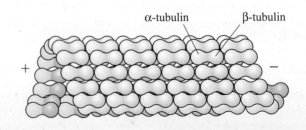

Figure 12.6 Microtubule structure and assembly. Heterodimers of α-tubulin and β-tubulin assemble end-to-end to form filamants, with α-tubulin at the plus end. Thirteen filaments assemble in a ring to form a microtubule.

Consider the plus end of a microtubule. Provided the concentration of tubulin-GTP is above the critical value, the tubule will continue to grow by addition of new tubulin-GTP monomers, and new monomers will be added before the previous ones have had time to hydrolyse their GTP. Consequently a tubule with a GTP cap will grow slowly. If, however, the concentration of tubulin-GTP falls below the threshold, or the conditions for polymerization change, new monomers are added too slowly and tubulin-GDP subunits in the microtubule become exposed. As these dissociate more quickly, the tubule will shrink rapidly, until it is rescued by the addition of new tubulin-GTP dimers (Figure 12.7). Dynamic instability is also seen in actin microfilaments, for the same reasons, but as the rate of growth and retraction of microfilaments is lower than that of microtubules, the effect is less dramatic.

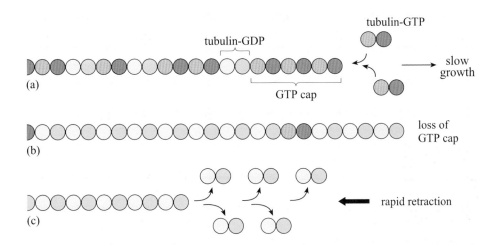

Figure 12.7
Dynamic instability of tubulin. Microtubules grow slowly by the addition of tubulin-GTP to the plus end of the tubule. The GTP cap so formed is relatively stable (a) but if the tubule loses its cap (b) tubulin-GDP is exposed and the tubule retracts rapidly with dissociation of tubulin-GDP heterodimers (c). (Note that, for simplicity, only one of the 13 filaments in the microtubule is shown.)

Although you may have gained the impression that microtubules are very dynamic (and this is certainly evident in the videos of *Dictyostelium* entitled 'Endosome traffic on microtubules'), some microtubules are permanent features of the cell. For example, in neurons, bundles of microtubules extend all the way down axons from the cell body to the nerve terminal. Such bundles are stabilized by cross-linking proteins that bind to the sides of microtubules and are called **microtubule associated proteins (MAPs)**. A MAP called tau, which cross-links bundles of microtubules in axons, has received a lot of attention in recent years, because of the possibility that it is involved in the development of Alzheimer's disease. Tau has multiple tubulin-binding domains that allow it to cross-link microtubules at regular intervals. Thus a nerve axon may contain a bundle of hundreds of regularly spaced, cross-linked microtubules. Cross-linking of the tubules is modulated by the phosphorylation of tau, and one theory proposes that phosphorylation of tau is abnormal in people with Alzheimer's disease. In the case of nerve axons, the bundle of microtubules serves two functions: it acts as a structural element of the cell, giving stability to the axon, but it also acts as a trackway for the transport of vesicles.

◯ Can you see any potential conflict between these two roles?

⬤ If there were too many tau molecules cross-linking and stabilizing the structure of the axon or if they were permanently in place, it might prevent the free passage of vesicles down the microtubules to the nerve terminals.

For this reason, it is thought that the microtubule networks must be subject to some degree of remodelling, in order to facilitate vesicular traffic, but that this is limited by the requirement to maintain axon structure. The 'tau hypothesis' of Alzheimer's disease suggests that the balance of these functions is disturbed so that normal axon structure and neuronal function are impaired.

Numerous other proteins associate with microtubules and perform analogous functions to those proteins that associate with microfilaments, including stabilization, destabilization and cutting. For example, the protein catastrophin pulls apart the plus end of microtubules and promotes dynamic instability.

☐ Can you think of one place in the cell where microtubule-capping proteins would be located during mitosis?

⬤ The centromeres of the chromosomes have capping proteins that attach to microtubules emanating from the mitotic spindles. These serve to stabilize the microtubules during mitosis and to act as attachment points on the chromosomes.

Before going on to look in more detail at the function of microtubules in facilitating intracellular traffic, we shall complete our review of the cytoskeleton by looking at intermediate filaments.

12.1.4 Specialized intermediate filaments

Compared with other cytoskeletal elements, intermediate filaments are more like a fixed scaffolding for the cell. They have a higher tensile strength than microtubules and microfilaments. Consequently they contribute greatly to the overall integrity of the cell and preservation of its shape. Not all eukaryotic cells have cytoskeletal intermediate filaments, and of those that do, each cell type has its own distinct set of intermediate filaments. The intermediate filaments, being cell-type specific, are more related to maintaining the characteristic architecture of each cell type. Intermediate filaments appear to have arisen by gene duplication and diversification on a number of separate occasions from the nuclear lamina (see Chapter 8). One of the largest families is the **keratins** with more than 20 different members in epithelial cells, and about 10 of them are specific to cells that form hair and nails (Table 12.1).

Table 12.1   Examples of intermediate filament proteins.

Intermediate filament	Polypeptides	Expressed in
nuclear	lamins A, B and C	nuclear lamina
epithelial	keratins	epithelial cells
axonal	neurofilament proteins	neurons
vimentin-like	vimentin	many mesenchymal cells
	desmin	muscle
	glial fibrillary acidic protein (GFAP)	astrocytes, some Schwann cells

Intermediate filaments are elongated molecules with a central section of α helix (Figure 12.8a). Two molecules associate to form a coiled-coil dimer (Figure 12.8b), and the dimers associate in a staggered head-to-tail arrangement as shown in Figure 12.8c and d, which further pack together to yield a rope-like filament (Figure 12.8e). This arrangement gives the intermediate filaments their tensile strength. Although intermediate filaments are dynamic structures, much less is known about how they are controlled than microfilaments or microtubules. Cells can change their expression of intermediate filaments in response to activation or a change in requirements. For example, astrocytes are cells in the brain that express the vimentin-like intermediate filament, glial fibrillary acidic protein (GFAP); in resting astrocytes the level of expression is quite low, but this increases greatly when the cells are activated, as occurs in individuals with multiple sclerosis. Activation is associated with an increase in the size and mobility of the astrocytes, which clearly places additional requirements on the cytoskeleton to maintain the structural integrity of the cell.

Figure 12.8
A model of intermediate filament assembly. (a) A monomer with an α-helical region. (b) Two monomers pair up to form a coiled-coil dimer. (c) Two dimers then align side-to-side to form an antiparallel tetramer of four polypeptide chains, slightly offset from each other, which allows (d) alignment with another tetramer. (e) In the final rope-like filament, tetramers are packed together in a helical array. An electron micrograph of intermediate filaments is shown upper left.

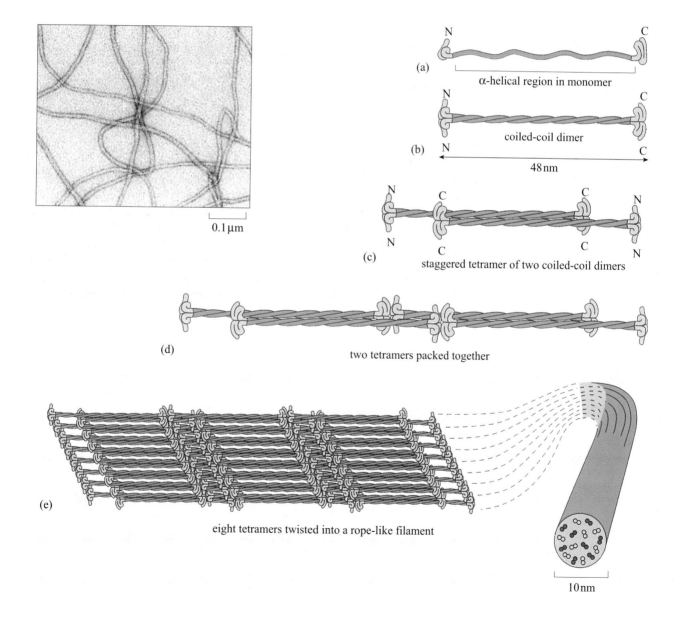

0.1 μm

(a) α-helical region in monomer

(b) coiled-coil dimer

48 nm

(c) staggered tetramer of two coiled-coil dimers

(d) two tetramers packed together

(e) eight tetramers twisted into a rope-like filament

10 nm

Summary of Section 12.1

1   The cytoskeleton is formed of microtubules, microfilaments and intermediate filaments. Microtubules are formed by polymerization of tubulin and microfilaments by polymerization of actin. Assembly and disassembly are faster at the plus end of the filament. Both microtubules and microfilaments can display treadmilling and dynamic instability, in appropriate conditions.

2   Actin is an ATPase, and actin-ATP is less readily dissociated from the ends of microfilaments than actin-ADP. Tubulin is a GTPase and tubulin-GTP is less readily dissociated from microtubules than tubulin-GDP.

3   Capping proteins stabilize the ends of microfilaments and microtubules. The minus ends of microtubules are stabilized and nucleated by the MTOC. The minus ends of microfilaments are nucleated as branches on the actin network or at the plasma membrane.

4   Microtubule associated proteins modulate the formation, stability and disruption of microtubules: an analogous set of proteins acts on microfilaments in a similar way.

5   Intermediate filaments are structural elements found only in some types of cell. They are found in a wide variety of cell-specific types and they have high tensile strength, which helps to maintain cellular integrity.

12.2 Cellular compartments and traffic

This section reminds you of the numerous specialized intracellular compartments of the eukaryotic cell, which were introduced in Chapter 1. Here, we are concerned not just with the variety of cellular compartments, but also with how molecules are moved rapidly and specifically between them in eukaryotic cells.

☐   What are the principal membrane-bound compartments of the cell and the trafficking pathways that connect them?

⬤   Early and late endosomes, lysosomes, peroxisomes, the endoplasmic reticulum, the *cis*, medial and *trans* Golgi network, and secretory vesicles. The pathways of vesicular traffic between these compartments were shown in Figure 1.6. In addition, you may have thought of the nucleus, mitochondrion and chloroplast.

On average, these compartments occupy about half of the volume of the cell. Their associated membranes in a liver cell (hepatocyte), for example, constitute about 50 times more of the total area than the plasma membrane (Table 12.2). The extent of the intracellular compartments varies between cell types, but the contemporary picture of a cell is a labyrinth of membrane-bound intracellular compartments, endosomes and organelles, with a highly developed interconnecting system of transport vesicles.

Vesicular transport is the mechanism by which molecules are ferried in membrane-bound vesicles between the membrane-bound compartments listed above, or between these compartments and the plasma membrane. Small **transport vesicles** pinch off from one compartment, and diffuse, or are more often actively transported, to another compartment, where they fuse and discharge their cargo (Figure 12.9). The size and shape of the vesicles, their cargo, their packaging and

Table 12.2 Relative amounts of membrane in two eukaryotic cells (% of total membrane, by surface area).

Membrane type	Hepatocyte	Pancreatic exocrine cell
plasma membrane	2%	5%
rough ER	35%	60%
smooth ER	16%	<1%
Golgi apparatus	7%	10%
mitochondrial inner membrane	32%	17%
mitochondrial outer membrane	7%	4%
nuclear membrane	0.2%	0.7%
lysosomes, peroxisomes, endosomes, secretory vesicles	<2%	<4%

The volume of the hepatocyte is approximately 5000 μm^3 with 110 000 μm^2 of membrane surface; the volume of the pancreatic cell is 1000 μm^3 with an estimated 13 000 μm^2 of membrane surface. Note that the large amount of rough endoplasmic reticulum (ER) in the pancreatic cell reflects its function of secreting digestive enzymes; the relatively large number of mitochondria in liver cells relates to their high metabolic activity. (Based on Alberts *et al*., 2002.)

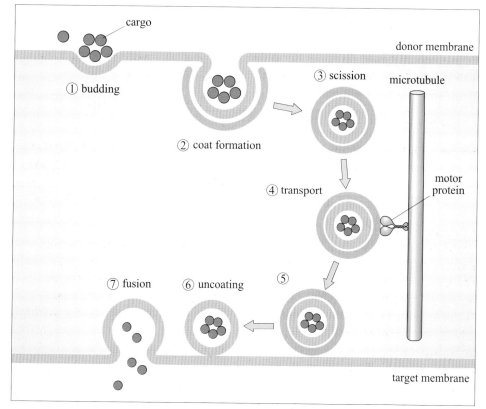

Figure 12.9

Vesicles are coated with proteins such as clathrin or caveolin as they bud from a donor membrane (steps 1 and 2). The vesicle is pinched off (scission) and is transported to its destination, a process that is often directed along the microtubule network by motor proteins (steps 3–5). At the target membrane the protein coat is removed and the vesicle fuses to release its cargo (steps 6 and 7).

their means of transportation vary depending on the trafficking pathway involved. The cargo itself may be soluble within the compartment (e.g. a secreted hormone) or may be associated with membrane proteins. Topologically, the extracellular space, the ER, the Golgi network, the endosomes, secretory vesicles and transport vesicles are all equivalent spaces, each separated from the cytosol by one phospholipid bilayer. For molecules to move from the cytosol into one of these compartments they have to cross one membrane. In this chapter we are concerned only with transport between these topologically equivalent compartments mediated by the budding and fusion of vesicles.

Transport of proteins to the correct cellular compartment depends on **signal sequences** in the polypeptide chain.

☐ You have already encountered signal sequences in the context of protein translation (Chapter 11). What was their function?

⬤ Signal sequences at the N-terminus of newly synthesized polypeptides are recognized by a signal recognition protein, which directs them to sites on the ER, where they are transported into the lumen of the ER as they are translated. The signal sequence is enzymatically removed from most proteins after translation. For multipass membrane proteins, internal stop-transfer and start-transfer signals are required to produce the correct looping across the membrane.

Proteins destined for specific cellular compartments also contain signal sequences, although these may be non-contiguous within the polypeptide chain, and are referred to as **signal patches**. Unlike the N-terminal signal sequences, signal patches are integral to the final protein and are not cleaved off. The signal patches serve to sort the proteins for their appropriate compartment and/or ensure that they remain in that compartment. Proteins called **sorting receptors** recognize the signal patches and group the proteins in appropriate vesicles for transport. We shall start by looking at how particular proteins are selectively localized in particular compartments.

12.2.1 Traffic in the endoplasmic reticulum and the Golgi network

The ER extends as a network of membranous tubes and sheets throughout the cytoplasm and is the site of synthesis of proteins ultimately destined for the Golgi apparatus, endosomes, lysosomes, the plasma membrane, secretory vesicles and beyond. In animal cells, the Golgi apparatus is usually a single structure located near the nucleus of the cell, consisting of between four and ten flattened cisternae, which are designated the *cis*, medial or *trans* Golgi network, depending on their position within the stack. The *cis* Golgi comprises the cisternae that receive transport vesicles from the ER, and the *trans* Golgi sorts proteins for onward delivery to the plasma membrane, endosomes, etc. The organization of the Golgi apparatus depends on the integrity of the microtubule network.

The movie entitled 'The endosomal network' demonstrates the labyrinthine nature of the ER and shows the highly active structure of this compartment, which undergoes continuous remodelling. The movie 'ER to Golgi transport' demonstrates the movement of a protein in transport vesicles from the ER towards the Golgi network.

Only proteins that are correctly folded are released from the ER and transported to the *cis* Golgi where they are further modified and processed (see Figure 11.26). Protein synthesis has numerous quality-control steps of this type, and this extends to protein localization. Vesicles carrying proteins move between the ER and the *cis*, medial and *trans* faces of the Golgi apparatus *in both directions* (see Figure 12.16). Primarily, these will be proteins destined for onward delivery to downstream compartments, such as secretory vesicles, but some proteins are required in the Golgi itself and these have the appropriate signal patches to ensure they are retained in this compartment.

○ Give some examples of proteins that are normally located and function in the ER or the Golgi apparatus.

● The molecular chaperones calnexin and calreticulin (see Figure 11.27) are required in the ER. The transglycosidases, which glycosylate proteins, function in the Golgi (Chapters 3 and 11). You can also infer that proteins responsible for sorting must be located in their own specific compartments.

However, there is always some degree of error in biological systems, so that proteins intended to function in the ER will occasionally be carried to the Golgi apparatus. A reverse transport system, or **ER retrieval pathway**, ensures that they are returned to their correct compartment. Signal sequences at the C-terminus of membrane-bound ER proteins and different sequences in soluble ER proteins control their localization, as described in Section 12.3.4.

Proteins that are destined for endosomal compartments, the plasma membrane or secretion are carried in vesicles that bud from the *trans* Golgi. The pH in the ER is neutral, but as proteins move from the *cis* to the *trans* Golgi they are exposed to increasingly acidic conditions. The pH affects the activity of the enzymes in the different compartments and may regulate how well proteins bind to sorting receptors in each compartment. Beyond the Golgi, specialized endosomal compartments in some cells have even lower pH values, maintained by proton pumps. One of the key functions of protein sorting is to move molecules to a compartment where they are in an appropriate environment to function, or where they can be stored.

12.2.2 Sorting for the basolateral and apical zones of the plasma membrane

Many cells are permanently polarized, and this means that surface proteins are selectively localized to different areas of the plasma membrane, depending on their function. For example, endothelial cells have adhesion molecules on the surface that contacts the basal lamina, but receptors that take up molecules from the blood (e.g. the transferrin receptor – see below) are located on the surface of the cell that is in contact with the blood. Cell surface molecules can normally diffuse laterally within the plane of the membrane, although they may be excluded from, or concentrated in, particular areas such as lipid rafts. However, for some cells, such as the epithelial cells in the gut, the plasma membrane is divided into two distinct zones termed the **basolateral** and **apical domains**, which are separated from each other by a belt of continuous tight junctions around the cell. This structure severely restricts the free diffusion of molecules through the extracellular spaces between neighbouring cells, and is seen in a number of other tissues.

Basal membranes are now more often called basal laminae, to emphasize the fact that they are not phospholipid bilayers, but sheets of extracellular matrix.

For example, the endothelial cells in the blood vessels in the brain have a ring of continuous tight junctions, which forms a barrier betweeen the blood and the brain tissue that contributes to the so-called blood–brain barrier. The tight junctions also prevent the lateral diffusion of proteins and lipids within the plasma membrane from one zone to another.

○ Predict what requirement this places on the transport systems within cells that have such differentiated zones of the plasma membrane.

● Proteins and lipids must be directed to either the basolateral or the apical zones by different routes.

Proteins destined for these zones are initially sorted in the Golgi apparatus and packaged in different vesicles before being directed to the appropriate zone of the membrane (Figure 12.10). Sorting signals have been identified in the C-terminus of proteins destined for the basolateral membrane, which ensure that the proteins reach the correct zone and are returned there should they be internalized by endocytosis.

> The two movies entitled 'Post-Golgi sorting I' and 'Post-Golgi sorting II' show how proteins destined for the apical and basolateral membranes of a cell are sorted in the *trans* Golgi network into separate vesicles.

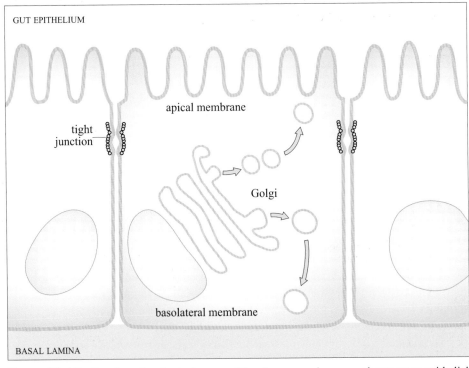

Figure 12.10   Basolateral and apical zones of the plasma membrane are shown on an epithelial cell, lining the lumen of the gut. Tight junctions between cells separate the two zones of the membrane. Proteins intended for each zone are sorted into separate vesicles at the *trans* Golgi network.

12.2.3 Exocytosis and the secretory pathways

Exocytosis is the process by which molecules are released to the outside of the cell. This includes the release of proteins to the plasma membrane and the release of secreted molecules into the extracellular fluid. All eukaryotic cells need a system to transport molecules to their plasma membrane, and many cells secrete proteins into the extracellular environment. In addition, cells in multicellular organisms communicate with each other via a variety of signalling molecules, which are released in appropriate circumstances. Intercellular signalling is effected by hormones, cytokines and other small signalling molecules that are released from **secretory vesicles**. Even within the nervous system, which we think of as an electrochemical signalling network, the transmission of a signal from one cell to another occurs by the secretion of neurotransmitters into the synaptic cleft, in response to the arrival of an action potential.

Biologists distinguish two basic types of exocytosis. **Constitutive secretion** is carried out by all cells and serves to transfer molecules from the Golgi network to the outer surface of the cell. It is the default pathway for most molecules bound for the plasma membrane. **Regulated secretion** occurs in response to specific conditions, signals or biochemical triggers, and is the process underlying the release of cytokines, hormones, neurotransmitters and other small signalling molecules, such as histamine (Figure 12.11). (Although secretion usually implies the release of soluble molecules, these pathways also transfer membrane-associated molecules to the cell surface.) One should note in passing that constitutive secretion is not an unregulated process; it is just that the rate of release of the molecules to the cell surface depends on their rate of production, which is regulated by transcription and translation, i.e. at an earlier stage in the pathway.

Cytokines are soluble extracellular molecules that act locally on cells, whereas hormones are carried by the bloodstream to distant cells.

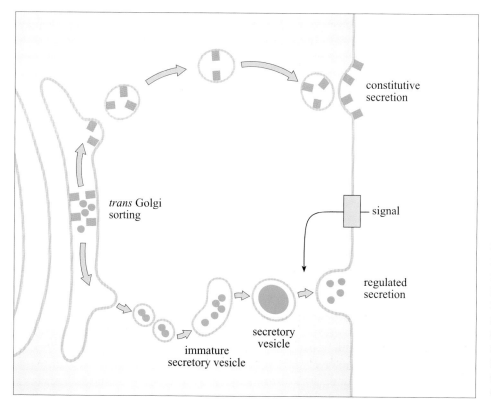

Figure 12.11

Secretory pathways. Molecules in the *trans* Golgi network are sorted into secretory vesicles either for regulated secretion if they contain appropriate signal sequences or for constitutive secretion if they do not. Proteins for regulated secretion are first assembled in immature vesicles, which mature into secretory vesicles located near the plasma membrane. Regulated secretion is typically controlled by external signals transduced via cell surface receptors. This example shows a constitutively secreted, membrane-bound molecule and a soluble, secreted molecule, but either type of molecule can be directed down either pathway.

Figure labels: constitutive secretion; *trans* Golgi sorting; signal; regulated secretion; secretory vesicle; immature secretory vesicle

○ Identify the fundamental difference between constitutive and regulated secretion, in terms of their function within an organism and the ways in which this is regulated.

● Constitutive secretion is a process concerned with the function of the individual cell, and is therefore primarily regulated by the mechanisms of protein production, which are intrinsic to the cell. Regulated secretion is related to a cell's interactions with other cells and therefore is responsive to external stimuli.

In mammals, the release of insulin by β cells of the pancreatic islets of Langerhans, in response to variations in blood glucose concentration, is a good example of regulated secretion. Insulin is retained in secretory vesicles that are triggered to fuse with the plasma membrane in response to a rise in intracellular Ca^{2+} concentration. Briefly, the series of interactions that links the concentration of blood glucose to the rate of insulin secretion is as follows:

1   A rise in blood glucose causes the ATP : ADP ratio in the β cell to rise, which closes a K^+ channel in the plasma membrane.

2   The resulting change in the β cell's membrane potential opens a Ca^{2+} channel, causing a rise in intracellular Ca^{2+} concentration and the secretion of insulin.

The way in which Ca^{2+} controls the fusion of vesicles with the plasma membrane is discussed in Section 12.7.1, in relation to the release of neurotransmitters from synaptic vesicles.

> The movies entitled 'Exocytosis I' and 'Exocytosis II' use the technique of evanescent wave micrography to demonstrate how proteins are transported to the cell surface to be released by exocytosis.

12.2.4 The endocytic pathways and lysosomes

Endocytosis is the process by which cells internalize molecules from the outside, and it includes **pinocytosis**, the uptake of small soluble molecules in vesicles, and **phagocytosis**, the internalization of large insoluble particles. These are two ends of a spectrum as seen microscopically, but the receptors, the subsequent intracellular trafficking pathways and the fate of the internalized molecules, vary depending on the cell type and its functions. The endocytic pathway comprises two distinct kinds of endosome, **early endosomes** and **late endosomes**. Material taken up by endocytosis passes from the early endosomes to the late endosomes and from there may intersect with trafficking pathways from the Golgi apparatus, or may be directed to lysosomes or to the Golgi. The exact pathway depends on the cell and the material that has been internalized.

It is important to distinguish **receptor-mediated endocytosis** from the general non-specific endocytic uptake of material from the medium. For example, transferrin (the iron transport molecule present in blood plasma) is taken up after binding to a transferrin receptor, which is expressed on a variety of cells. The receptor with its bound transferrin is internalized by budding of vesicles from the plasma membrane, and these fuse with endosomes. In the acidic environment of the endosome, iron dissociates from transferrin to give apotransferrin, which is then recycled back to the plasma membrane to collect more iron (Figure 12.12). The receptor is similarly recycled.

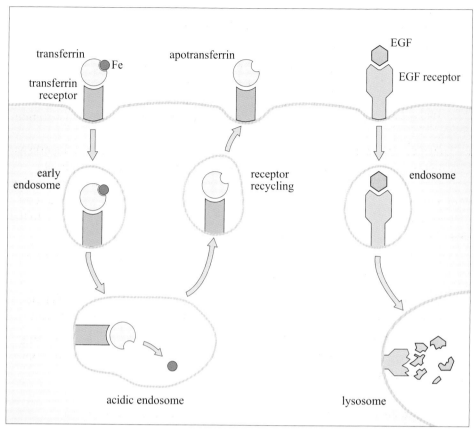

Figure 12.12 Pathways of endocytosis. Transferrin with a bound iron molecule binds to the transferrin receptor on the plasma membrane and is internalized. Within an acidic endosome, iron is released from transferrin (now designated apotransferrin) and the apotransferrin and the receptor are recycled to the cell membrane. A different pathway is illustrated by the EGF receptor, which is internalized via endosomal compartments and is then directed to lysosomes for degradation.

A different pathway is taken by receptors such as the EGF (epidermal growth factor) receptor, which together with its ligand moves from an early endosomal compartment to a late endosome and from there to lysosomes for degradation (Figure 12.12). This is a mechanism for reducing the number of receptors on the cell surface, a process that is controlled, in many cases, by the phosphorylation of the receptors, as described in Chapter 13.

Notice that the transferrin receptor can be used many times to take up iron, whereas the EGF receptor has a single function – signalling cell division. Once the cell has received the appropriate signal then the EGF receptor is no longer required (at least for a while) and, by degrading the receptor, the cell becomes less sensitive to further signals.

The movies 'Endocytosis' and 'Segregation of vesicles II' demonstrate how molecules such as transferrin are endocytosed, and that endosomal compartments generally remain distinct from those of the secretory pathways. Note that this is not always true and in some cells the secretory and endocytic pathways may intersect – see for example Section 12.6.5.

12.2.5 Transcytosis

The components of the endocytotic pathways also function to transfer material within a cell. In vertebrates, most cells depend on nutrients from the blood even though they are not in direct contact with the blood. Diffusion of molecules from the blood to the tissues would in many cases be just too slow. **Transcytosis** is the transfer of molecules across cells from one side to the other, a process that entails endocytosis, vesicular transfer and exocytosis, and which speeds the bulk movement of molecules through tissues. In some cases, transcytosis is receptor-mediated, and is often carried out by vesicles called **caveolae**, which are distinct from those involved in endocytosis and exocytosis as described above.

○   Which cells in a vertebrate would you expect to contain abundant caveolae?

●   The endothelial cells that line blood vessels have large numbers of caveolae, which are particularly evident in clusters near the plasma membrane.

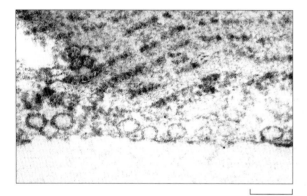

Figure 12.13 shows a cluster of caveolae adjoining the membrane of an endothelial cell from lung.

Receptor-mediated transcytosis can also carry specific molecules across cells. For example, in humans and some other mammals, antibodies are transported across the placental cells that form the interface between the maternal and fetal circulation. The transported maternal antibodies protect the fetus in utero and in neonatal life. A related process occurs in the gut epithelial cells of some neonatal animals, which have receptors that transfer antibodies from maternal milk intact across the gut epithelium and into the tissues, to protect the neonatal animal. The reverse process occurs in the gut of adult mammals that have a system for transferring a different type of antibody (IgA) from the tissues into the lumen of the gut, to protect against infection (Figure 12.14).

100 nm

Figure 12.13   Electron micrograph of lung endothelium showing caveolae, small goblet-shaped vesicles, which are prominent near the cell membrane.

Figure 12.14
Receptor-mediated transcytosis. The antibody IgA is transported across an epithelial cell from the submucosal tissue side to the lumen of the mucosal epithelium. The antibody first binds to a poly-Ig receptor and is then transferred from the basolateral to the apical zone of the membrane, where the receptor is cleaved, to release the antibody with a segment of the receptor, called 'secretory component', still bound.

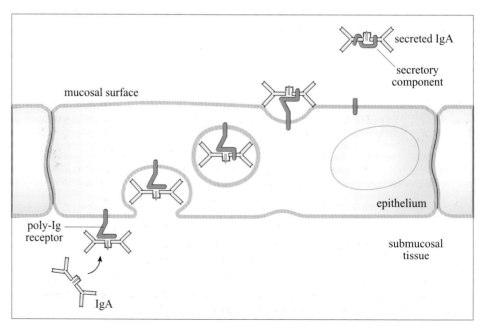

The role of antibodies in protection against infection is extensively discussed in S320, Book 3 *Immunology*.

Transcytosis may also be important in moving proteins involved in differentiation and body pattern development. An interesting example is the Wg protein produced in a row of cells at the posterior of each segment of *Drosophila*, which is distributed throughout the segments to control the normal development of elements of the segment (mutations of the *Wg* gene which produces the Wg protein may result in a wingless phenotype). In this example, transcytosis distributes the protein laterally in the plane of the polarized epidermal epithelium. This differs from the basal–apical transcytosis of IgA, described above.

Summary of Section 12.2

1   Eukaryotic cells contain numerous distinct types of membrane-bound compartment. Transport vesicles move proteins and other molecules between the compartments.

2   Proteins contain signalling sequences or patches that specify their destination compartment.

3   Proteins destined for lysosomes, secretion or the plasma membrane are synthesized in the ER, transported to the *cis* Golgi, modified in the Golgi apparatus, and sorted and packaged in vesicles at the *trans* Golgi for onward delivery to endosomes or secretory vesicles. The pH and the proteins in each compartment of the ER and Golgi are different. Misplaced proteins are returned to the ER. Proteins are sent from the Golgi to the basolateral and apical regions of the plasma membrane (if separate) in different vesicles.

4   Molecules are internalized either by non-specific or receptor-mediated systems. Receptors may be recycled to the plasma membrane or routed for breakdown in lysosomes, depending on the receptor and the requirements of the cell.

5   Molecules can be transported across cells either in solution in a non-specific manner, or by receptor-mediated mechanisms.

12.3 Trafficking vesicles

In the following sections, we shall describe the sequential steps involved in the movement of vesicles from one membrane to another (see Figure 12.9). Some of these steps are quite well defined, but for others there are gaps in our knowledge. Although we have emphasized the importance of proteins as cargo, vesicles also transfer membrane lipids between compartments, and so are important in maintaining the lipid composition and relative proportions of membrane lipids between different compartments, a process that is much less well understood.

The first stage of vesicular transport is the production of the transport vesicles. Vesicle formation requires deformation of the lipid bilayer, forming a goblet-shaped invagination of the membrane that will eventually be pinched off to form the vesicle, a process called **budding**. The induction of membrane curvature required for vesicle formation is an energy-dependent process mediated by proteins such as epsins, which are required specifically for budding. When a vesicle is generated, it carries proteins that were resident in that stretch of membrane as well as soluble molecules. Fusion of the vesicle with a target membrane is essentially a reversal of the process by which it originates. The proteins that direct the targeting of the vesicle to the correct cellular location also mediate fusion, and in some systems regulate the precise time at which fusion occurs.

☐ We emphasized the importance of signal sequences in proteins, which ensure they are packaged in the right vesicles. What other proteins are needed to ensure they reach their correct destination?

⬤ To deliver their cargo to the right compartment, the transport vesicles must be able to recognize and fuse with the correct target membrane. This means that they need to carry molecules that address them to the target membrane.

Some vesicles have a coat of proteins surrounding their membrane and are therefore called **coated vesicles**. The coat is acquired as the vesicle buds from the donor membrane and is shed before the vesicle fuses with the target membrane (see Figure 12.9). One purpose of the coat is to enable the type of vesicle to be identified, so that is directed to the appropriate target membrane; it may also be involved in the selection of cargo to be transported.

Figure 12.15 shows in more detail how the vesicular coat is assembled, a process that involves small G proteins (see Section 3.6.2). Budding is initiated by recruitment of small G proteins to a region of membrane curvature, which then assemble the complex of coat proteins and adaptor proteins, which link the coat to molecules in the membrane. The G proteins exchange GDP for GTP, converting into the active form, which can then insert spontaneously into lipid bilayers, by means of a hydrophobic tail. It seems that the G protein activity and ability to recycle is controlled by hydrolysis of GTP. The G proteins associate with proteins in the membrane, and there is some evidence that they may interact with receptors in the donor membrane. In other words, the function of these G proteins is to provide the binding sites at which coat proteins can assemble. Examples of such G proteins and the types of coated vesicle they associate with are shown in Table 12.3.

Three types of different coat protein involved in vesicular transport have been particularly well studied (Table 12.3 and Figure 12.16).

▶ Endocytic and secretory vesicles have **clathrin** as the most prominent protein in their coats and they are called **clathrin-coated vesicles**.

▶ The vesicles involved in transport between Golgi cisternae are called **COPI-coated vesicles** (COPI is an acronym for **CO**at **P**rotein **I** (roman one).)

▶ The vesicles involved in trafficking from the ER to the *cis* Golgi have a different coat (**COPII**), and are called **COPII-coated vesicles**.

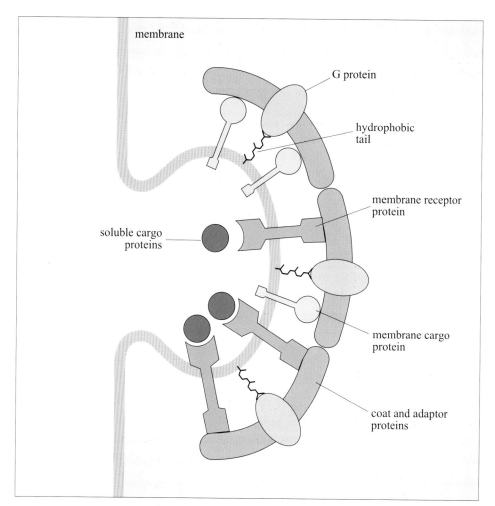

membrane

G protein

hydrophobic tail

membrane receptor protein

soluble cargo proteins

membrane cargo protein

coat and adaptor proteins

Figure 12.15
Assembly of a coated vesicle. Small membrane-bound G proteins, attached to the membrane, recruit coat proteins and adaptor proteins. The cargo may be a soluble molecule that binds to membrane receptors that are attached to adaptors within the coat. Alternatively, the cargo may be a membrane protein that is carried in the membrane of the vesicle. (Note that the lipid tail of the G proteins would be fully buried in the membrane.)

Table 12.3 Protein and G protein components of coated vesicles.

Vesicle	Coat and adaptor proteins	Small G protein	Transport step
clathrin	clathrin heavy and light chains, AP2	ARF	plasma membrane → endosome
	clathrin heavy and light chains, AP1	ARF	Golgi → endosome
	clathrin heavy and light chains, AP3	ARF	Golgi → lysosome
COPI	COP α, β, β', γ, δ, ε, ζ	ARF	Golgi → ER; between Golgi cisternae
COPII	Sec23/Sec24 complex; Sec13/Sec31 complex; Sec1β	Sar1	ER → Golgi

Each of the coat proteins (clathrin, COPI and COPII) is a complex of subunits, sometimes referred to as a coatamer. ARF is an acronym for ADP ribosylation factor. AP = adaptor protein.

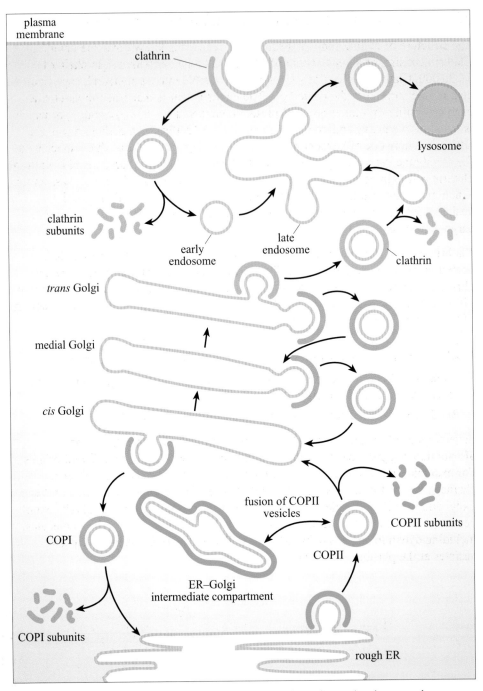

Figure 12.16   Clathrin-coated vesicles are involved in the endosomal pathways and in transport of proteins from the *trans* Golgi network. COPI-coated vesicles are involved in retrograde transport from the *trans* Golgi back through the Golgi cisternae to the ER. COPII-coated vesicles are required for transport from the ER to the *cis* Golgi.

12.3.1 Formation of clathrin and COP-coated vesicles

The structure of clathrin and clathrin-coated vesicles is known in some detail. Clathrin consists of a heavy chain of M_r 180 000 together with a light chain of M_r 35 000. Clathrin molecules successively assemble into a polyhedral, cage-like coat on the surface of the coated pit. The clathrin coat is made of sub-assemblies, each consisting of a three-pronged protein complex, a triskelion, each leg of which is made of one heavy and one light chain (Figure 12.17a). The triskelion forms a lattice-like network of hexagons and pentagons (Figure 12.17b), which attaches to the membrane via an **adaptor protein** (**AP**) complex. Adaptor proteins bind both to clathrin and to integral membrane proteins of the vesicle and stimulate its assembly. Much more importantly, by binding to the molecules in the membrane of the vesicle, adaptor proteins appear to be responsible for recognizing the appropriate cargo molecules.

Clathrin concentrates in specific areas of the plasma membrane, forming clathrin-coated membrane invaginations, called **clathrin-coated pits**. Cell surface receptors cluster in the pits, and then through a series of highly regulated steps the pits pinch off to form clathrin-coated vesicles (Figure 12.18). Although the detail and ordering of the process is not fully defined, the main steps are:

◗ Recruitment of the G-protein ARF (ADP-ribosylation factor-binding protein), adaptor proteins and clathrin to defined sites on the plasma membrane;

◗ Assembly of clathrin, formation of clathrin-coated pits and cargo recruitment, specified by adaptor proteins;

◗ Budding and detachment of the nascent clathrin-coated vesicles.

Several types of adaptor protein have been characterized (Table 12.3); their distribution suggests that they correspond to coated vesicles with different origins. For example, the AP2 adaptor, found on coated pits at the plasma membrane, characterizes endocytic vesicles. The AP1 adaptor is found on coated pits of the Golgi and identifies vesicles that are targeted to endosomes. The role of AP3 is not yet fully understood. In addition to clathrin and APs, a number of other molecules, including dynamin and epsin, have been implicated in the formation of coated vesicles at the plasma membrane.

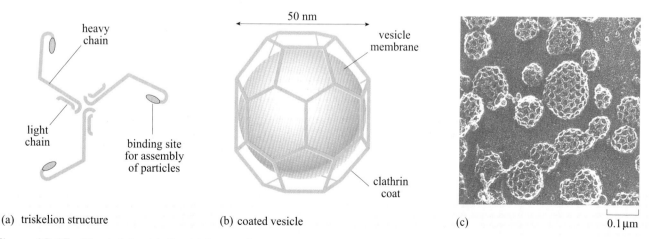

(a) triskelion structure   (b) coated vesicle   (c)

Figure 12.17   The clathrin triskelion (a) forms a skeleton of hexagons and pentagons around the coated vesicle (b). (c) Scanning electron micrograph of clathrin-coated vesicles.

Within the past few years a novel family of proteins has been identified as molecules that also interact directly with ARF, clathrin and vesicle cargo. These proteins appear to be ARF-dependent clathrin adaptors that facilitate specific membrane trafficking events, such as cargo sorting and vesicle formation at the *trans* Golgi network. They are named GGA proteins (Golgi-localized, gamma-ear containing, ADP-ribosylation factor-binding proteins). GGA proteins are cytosolic monomeric proteins containing four distinct domains, one of which, the 'hinge' domain, contains one or more clathrin-binding sites (Figure 12.19).

As mentioned above, the deformation and scission of the vesicle is energy-dependent, and a family of proteins called **epsins** appear to be involved in this process. Epsin-1 induces membrane curvature and promotes the polymerization of clathrin. Another protein, AP180, appears to limit the vesicle size, and vesicle scission is mediated by another protein, **dynamin**, a GTPase of M_r 100 000 that collaborates with the coat proteins to induce budding of clathrin-coated vesicles. Dynamin self-assembles into rings and forms collars at the neck of invaginated coated pits. These collars constrict the neck of the coated pits, which are then severed by hydrolysis of GTP (Figure 12.20).

Although the mechanisms are broadly similar, different coat structures seem to be involved in different transport steps. Hence, COPI-coated vesicles shuttle molecules from exit sites on the *cis* Golgi complex towards the ER, while COPII-coated vesicles shuttle them from the ER towards the Golgi. This type of spatial organization of transport maintains an asymmetric intracellular distribution

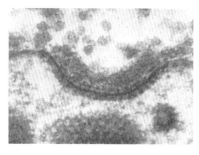
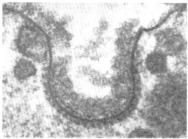
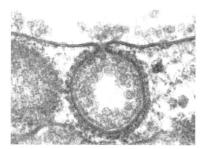
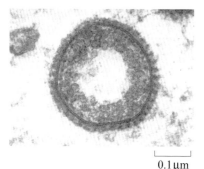

0.1 μm

Figure 12.18
Transmission electron micrographs demonstrating successive stages in the progression from a clathrin-coated pit to a clathrin-coated vesicle.

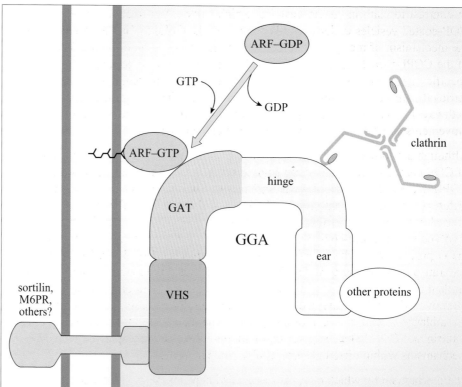

Figure 12.19   GGA proteins have been shown to act as multifunctional adaptors at the *trans* Golgi network. They bind to ARF–GTP and also bind to sorting proteins (sortilin and mannose 6-phosphate receptor, M6PR), clathrin and possibly other molecules. GGA proteins have four distinct domains, labelled VHS, GAT, hinge and ear.

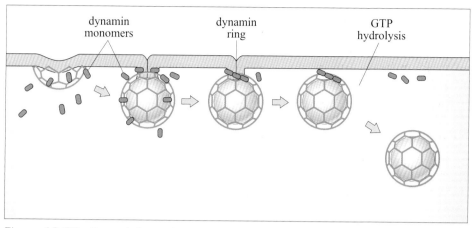

Figure 12.20 Dynamin is recruited by vesicle-associated proteins and forms rings around the neck of the invagination. GTP hydrolysis leads to constriction of the dynamin ring followed by pinching off of the vesicle.

of different proteins, such as enzymes, and permits the transport of newly synthesized proteins to the plasma membrane. For example, in the Golgi network, modifying enzymes are spread in a unique gradient-like distribution across several discontinuous membrane-bound compartments that collectively make up the Golgi stack; in the ER, enzymes mediating post-translational modifications of proteins either coexist in a continuous membrane or are segregated spatially into ER subregions.

In contrast to clathrin-coated vesicles, which carry rather specific proteins, COP-coated vesicles undertake bulk flow from the Golgi to the ER and back, and the mechanism of recognizing the protein cargo seems to be different. The cargo of the COPI-coated vesicles is selected by binding of the cargo molecules to specific membrane receptors. COPI-coated vesicles are involved in the ER retrieval pathway; thus, this pathway is often called the retrograde transport pathway. In contrast, the transport from the ER to the Golgi, achieved by movements of COPII-coated vesicles, is called anterograde.

Although the formation of clathrin-coated vesicles is similar in principle to that of COP-coated vesicles, there are some differences in the detail. Formation of COPII-coated vesicles requires the ordered assembly of the coat from many different cytoplasmic components (Table 12.3), but the formation of the prebudding complex as well as severance of the neck differs from the processes involved with clathrin-coated vesicles. Budding of COPII vesicles is initiated by the G protein Sar1, which recruits two further proteins, Sec23 and Sec24, to generate a pre-budding complex. The elongated COPII prebudding complex is in marked contrast to the open honeycomb-like clathrin-coated prebudding complex. Moreover, the architecture and folding of the COPII-coat components bears no resemblance to clathrin adaptor complexes. These structural differences between clathrin and COPII coats suggest that budding might be accomplished by distinct mechanisms within different intracellular compartments.

The mechanism by which cargo is recognized depends on both lumenal and transmembrane proteins of the vesicles as well as the receptors that reside in the Golgi complex. For example, COPI vesicles select proteins containing a dilysine motif near their C-terminus, in the form of -KKXX-COOH, where K is lysine and X is any amino acid residue.

After vesicle scission and transport to the target membrane, the delivery of the cargo occurs by vesicle fusion with the target membrane. The coat components would be an obstacle to membrane fusion, so they must be removed. Shedding of the coat is regulated by hydrolysis of GTP in ARF–GTP (Figure 12.21). Studies on transport in nerve terminals have shown that proteins including ARF, dynamin and some epsins, which are phosphorylated in resting nerve terminals, become coordinately dephosphorylated following nerve terminal stimulation. This dephosphorylation is believed to promote recycling of the components of the clathrin- and COP-coated vesicles (Figure 12.22).

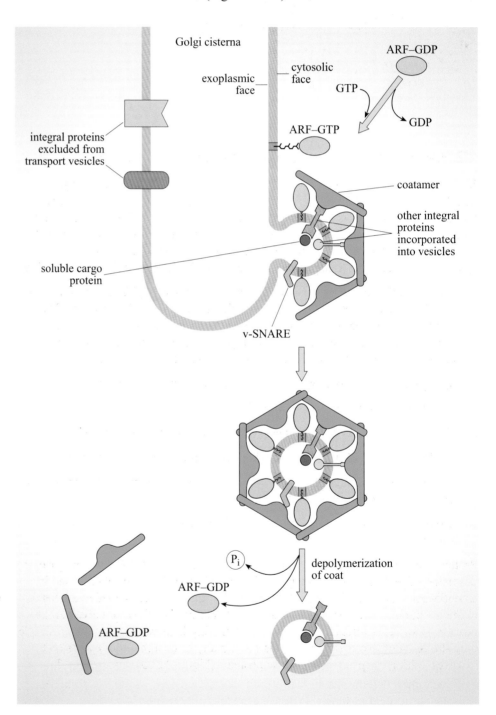

Figure 12.21
Assembly of vesicles at the Golgi cisternae. ARF–GTP binds to the membrane of the cisternae and recruits coat proteins and vesicle-targeted proteins carrying soluble cargo molecules (other proteins are excluded from the vesicle). v-SNARE molecules, which are required for fusion with the target membrane, are also incorporated into the vesicle membrane. The vesicle buds off and moves towards the target membrane, where hydrolysis of GTP in ARF–GTP leads to depolymerization of the coat.

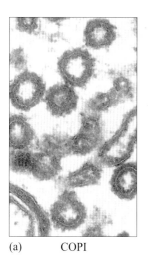 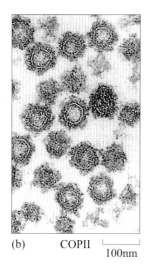

(a) COPI (b) COPII

100nm

Figure 12.22
Electron micrographs showing COPI- and COPII-coated vesicles.

12.3.2 Fusion of vesicles with the target membrane

In this section, we shall look at how vesicles fuse with the appropriate target membrane. The targeting of different classes of transport vesicles to their distinct membrane destinations is essential in maintaining the distinct characteristics of the various eukaryotic organelles. Because coat proteins, such as clathrin, are found in different trafficking pathways, it follows that other proteins in the coat must specify the direction of transport of a particular vesicle and its ultimate destination.

What controls the specificity of vesicle targeting and docking? The interaction and fusion of the membranes of the vesicle and the target is a multistage event. The first stage is membrane recognition. The next step is a loose interaction called **tethering**. The subsequent interaction brings the opposing membranes much closer to each other and is called **docking**. Docking leads to membrane fusion.

Thus, targeting specificity might be thought of as a series of events that includes:

1 specification of the vesicle delivery site;

2 the recruitment of components capable of initiating vesicle 'capture';

3 the formation of a bridge between the vesicle and the target membrane;

4 conformational change that allows the vesicle and target membrane proteins to come close enough to interact;

5 dissociation of the tethering proteins, to free them for another round of transport.

Proteins involved in the tethering processes are called **TRAPPs (transport protein particles)**. The TRAPP complex ($M_r \sim 1\,100\,000$) is made of 10 subunits and is essential for vesicle trafficking. TRAPP proteins are highly conserved and integral to the membrane. The discovery of different tethering complexes involved in the process of vesicle trafficking suggests that tethering is more complex than a simple cross-bridging of two membranes. It is more likely to be a series of events that involves pairing of specific membrane proteins (Figure 12.23).

Figure 12.23

A model for vesicle docking, based on transport from the ER to the Golgi in yeast. A TRAPP complex on the target membrane recruits a GTPase of the Rab family. A tethering protein captures the transport vesicle by linking it to the TRAPP/Rab–GTP complex. Binding causes the protein that blocks t-SNARE binding (pale green) to be released from the t-SNARE, which is then free to bind to the v-SNARE on the vesicle. Several additional proteins are thought to be involved in this scheme, with variations between species and trafficking pathways.

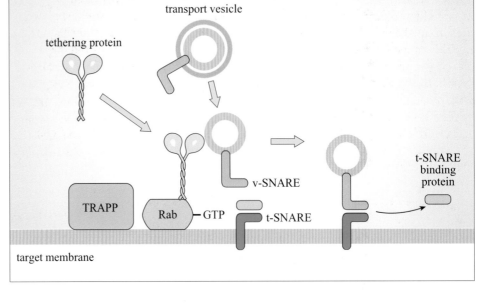

SNAREs may be categorized according to their amino acid sequence as well as by the v/t nomenclature. Components involved in the fusion between the donor membrane of the vesicle and the target membrane were identified because of their interactions with a soluble ATPase called NSF, identified by its sensitivity to NEM (*N*-ethylmaleimide). Thus SNARE is an acronym for Soluble NEM-sensitive factor Attachment protein REceptors.

Two families of integral membrane proteins 'tag' the membrane of the target organelle and the vesicle. Members of one family are known as vesicle **SNAREs** (v-SNAREs) and members of the other family are known as target SNAREs (t-SNAREs).

What are SNAREs and how is SNARE function studied? Most of the discoveries on SNARE function and their interactions in membrane trafficking have been made through studies of the proteins that attach to the membrane of synaptic vesicles (Box 12.2). We shall use this example to illustrate how SNAREs function.

Box 12.2   Synaptic vesicles

Synaptic vesicles are secretory vesicles containing neurotransmitters that are found clustered near the plasma membrane at the terminals of a nerve axon. These vesicles fuse with specialized areas of the plasma membrane called 'active zones', releasing the neurotransmitter into the extracellular space (the synaptic cleft). This process is the basis of signal transmission between nerves and it depends on the v/t SNARE complex.

Relatively pure synaptic vesicles from the nervous system may be prepared by subcellular fractionation. Brain tissue is homogenized in a medium that allows subcellular organelles, such as mitochondria and synaptic vesicles, to remain intact. Different organelles can be separated according to their buoyant density by sedimentation in sucrose density gradients. In this way it is possible to obtain relatively pure preparations of vesicles from neuronal as well as other secretory tissues. The availability of pure vesicles has enabled some of the key molecules in the process of exocytosis to be identified and the relationship between these molecules to be unravelled.

The synaptic SNARE complex, which comprises a v-SNARE (synaptobrevin) and two t-SNAREs (syntaxin and SNAP-25), is made of three proteins: synaptobrevin, syntaxin and SNAP-25 (named for SyNaptosomal Associated Protein of M_r 25 000).

The v-SNARE synaptobrevin is a transmembrane synaptic vesicle protein with a short C-terminal region inside the vesicle and the bulk of the protein in the cytoplasm. The t-SNARE syntaxin has a very similar structure but is located in the plasma membrane of the synapse, with the bulk of the protein also in the cytoplasm. In contrast, the t-SNARE SNAP-25 is firmly anchored to the plasma membrane by palmitoyl chains (see Section 3.3.3). These three proteins together form a complex that links the synaptic vesicle to the plasma membrane and whose structure has been determined by X-ray crystallography. They assemble with a 1 : 1 : 1 stoichiometry into a tight ternary complex called a fusion or SNARE complex (Figure 12.24). Much of our knowledge of these processes has been gained from the study of neurotoxins (Box 12.3).

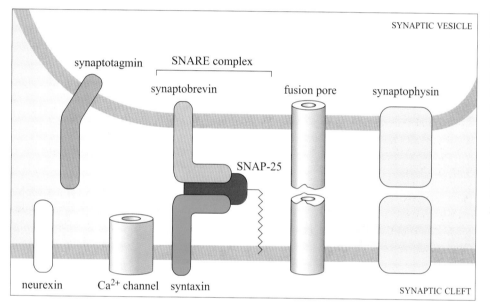

Figure 12.24
Fusion of the synaptic vesicle with the active zone of the plasma membrane at the synaptic cleft is brought about by the SNARE complex, consisting of synaptobrevin, SNAP-25 and syntaxin. The complex is associated with a Ca^{2+} channel and other proteins (synaptotagmin, neurexin and synaptophysin) that are involved in triggering the fusion process. It is postulated that the initial fusion is effected by fusion pores on either membrane.

Box 12.3 Neurotoxins and SNARE research

Important insights into the function of SNAREs have been gained through the use of toxins that poison the nervous system (neurotoxins). In the case of neurotransmitter release, evidence that SNAP-25 and synaptobrevin are essential for membrane docking was obtained in studies using tetanus toxin and botulinum toxin, which are bacterial neurotoxins, which cause paralysis by blocking neurotransmitter release. They are produced by bacteria as single proteins that are then cleaved into two different subunits, known as the light chain and the heavy chain. The heavy chain binds to the external membrane of neurons and facilitates the entry of the light chain into the cytoplasm of the nerve cell at the synaptic terminal. Once the light chains enter the cytoplasm they act as proteases that rapidly destroy specific target proteins. For example, botulinum B and tetanus toxin destroy only synaptobrevin, whereas botulinum A selectively cleaves SNAP-25. Another toxin, botulinum C1, destroys syntaxin. Because each of these toxins is very specific in their action they have provided direct evidence that SNARE proteins are critical components of the process of neurotransmitter release.

Note that tetanus toxin produces spastic paralysis by preventing transmitter release in the CNS, whereas botulinum B toxin causes flaccid paralysis by preventing acetylcholine release at the neuromuscular junction.

All SNARE proteins share a characteristic motif that consists of a stretch of approximately 60 amino acids called the SNARE motif. The SNARE motif is the principal protein–protein interaction region; it is where synaptobrevin binds tightly to corresponding SNARE motifs in syntaxin and SNAP-25 to form an exceptionally stable complex.

After docking of the synaptic vesicle, SNARE proteins undergo a priming step that probably involves the transition of syntaxin to an open conformation required for SNARE complex formation. Another protein, called Unc (named after uncoordinated phenotype of *C. elegans*), interacts with the syntaxin in its open state to stabilize the conformation, which enables the SNARE complex to form. The stable assembly of the SNARE complex is believed to drive membrane fusion, which involves a number of other proteins shown in Figure 12.24, although the precise interactions are not yet known.

For fusion and cargo release to proceed normally, the SNARE complex must become disassembled. In nerve terminals, this process occurs at some point after fusion, and is a step required for recovery and recycling of the membrane. Disassembly is carried out by proteins called NSF and three different SNAPs (unrelated to SNAP-25), which prise apart the SNARE complex in a process that requires ATP hydrolysis (see Figure 12.26).

v/t SNARE pairing presents an attractive lock-and-key mechanism, which may underlie the specificity of vesicle targeting and docking. In other words, the v/t SNARE recognition process could provide a means by which a cell controls the specificity of a vesicle–target membrane fusion. Direct evidence for the involvement of SNAREs in bilayer fusion was lacking until recently, when studies in which SNAREs were reconstituted into liposomes and the liposomes placed inside permeabilized living cells provided strong evidence that SNARE complex formation is associated with the physiological fusion step.

However, several lines of evidence indicate that the same v-SNARE can reside both on vesicles moving towards the plasma membrane and on those being recovered from it. Also it appears that one single v-SNARE can interact with several t-SNAREs. Hence the v–t interaction is not sufficient to ensure the necessary targeting/docking/fusion specificity. This suggests that SNAREs cannot be the sole determinants of vesicle docking that occurs prior to fusion.

12.3.3 The function of Rab proteins in directing traffic

The SNARE proteins are just one component of the vesicle targeting system. Other participants in this process are the **Rab family of GTPases,** which regulate traffic between different cellular compartments and which are implicated in directing vesicles to their appropriate target compartments. The Rab family is the largest family of GTPases, with more than 30 members. They are distributed in specific organelles where they mediate the assembly of distinctive groups of proteins. Moreover, Rabs act in a combinatorial manner with **Rab effector proteins** to regulate almost all stages of membrane traffic, hence they are the key to recruitment of the tethering and docking proteins that facilitate membrane fusion. Rabs are selectively distributed to different membranous systems in the cell (Table 12.4) and attach to membranes via prenyl or palmitoyl groups at the C-terminus. Localization of Rabs onto their membranes occurs when they are activated by a guanine nucleotide exchange factor (GEF), which allows them to bind Rab effector proteins and to recruit other specific proteins to the cluster (Figure 12.25).

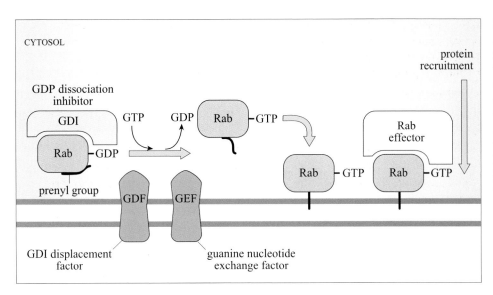

Figure 12.25
A model for the role of Rabs in protein recruitment. Rab–GDP is present in the cytosol, bound to a GDP dissociation inhibitor (GDI). At the appropriate membrane a protein (GDF) displaces the inhibitor and a guanine nucleotide exchange factor (GEF) activates Rab, exposing the prenyl group, which attaches to the membrane. Rab–GTP then binds to Rab effector proteins, which recruit a specific set of proteins to the cluster.

Table 12.4 Intracellular localization of some Rab proteins.

Type of Rab	Cellular compartment
Rab1	ER and Golgi network
Rab2	*cis* Golgi network
Rab6	medial and *trans* Golgi network
Rab5A	clathrin-coated vesicles
Rab5C and Rab4	early endosomes
Rab7	late endosomes
Rab8	basolateral secretory vesicles
Rab3	synaptic and secretory vesicles

Although Rab proteins are structurally similar, their C-termini are highly variable, and it is this part of the molecule that determines their membrane specificity. Rab proteins and their effectors collect integral and peripheral membrane proteins into specific domains by regulating protein–protein interactions. In this way they can link appropriate addressing molecules, such as SNAREs, to the vesicles. Although Rabs are fairly similar in structure, the Rab effectors are very diverse. Rabs remain associated with the vesicles as they move and may also be involved in getting the correct motor proteins attached to the vesicle. After all, there is little point in knowing the address of where you are going if you are on the wrong road to get there.

Once a vesicle has fused with its target membrane, Rab proteins hydrolyse their bound GTP and the inactive Rab–GDP protein returns to the cytoplasm.

▢ Rabs are small GTPases associated with vesicles that shuttle between compartments. What other small GTPases have you encountered that are involved in this process?

● The proteins ARF and Sar1, which initiate assembly of the coats, and go through a similar cycle of activation, protein recruitment, transfer on vesicles and GTP hydrolysis and dissociation at the target membrane.

Despite the partially unresolved mystery about some functions of Rabs, such as their ability to link membranes to molecular motors, at least two facets are clear: (i) Rabs contribute to organelle identity and (ii) they catalyse the selective recruitment of proteins onto membranes to promote specific vesicle formation, tethering and fusion. As such, Rab GTPases are thought to be 'master regulators' of membrane trafficking in eukaryotic cells.

Our attention has been focused very much on proteins, but numerous aspects of membrane fluidity, specificity and permeability as well as fusion are regulated by lipids. Thus, lipids should not be forgotten because they are inevitably involved in vesicle trafficking. Membrane phospholipids and phosphoinositides in particular regulate many aspects of vesicular trafficking by binding to proteins implicated in tethering and in mixing the membrane bilayers.

12.3.4 Cycling and re-use of membranes and traffic proteins

As already mentioned, a vesicle follows a cycle in which it gains its coat, is released from a donor membrane, moves to the target membrane, becomes uncoated, and fuses with the target membrane. Once a vesicle releases its contents by fusing with the target membrane, its components become part of the target membrane or of the lumen of the compartment bounded by the target membrane. The vesicular membrane that has fused with the target membrane needs to be retrieved to form new vesicles. Recovery of the membrane is achieved by the process of budding and membrane scission, i.e. formation of a new vesicle. For example, the recovery of synaptic vesicles involves a new round of budding and scission and involves the same set of coat components used for vesicle release.

☐ Which coat protein, adaptor protein and GTPase would be involved in recovering synaptic vesicle membrane from the plasma membrane at an axon terminal?

● Clathrin, AP2 and ARF (see Table 12.3).

In the synaptic vesicle recovery pathway, the adaptor protein AP2 binds directly to synaptotagmin (see Figure 12.26), a vesicle protein that may flag the stretch of membrane that contains other recently fused vesicular components. The formation of the clathrin coat and the recovery of the underlying membrane involves close interaction of the proteins with the lipids of the membrane, and the process is regulated by specific enzymes that act on phospholipids. After the coated vesicle buds from the plasma membrane, it moves to an early endosome (Figure 12.26).

After fusion of the coated vesicle with an early endosome, the retrieved synaptic vesicle proteins are ready to be reformed into new synaptic vesicles. To make a mature synaptic vesicle, it must first be replenished with neurotransmitters. Before this happens the interior of the vesicle is acidified by the activity of an ion pump, which uses ATP to pump protons across the membrane into the lumen of the vesicle. The acidic environment is essential in that it drives the uptake and storage of neurotransmitter by specific proteins present in the membrane of the vesicle.

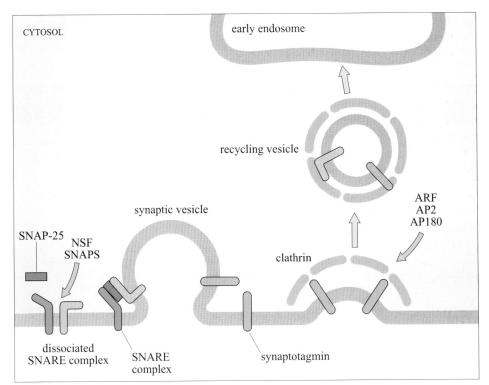

Figure 12.26
Recycling synaptic vesicle components. After synaptic vesicle fusion the SNARE complex is dissociated by the action of NSF and SNAPS in a process driven by ATP hydrolysis. Regions of the membrane that have recently fused with vesicles are marked by synaptotagmin, which identifies regions of membrane for recycling to early endosomes via the assembly of clathrin-coated recycling vesicles, in a process mediated by ARF and the adaptor proteins AP2 and AP180.

Many small neurotransmitters are recovered after release into the synaptic cleft, in order to replenish the synaptic vesicles. Small neurotransmitters such as acetylcholine are regenerated by enzymes near the nerve terminal. For example, after its release, acetylcholine is rapidly cleaved into acetate and choline. Most of the choline is then taken up again into the nerve terminal, by a high affinity sodium-dependent choline uptake system, and used for resynthesis of acetylcholine. Thus, the depletion of neurotransmitters is prevented by their rapid resynthesis and packing into the small synaptic vesicles retrieved by the process of endocytosis. Vesicles can be recycled many times at the terminal by repeated exocytosis/endocytosis, which entails retrieval of vesicle proteins and refilling with neurotransmitters.

Membrane recycling also occurs between the Golgi cisternae and the ER. The fidelity of synthesized proteins is checked during the process of anterograde transport, and all proteins that are not properly modified or folded (see Section 11.6) are returned to the ER in vesicles that also carry biologically dysfunctional proteins as well as ER-resident proteins that had escaped. An intermediate compartment between the ER and the Golgi is involved in the sorting process.

○ Which coat proteins are components of the vesicles moving in the retrograde and anterograde directions?

● COPII coats the anterograde vesicles and COPI the retrograde vesicles (see Figure 12.16).

The process that regulates the exchange of a COPII to a COPI coat is still unknown. It seems that sequential coupling between COPII and COPI coats may be essential to coordinate bidirectional vesicular traffic between the ER and the pre-Golgi intermediate compartments.

The one-letter abbreviations of all 20 naturally occurring amino acids are listed on *Bookmark 1*.

COPI-coated vesicles also move proteins that were involved in anterograde transport back to the ER and between the Golgi cisternae, so that these components are continuously replenished. After reaching the Golgi complex and delivering their cargo, the vesicles depend for recycling on the retrieval signal and retrograde transport. For example, ER membrane proteins carry a dilysine motif (KKXX) that binds directly to the COPI coat. The recycling of the soluble ER proteins involves a C-terminal tetrapeptide (KDEL) that binds to a receptor (Section 12.3.1), which packages the protein into the COPI-coated vesicle. The affinity of the KDEL receptor varies depending on whether it is in the ER or the Golgi compartment (high in the Golgi; low in the ER), so the receptor binds the proteins in the Golgi and releases them in the ER.

☐ How could a receptor have one affinity for its substrate in the ER and a different affinity in the Golgi apparatus?

⬤ The lumens of the two compartments have different pH values (Section 12.2.1), which affects the charge on amino acid side-chains and therefore protein folding and conformation.

The KDEL-containing proteins and KDEL receptors are not the only molecules that are recycled between ER and Golgi compartments; v- and t-SNAREs and many Golgi enzymes are also returned to their correct compartments.

There is growing evidence for more than one mechanism for protein recycling between the Golgi and the ER. Some proteins clearly have KDEL-like sequences whereas others, such as some glycosylation enzymes, lack such motifs but nevertheless find their way from the Golgi complex to the ER. The KDEL-receptor independent/COPI-independent pathway of recycling is much slower than the COPI-dependent one. This transport process, like the COPI-dependent pathway, requires the cytoskeleton and motor proteins, but it seems that these two mechanisms are completely unrelated, because no increase in COPI-independent recycling is observed in cells that have had their COPI-dependent pathway inhibited. Investigation of the two transport mechanisms has been greatly assisted by the use of toxins (Box 12.4).

Box 12.4   Transport of toxins

The orientation of intracellular trafficking (anterograde vs. retrograde) is often studied by use of protein toxins that enter the cell and are transported subsequently from the Golgi to the ER. For example, *Pseudomonas* exotoxin (PE), cholera toxin (CT) and Shiga-like toxins (verotoxins) enter the cell by endocytosis and travel to the *trans* Golgi network from where they are recycled to the ER. Upon arrival in the ER, the toxins translocate to the cytoplasm to exert their effects. Both PE and CT contain C-terminal KDEL or KDEL-like motifs, which facilitate their transport from the Golgi to the ER, through interaction with the KDEL receptor. These toxins provide conclusive evidence for the existence of COPI-mediated retrograde transport that recycles between the Golgi complex and the ER.

At present, biologists know something about the start and the end points of recycling pathways, but have less understanding of the routes of recycling or detailed molecular mechanisms. Moreover, there is very little knowledge on how the

ER and the Golgi disassemble during mitosis. It is believed that an interruption in vesicular trafficking is likely to occur through a collapse of the Golgi back into the ER, increased fragmentation of ER membranes and inhibition of COPI vesicular fusion. This complex process of disassembly must be followed by reassembly, which involves activation of Rabs, TRAPPs, SNAREs and NSF-related factors and seems to be controlled by cell-cycle dependent kinases and phosphatases (see Section 8.3.2).

Yet again, lipids should not be forgotten. Lipid rafts also affect trafficking between the ER and Golgi compartments. Although the major metabolic pathways of cholesterol and sphingolipids have been elucidated, our understanding of the molecular mechanisms of lipid trafficking between subcellular organelles is, compared with our knowledge of protein trafficking, still elementary.

12.3.5 Membrane fusion mediated by viral proteins

Until now, we have focused on the transport of material between different intracellular membrane-bound compartments and fusion of cytoplasmic membranes. This type of fusion is **endoplasmic fusion**. Another type of membrane fusion, called **ectoplasmic fusion**, is used by enveloped viruses to infect cells (enveloped viruses have an outer phospholipid bilayer). The biophysical and structural studies of viral proteins involved in the processes of membrane fusion provide a foundation for understanding their functions at a molecular level.

The proteins involved in promoting ectoplasmic fusion reactions are virally encoded membrane glycoproteins, and the best studied are the influenza virus haemagglutinin and the gp120 protein of human immunodeficiency virus (HIV).

> The diseases caused by influenza virus and HIV and the way they replicate are discussed in detail in S204, Book 4 *Microbes*.

In the case of influenza virus, the virus attaches to the host cell and is taken up by endocytosis, a process mediated by binding of the haemagglutinin in the viral envelope to sialic acid residues that are present on glycophorins, a widely distributed group of cell-surface proteins. The extracellular domain of the haemagglutinin contains a non-polar peptide sequence of 16–23 amino acid residues (known as the fusion peptide), which is essential for fusion of the viral envelope with the membrane of the endosome. In inactive haemagglutinin the peptide is folded in the extracellular domain. This inactive form is converted into an active form in the endosome because the pH is low. This causes the haemagglutinin to unfold so that the fusion peptide is exposed at the tip of the protein farthest from the viral envelope. In this conformation the fusion peptide, being non-polar, can penetrate the endosome membrane, insert into the phospholipid bilayer and thereby facilitate fusion with the viral envelope.

Analysis of the viral proteins and eukaryotic proteins involved in membrane fusion shows significant structural similarities. In particular, the parallel topology of α helices from opposing membranes within the v/t SNARE complex is similar to the coiled arrangement seen in viral fusion proteins (Figure 12.27). It is believed that proteins such as haemagglutinins and SNAREs help to overcome several energetically unfavourable transition states during the process of fusion pore formation. The similarity seen between viral and non-viral fusion proteins may

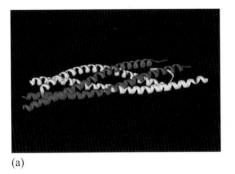

(a)

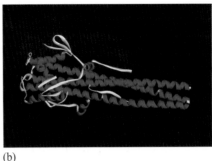

(b)

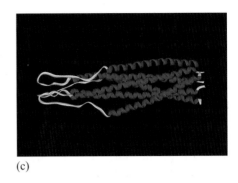

(c)

Figure 12.27   Structural similarities between protein components of (a) a v/t SNARE complex, (b) the haemagglutinin of influenza virus (HA-A2) at low pH, and (c) the core of HIV gp41.

reflect a common mechanism in which the free energy contained in the coiled formation is transformed into the mechanical work needed to fuse membranes.

In the case of HIV, the virus enters the cell by binding to a protein, CD4, which is expressed on the surface of some lymphocytes and phagocytes. Binding is mediated by the viral protein gp120, which is bound to the HIV fusion protein. The release and consequent insertion of the viral fusion protein into the lymphocyte membrane is mediated by the action of another lymphocyte membrane protein. The viral fusion protein spontaneously rearranges, and the energy released in this process, as in the case of influenza virus, is transformed into the mechanical work required for membrane fusion.

Summary of Section 12.3

1   The formation of transport vesicles is initiated by small G proteins that insert into the donor membrane and assemble coat proteins. The coat proteins are COPI, COPII or clathrin, depending on the pathway, and the coat includes adaptor proteins that link the coat to the vesicle and its cargo. Epsins and dynamin are involved in the budding process.

2   The vesicle cargo depends on the adaptor proteins, sorting proteins and receptors that are assembled in the vesicle.

3   After vesicles have moved to the target membrane, GTP is hydrolysed and the coat proteins depolymerize to uncoat the vesicle.

4   The initial tethering of vesicles with the target membrane is mediated by TRAPPs, and docking is mediated by SNAREs, but other proteins and ion channels are involved in triggering fusion.

5   Rab GTPases act as master regulators of vesicle trafficking, by binding to membranes and, in association with Rab effectors, assembling appropriate groups of proteins to mediate transport to and fusion with the target membrane. There are numerous Rabs, each selectively localized in particular membranes or organelles.

6   Membrane components and proteins involved in controlling vesicular traffic and vesicle coating are recycled to their original compartment for re-use. Misdirected cargo proteins are returned to their correct compartment, by a process involving their signal sequences. Misfolded proteins are returned to the endoplasmic reticulum.

7   Enveloped viruses must also fuse with cell membranes in order for the virus to enter the cytoplasm of the cell. Viral fusion proteins have structural similarities with eukaryotic fusion proteins.

12.4 Signals for compartmentalization

We have noted how proteins for different destinations are packaged in transport vesicles, a process that depends on signal sequences in the proteins. In this section we shall look in a little more detail at the nature of the signal sequences. Except for the few proteins synthesized in the mitochondria or chloroplasts, cellular proteins are encoded by nuclear genes and synthesized on ribosomes in the cytosol or at the ER. Consequently, these proteins, if destined for organelles, must be sorted to the correct target membrane and translocated to the organelle. Sorting of proteins for their ultimate destinations occurs in conjunction with a variety of post-translational modifications. These modifications represent 'recognition signatures' for a variety of biological processes, including organelle targeting, subcellular anchoring and the formation of macromolecular complexes.

○ In the absence of a signal sequence, or if the signal sequence is removed by genetic modification, where is the protein likely to end up?

● At the plasma membrane. Constitutive secretion is the default pathway (Section 12.2.3) and specific signals are needed to retain proteins in the ER and the Golgi or to direct them to the secretory pathways or lysosomes.

12.4.1 Peptide signal sequences

The distinct chemistry of proteins at the N- and C-termini provides protein molecules with two positionally and chemically unique sites for post-translational modifications and with the means to control their spatial and temporal interactions and position. This feature of proteins is crucial for a variety of biological processes from protein degradation to protein sorting for specific cellular compartments. The N- and C-termini of proteins have distinct roles, and we have already emphasized the importance of the N-terminal signal sequence in controlling translation across the ER (Section 11.5.2).

Proteins destined for other cellular compartments also have signal sequences. For example, more than 98% of mitochondrial proteins are synthesized as pre-proteins in the cytosol, and these proteins contain a targeting sequence at the N-terminus, called a presequence, which is made up of 20–50 amino acid residues with characteristic properties. This sequence is enriched with positively charged hydroxylated and hydrophobic residues and has the potential to form an amphiphilic α helix. The sequence is recognized by protein translocator complexes located in both the inner and outer mitochondrial membranes.

Import of proteins to the nucleus and to the chloroplast also depends on the N-terminal signal peptides. It is possible to change the localization of a protein by genetic engineering – attachment of appropriate presequences can direct non-mitochondrial proteins to mitochondria and across both outer and inner membrane into the matrix. This demonstrates that they contain all the information needed for targeting and membrane translocation properties. In plants, a group of proteins known as dual-targeted proteins have a targeting peptide capable of leading the mature protein to both organelles, that is to mitochondria and chloroplasts. Dual-targeted proteins not only have to be recognized by the import apparatus of two different organelles, but their targeting peptide must be correctly removed once the protein is inside the organelle.

Signals at the C-terminus are also important, but have different functions. We have already mentioned the tetrapeptide signals KDEL and KKXX of lumenal and transmembrane ER proteins, and their interaction with corresponding receptors that forms the basis for ER localization and retrieval activity. Other examples are the di-acidic DXE motif or the FCYENE motif both involved in ER export. The sorting function of a signalling peptide is not restricted to proteins that enter the secretory pathway. For example, two types of peroxisomal targeting signal mediate the import of most peroxisomal matrix proteins.

Abnormal proteins can arise as a result of various mechanisms, including premature termination of translation. To channel these proteins into a degradation pathway, an 11-residue C-terminal sequence with a non-polar tail, -AANSENYALAA-COOH, is added to the protein. This sequence serves as a signal for protease recognition in various cellular compartments. Although it is relatively easy to spot signal sequences in molecules, signal patches that rely on particular protein folding are less easy to identify. Table 12.5 shows some examples of signal sequences.

Table 12.5   Signal sequences

Function of signal sequence	Example of signal sequence
import into nucleus	PPKKKRKV
export from nucleus	LALKLAGLDI
import into mitochondria	^+H_3N-MLSL**R**QSI**R**FF**K**PAT**R**TLCSSRYLL
import into peroxisome	SKL-COO$^-$
import into ER	^+H_3N-MMSFVSLLLVGILFWATEAEQLTKCEVFN
return to ER	KDEL-COO$^-$

Important hydrophobic amino acids are underlined; ^+H_3N indicates the N-terminus of a protein; COO$^-$ indicates the C-terminus; the positions of a key set of positively charged residues in the mitochondrial import sequence, which cluster on one side of the α helix, are shown in bold. (Information derived from Alberts, *et al.*, 2002).

Because many viruses replicate in the nucleus of their host cells (e.g. influenza virus, HIV-1), they have developed several methods for transporting their genome into this compartment using the complex machinery that cells have evolved for protein and nucleic acid trafficking. After viral entry into the cell, either through endocytosis (influenza virus) or via fusion with the plasma membrane (HIV-1), the nucleic acids (associated with virus-specific proteins) are discharged into the cytoplasm. This nucleoprotein capsid must make its way to the nucleus. To gain access to the nucleus, viruses use two different methods: (i) they wait in the cytosol until the cell undergoes mitosis, or (ii) they use strategies that enlist the cellular nuclear transport machinery, but which also depend on the size of the viral capsid. The only way for macromolecules to enter the nucleus is through the nuclear pore complex (NPC), and the mechanism depends on the 'nuclear localization sequences' (NLS) exposed on the surface of the capsid particle.

12.4.2 Glycosylation sequences and protein glycosylation

In Chapters 3 and 11 we introduced the different types of glycosylation seen on proteins. The structures may be simple or branched and are almost completely confined to those proteins destined for the cell surface or secretion. The sites and types of glycosylation are determined by the primary structure of the protein and by the availability of enzymes to carry out glycosylation (glycosyltransferases).

○ To which amino acid residues and which functional groups are carbohydrate units attached, and where does this occur?

● N-linked polysaccharides are attached to the $-NH_2$ groups of asparagine and O-linked polysaccharides are attached to the $-OH$ groups of serine and threonine (Section 3.3.3). N-linked glycosylation occurs in the rough ER as the protein is synthesized (Figure 11.26).

Glycosylation of proteins is important for two reasons: it alters the properties of proteins, changing their stability, solubility and physical bulk, and carbohydrate units may act as recognition signals that are central to aspects of protein targeting and cellular recognition.

N-glycosylation begins in the ER lumen and carbohydrates are further processed after transport of the protein to the Golgi apparatus. A specific sequence NXT/S is required, in which N is asparagine and T/S is either threonine or serine and X may be any amino acid except proline or aspartic acid. Not all NXT/S sequences in protein molecules are glycosylated because in some cases they are masked by protein folding. The process of linking the carbohydrate unit through the amide nitrogen atom of asparagine occurs in the ER, whereas the process of linking the carbohydrate unit through the hydroxyl group of serine or threonine occurs in the Golgi. *N*-glycosylation is the most conserved form of protein glycosylation in eukaryotes, but the modifications of N-linked oligosaccharides in plants and invertebrates often differ greatly from those in vertebrates.

The initial step in *N*-glycosylation is the transfer of a pre-assembled branched oligosaccharide from a special lipid molecule **dolichol** to the target asparagine residue, in a single enzymatic step (Figure 12.28). Dolichol acts as an anchor upon which the carbohydrate unit is assembled by successive addition of monosaccharide units. Assembly of the carbohydrate starts on the cytosolic side of the ER and is completed in the lumen of the ER.

After the addition of the oligosaccharide, and provided the protein has folded correctly, the terminal glucose units are trimmed back by an ER glucosidase, and an ER mannosidase (Figure 12.29), before being despatched to the Golgi network.

○ If the terminal glucose residues are not removed, what happens to the protein?

● The protein will then bind to chaperone molecules, such as calnexin and calreticulin, and will be retained in the ER until properly folded and released for transport to the Golgi. If it is incorrectly folded it will be released for degradation (Section 11.6.4).

Figure 12.28
N-linked protein glycosylation. The core oligosaccharide, which has been assembled on dolichol, is transferred en bloc to an asparagine residue (Asn) in the nascent polypeptide chain by the action of oligosaccharyl transferase. Energy for the reaction comes from the phosphoanhydride bonds that link the carbohydrate unit to dolichol.

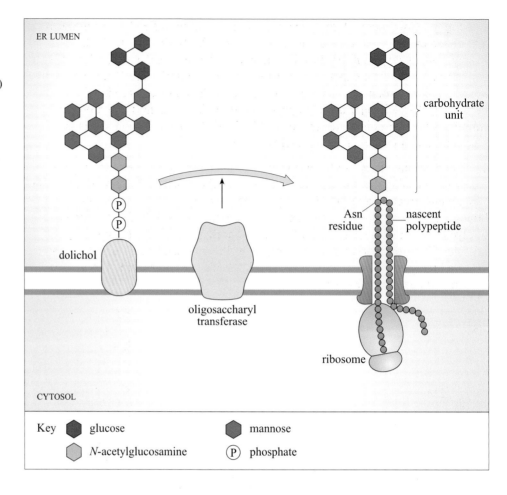

Figure 12.29
The oligosaccharide unit is trimmed back within the ER by the action of ER glucosidase and ER mannosidase.

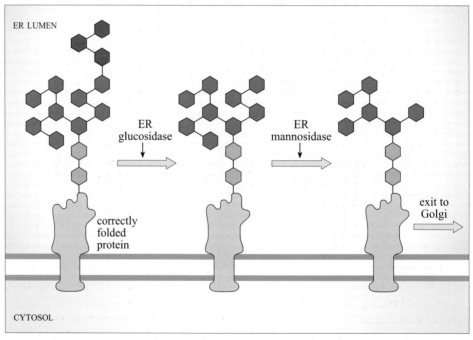

Once in the Golgi network the carbohydrate is further modified by enzymes that add or remove monosaccharide residues (Figure 12.30). Some carbohydrate residues on glycoproteins are heavily sulfated. For example, the molecules perlecan and agrin, which are components of the extracellular matrix (see Chapter 16) carry heparan sulfate groups, which are polymeric carbohydrates that are highly negatively charged under physiological conditions. The enzymes that promote the sulfation of the carbohydrates are located in the Golgi network, and this is the final stage in the maturation of such proteins.

The implications of glycosylation for the structure and function of a glycoprotein are so far-reaching that the regulation of protein glycosylation and its effect on the subsequent structure and function of proteins are extremely important in cell biology. For example, recent research into prion diseases has highlighted the impact of glycosylation on the structure of the prion protein, PrP, and its propensity to misfold if incorrectly glycosylated. Misfolded PrP can recruit further PrP molecules that are highly resistant to degradation, which leads to PrP deposition in the nervous system and death of nerve cells.

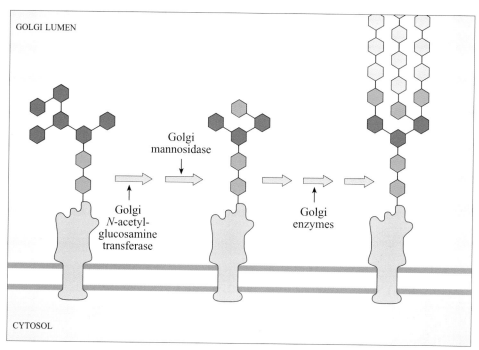

Figure 12.30   In the Golgi network the carbohydrate unit is further trimmed back by the action of a Golgi mannosidase, and further residues may be added by the action of different Golgi enzymes.

12.4.3 Lipidation

Lipid modification occurs in both prokaryotes and eukaryotes, including viruses. Lipidated proteins have an increased affinity for membranes, and the preferential partition of lipid-anchored proteins provides a number of physiological benefits, such as spatial specificity, increased local concentration and faster protein–protein interactions. A number of C-terminal motifs are sites for lipidation, including -CaaX, -CC and –CXC, where X is any amino acid and a is an aliphatic residue (see Section 3.3.3).

☐ List the principal types of lipid modification of proteins. If you are unsure, look back at Figure 3.25.

⬤ Prenylated proteins have either a farnesyl or a geranylgeranyl group linked to cysteine. Acylated proteins have myristoyl groups linked to the N-terminus or palmitoyl groups attached to cysteine. GPI-linked proteins have a composite structure which attaches to the C-terminus.

Prenylation and acylation affect the ability of the protein to interact with membranes (Table 12.6), which in turn alters their ability to interact with substrates and can also affect sorting to different compartments. For example, segregation to the apical and basolateral membranes appears to involve partitioning of newly synthesized proteins into glycosphingolipid-enriched domains.

Table 12.6 Lipid modification of proteins and their membrane affinity.

Modification	Addition	Substrates	Membrane affinity, K_D
farnesylation	post-translation	cytosolic proteins	$100\,\mu mol\,l^{-1}$
geranylgeranylation	post-translation	cytosolic proteins	$2\,\mu mol\,l^{-1}$
N-myristoylation	co-translation	nascent polypeptide	$80\,\mu mol\,l^{-1}$
palmitoylation	post-translation	membrane protein	$5\,\mu mol\,l^{-1}$

Summary of Section 12.4

1   Targeting sequences at the N-terminus of proteins direct translation across the ER, and act as signals for import to the nucleus, mitochondrion and chloroplasts. Sequences at the C-terminus control traffic through the ER and the Golgi and to peroxisomes.

2   Glycosylation is directed by signal sequences that act as targets for N-linked glycosylation in the ER and O-linked glycosylation in the Golgi apparatus. Glycosylation and remodelling of polysaccharides is important in controlling protein folding and release from the ER, and in affecting the stability and function of the completed glycoprotein.

3   Lipidation affects the ways in which proteins attach or partition to membranes, and may also contribute to sorting.

12.5 The cytoskeleton and motor proteins

12.5.1 The role of the cytoskeleton in intracellular transport

In Section 12.3 we explained how vesicles bud from donor membranes and fuse with target membranes, which may be quite distant. In such cases, vesicles are actively transported from one site to another, a process that involves motor proteins attached to the vesicle, which propel the vesicle along the cytoskeleton. The microtubule network in particular acts as a trackway for long-range movement of transport vesicles, and this is evident in the movies that show the dual staining of tubulin and secretory vesicle components.

You should look again carefully at the movies 'Secretory pathway I–III', which show transport of secretory vesicles along the microtubule network. Pay particular attention to the arrangement of the microtubule network, the ways in which the vesicles move and the routes that they take. Also review the movies 'Caveolae I–III', which show the movement of caveolae along microtubule networks.

☐ How is the microtubule network arranged in relation to the Golgi network and the ER and how might this facilitate long-range movement of transport vesicles? What implications does this arrangement have for the direction of travel of vesicles along the microtubules?

⬤ The microtubule network extends from the MTOC, which is located near the nucleus, and the Golgi network is also located near the nucleus. This means that vesicles travelling from the ER to the Golgi will generally be moving from the farthest (plus) end of the microtubules to the minus end, near the MTOC, whereas secretory vesicles will be moving from the Golgi (near the nucleus) to the periphery of the cell. Notice that in these cells, the microtubule network appears to be relatively stable, and this is related to capping at the periphery of the cell.

☐ What do you observe about the movement of the vesicles – the direction they move and the routes they take?

⬤ Secretory vesicles generally move away from the Golgi apparatus, but they can occasionally stop and even reverse direction or appear to branch onto another microtubule. Most of the traffic is confined to a limited number of microtubules, and these appear to be fast-tracks to the cell periphery – vesicles move along them without pausing.

The implication of these observations is that the microtubule network can act as a semi-permanent link between compartments, but that the directionality of migration is very carefully controlled – the network is doing much more than speeding up diffusion – vesicle migration is directional and depends on the vesicle and its cargo as well as on the orientation of the cytoskeletal elements and the action of motor proteins.

Microfilaments also affect vesicle movement, especially for vesicles positioned near the cell surface. For example, the mobility of caveolae located beneath the plasma membrane is affected by latrunculin, a drug that inhibits microfilament assembly, whereas their movement across the cell is blocked by nocodazole, a drug that causes microtubules to disassemble. For caveolae, the mobility of vesicles near the membrane appears to be limited by their interaction with the microfilaments.

12.5.2 Motor proteins

The final element that is needed for a vesicle transport system is **motor proteins,** as indicated in Figure 12.9. These proteins bind to vesicles and organelles and use energy from ATP to move them along the microtubule or microfilament network. Two families of motor proteins, the **kinesins** and **dyneins,** move vesicles along microtubules, and members of the **myosin** family move them along microfilaments (see Box 12.1). The myosin family is also important in cell movement, which is considered in Chapter 16.

The direction of movement of vesicles along the cytoskeleton is absolutely dependent on the polarity of the microfilaments and microtubules. Some motor proteins move from the minus end to the plus end and others in the opposite direction. For example, of the various myosins that have been discovered throughout the animal and plant kingdoms, all but one (myosin VI) move towards the plus end of the filament.

Kinesins have a tertiary structure that is similar to myosin II, even though there is no significant similarity in the primary structure. Both molecules have two heads with motor domains formed around an ATP-binding core, and a coiled tail that binds to the cargo (Figure 12.31). A number of other molecules are related to kinesin, and all of them share the kinesin motor domain, but very little else. These are the **kinesin-related proteins**. Kinesin itself moves towards the plus end of microtubules (Figure 12.32), but other members of the kinesin family move to the plus or minus end depending on the protein. Some of the kinesin-related proteins are involved in moving microtubules during mitosis – in this way the motor protein and the microtubule act in an analogous way to myosin and microfilaments in cell movement.

Figure 12.31
Molecular structure of kinesin. The model shows a truncated kinesin dimer. The heavy and light chains of the two motor domains are coloured in green and blue, and a space-filling model of ADP is shown in the binding site of each. The tail regions of the molecules (red) consist of paired α helices.

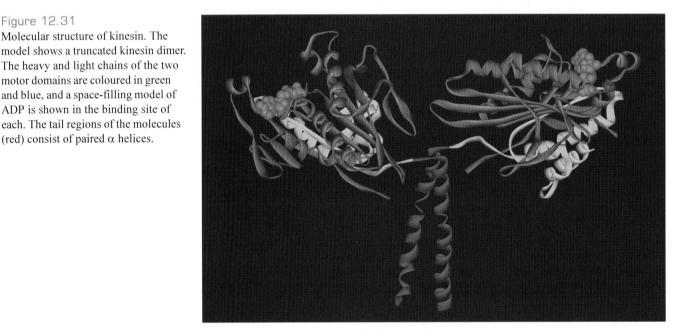

Figure 12.32
Kinesins and dyneins carry cargo along microtubules. Kinesin itself moves towards the plus end of the microtubule, whereas the dyneins move towards the minus end.

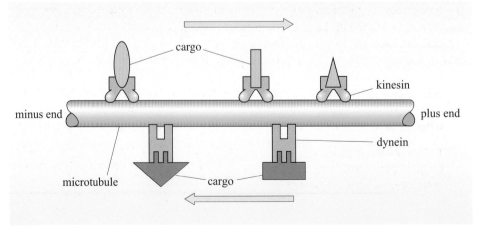

Dyneins are unrelated to either kinesins or myosins, and they move towards the minus end of microtubules. Each is composed of two or three heavy chains, with the cytoplasmic dyneins having two chains, each of which forms a large motor domain. In nerve cells, the axonemal dyneins, which have two or three motor domains, transport vesicles along microtubule bundles in the axons.

○ In which direction will dyneins transport vesicles along the axons?

● From the nerve terminal to the nerve body. Dyneins transport towards the minus end of microtubules, which is located in the MTOC near the nucleus.

The speed of the movement mediated by dyneins and kinesins is quite extraordinary. In vitro, kinesins can move along microtubules at $2\,\mu\mathrm{m\,s^{-1}}$ and dyneins at up to $14\,\mu\mathrm{m\,s^{-1}}$. Although these high rates of movement would not be achieved in the complex environment of a cell, they can explain, for example, how caveolar transcytosis of molecules across an endothelial cell can occur in 1–2 minutes. Movement and force generation by both classes of proteins involves ATP hydrolysis and allosteric shifts in the orientation of the motor domains, so that the proteins are thought to 'step' progressively down the microtubule.

> The process of 'stepping' down the microtubule is conceptually similar to the stepping of myosin along actin filaments – the cross-bridge cycle, described in S204, Book 3 *The Core of Life*, Vol. II, Chapter 7.

Notice however that the ATP-binding site of kinesin (Figure 12.31) is located at the distal tip of the motor domain, whereas in myosin the equivalent site is deep within the motor domain and covered by the myosin's actin-binding site. Therefore the mechanism of stepping is different in the two molecules. In particular, the α-helical linking region connecting the two motor domains of kinesin appears to transfer allosteric changes between them to coordinate ATPase activity and hence the stepping motion of the protein. It is interesting that the motor domains of kinesin-related proteins that move to the plus end and those that move to the minus end of the microtubule are similar, but the linkage between them is quite different. Kinesin has its motor domain near the N-terminus, whereas the molecule Ncd, which moves to the minus end of the microtubule, has its motor domain located near the C-terminus. It seems that whether the protein is directed to the plus or the minus end is dependent on the configuration of domains and the coordination.

The mechanical cycle of kinesin is outlined in Figure 12.33. Notice that kinesin is permanently attached to the microtubule, by either one head or the other. By comparison, the myosin heads (which are arranged in bundles in myofibrils) are only in contact with actin filaments for about 5% of each movement cycle.

○ What advantage can you see in the stepping mechanism of kinesin when compared with myosin? Remember that the kinesin molecule acts singly, whereas myosin acts in concert with other myosin molecules in the myofibril.

● It means that kinesin does not let go of the microtubule between steps, so the cargo is permanently attached and less likely to be lost from its trackway, which could lead to its misdirection.

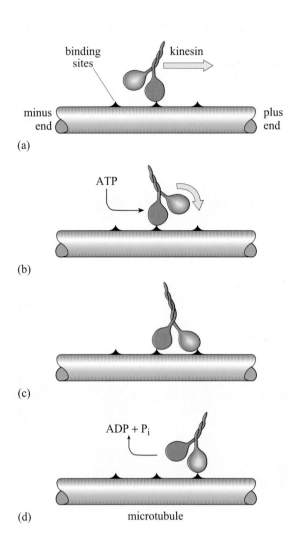

(a)

(b)

(c)

ADP + P$_i$

(d)   microtubule

Figure 12.33   Proposed motor cycle of kinesin.
The leading kinesin motor domain binds to a site on the
microtubule (a). As ATP binds to this domain, the trailing
head swings forward (b) to become the leading head, and
attaches to a new site on the microtubule (c). Release of
ADP and phosphate from the new trailing head causes it
to be released from the microtubule (d). Thus the molecule
takes one step for each molecule of ATP hydrolysed.

How are different motor proteins associated with different
trafficking vesicles? Figure 12.34 shows a basic hypothesis of
how a vesicle attaches to a microtubule, but the details of this
process are still largely unknown. Observation of moving
caveolae suggests that they tend to track initially to a large
endosomal compartment, the caveosome, located near the MTOC
and then switch to move away, as they traverse the cell.
However it is also clear that individual caveolae can alternately
move forwards or backwards along the microtubule network.
You can see this quite clearly in the movie 'Caveolae I'.

☐   What does this imply about the motor proteins that associate
with caveolae?

◼   Different motor proteins can associate with the same vesicle
– some moving to the minus end of the tubule and others to
the plus end.

It has been suggested that there is occasionally competition
between kinesin and dyneins to produce this shuffling back and
forth, but this is the exception. Observation of the movement of
secretory vesicles shows a rapid one-way transfer from the Golgi
to the plasma membrane, and the key to this transfer must be the

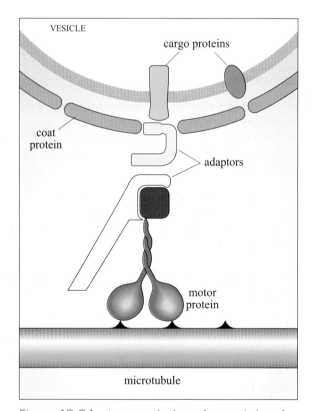

Figure 12.34   A proposed scheme for association of
a transport vesicle with a microtubule. Adaptors link
cargo molecules to the motor proteins, to ensure that the
appropriate motor is attached to each vesicle.

attachment of the correct motor protein as the vesicles bud from the *trans* Golgi network. However, this subject is not well understood. It is possible that small GTPases, such as those that assemble the vesicle and the coat proteins, could also be responsible for recruiting the correct motor protein to the vesicle, and there is good evidence for different adaptor proteins that link the motor protein to the vesicle. GGA proteins (Figure 12.19) could perform such a function, but at present the mechanisms of the process are unclear.

Summary of Section 12.5

1 The microtubule network provides an essential trackway for the rapid movement of vesicles around cells, and the microfilament network also contributes to the local organization and movement of vesicles.

2 Motor proteins can move vesicles and organelles (described as cargo) along microfilaments (myosins) or along microtubules (kinesins and dyneins). Kinesin and most kinesin-related proteins move to the plus end of microtubules whereas dyneins move to the minus end.

3 The motor domains (heads) of these proteins convert ATP into work. Kinesin is a two-headed molecule and dyneins have two or three heads, which step along the microtubule in a coordinated fashion.

4 Association of the correct motor protein with a trafficking vesicle ensures that the vesicle will move towards the correct region of the cell. However, the mechanisms by which the correct motor protein is attached to a vesicle are unclear.

12.6 Endocytic pathways

In the final two sections of this chapter, we shall look at some examples of endocytosis and exocytosis, in different types of cell. The molecules that are taken up or released by a cell and the triggers for secretion depend greatly on the type of cell, although the underlying transport processes are similar for many cell types, and relate to the systems described above.

The plasma membrane not only separates the cell interior from the extracellular environment, it also regulates and coordinates the entry and exit of different types of molecule. Many small molecules, such as amino acids, water, sugars and ions, can cross the plasma membrane.

○ Give three mechanisms by which small molecules can cross the plasma membrane, with examples.

● Water and most gases cross the membrane by simple diffusion. Glucose and amino acids are taken up by facilitated diffusion on carrier molecules. Ions cross through pores or specific transporters, which may require energy, depending on the ion, the membrane potential and the concentration gradient across the membrane.

Macromolecules, however, must be carried into the cell by endocytosis.

12.6.1 Endocytosis

Fluid-phase uptake by pinocytosis can be broadly categorized according to the size of the endocytic vesicle and this also relates to how the vesicle is coated (Figure 12.35). The rate of internalization is directly proportional to (i) the concentration of extracellular molecules, (ii) the volume enclosed by the vesicle and (iii) the rate of vesicle formation. Greater efficiency of endocytosis can be achieved by binding of the extracellular molecules to the membrane. The most efficient uptake occurs when molecules from the extracellular environment bind to specific receptors, i.e. receptor-mediated endocytosis. In contrast, phagocytosis is concentration-independent, but as with pinocytosis, the entry into the cell is determined by the type of cargo and its receptor. Both processes also serve to internalize and recycle membrane proteins and lipids.

In many cell types, stimulation by growth factors often induces membrane disturbance, which ultimately leads to macropinocytosis. **Macropinocytosis** is a non-specific mechanism for internalization, in which lamellipodia extend at a site of membrane ruffling to form irregular vesicles, containing large volumes of extracellular fluid. Macropinocytosis is often induced as part of the response to stimulation by growth factors. The extension of lamellipodia is driven by the extension of actin filaments, in a process controlled by small GTPases belonging to the Rho family. (Be careful not to confuse this family of molecules with the Rho protein involved in termination of transcription, as described in Section 10.1.3.) Rho was the first member of a large family of GTPases to be discovered. It is involved in numerous cellular events, including pinocytosis, cell signalling (Chapter 13) and cell migration (Chapter 16). Many of these events involve the reorganization of the cytoskeleton, for different purposes. Other members of the Rho family are Rac, Rap1 and Cdc42, and we shall discuss the functions of these molecules in some detail in Chapter 16.

In contrast to macropinocytosis, the mechanism of clathrin-coated-vesicle dependent, clathrin-coated-vesicle independent and caveolin-mediated endocytosis proceeds by involution of selective plasma-membrane domains that give rise to smaller pinocytic vesicles (Figure 12.35). Assembly of endosomal vesicles is often preceded by the formation of domains within the membrane, consisting of specific

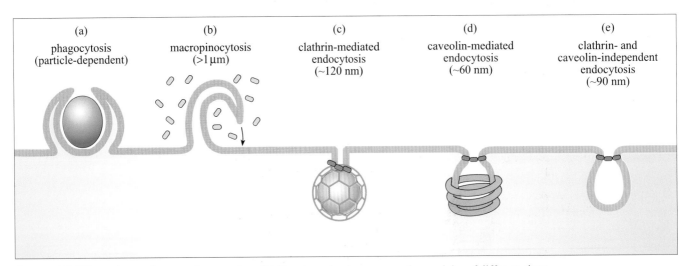

| (a) | (b) | (c) | (d) | (e) |
| phagocytosis (particle-dependent) | macropinocytosis (>1 μm) | clathrin-mediated endocytosis (~120 nm) | caveolin-mediated endocytosis (~60 nm) | clathrin- and caveolin-independent endocytosis (~90 nm) |

Figure 12.35   Endocytosis occurs by a number of different mechanisms, generating vesicles of different sizes.

lipids and proteins. For example, caveolae form from lipid rafts (cholesterol-rich domains within the membrane), which can selectively incorporate or exclude particular proteins. The cytoskeletal protein actin is thought to constrain the lateral mobility of rafts, increasing their stability in the membrane. Moreover, actin is involved in the initial intracellular movement of the caveolae.

○ What are the principal traffic pathways of material entering the cell by endocytosis?

● Molecules pass from early endosomes to late endosomes, and from there may move to lysosomes or recycle to the plasma membrane or intersect with secretory vesicles from the Golgi. Some molecules such as the bacterial toxins (Box 12.4) move to the Golgi network and the ER.

What are the sorting signals that guide proteins through the endocytic maze? In some cases of receptor-mediated endocytosis, covalent attachment of ubiquitin can act as a signal for endocytosis – several proteins appear to control this complex process and some of them are distinguished by the fact that they become tagged with a single copy of the molecule ubiquitin. Monoubiquitination (the addition of one ubiquitin molecule) is well established as a signal for endocytosis in yeast, and is implicated in the regulated removal of cell surface receptors in animal cells. This tagging requires sequentially acting enzymes, the last one being a ubiquitin ligase that attaches ubiquitin to a lysine residue of the target protein. It is not known how the ligase distinguishes between proteins destined for degradation, which will be tagged with several molecules of ubiquitin, and proteins destined for endocytosis, which will be tagged with a single molecule of ubiquitin by the very same ligase. This process has been studied in relation to the protein eps15, a molecule that associates with clathrin-coated pits and which regulates endocytosis (Figure 12.36).

The signals that trigger internalization vary according to the receptors. Some receptors are internalized continuously, but others remain exposed on the surface until ligand is bound to them, after which they become susceptible to endocytosis. In either case the receptors slide laterally into coated pits, and endocytosis starts by a common route that leads to several pathways in which receptors have different fates. It is not clear whether lateral diffusion can adequately explain receptor movement into coated pits or whether some additional forces are required.

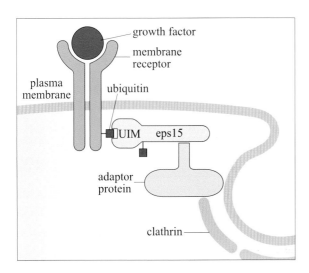

Figure 12.36
Proteins such as eps15 become monoubiquitinated, as a signal for endocytosis. The separate region of eps15 also contains a ubiquitin-interacting motif (UIM), and it is proposed that this could link eps15 to other monoubiquitinated proteins, such as growth factor receptors, leading them to be clustered into clathrin-coated pits.

Coated pits invaginate into the cytoplasm and pinch off to form coated vesicles. Clathrin forms an outer polyhedral layer on clathrin-coated vesicles, and the adaptins recognize the appropriate sequences in the cytoplasmic domains of receptors that are to be internalized, immobilizing the receptor in the pit. As a result, the receptor is retained by the coated vesicle when it pinches off from the plasma membrane. These vesicles move to early endosomes, fuse with the target membrane and release their content. The immediate destination for endocytic clathrin-coated vesicles is the endosome, a rather heterogeneous structure consisting of membrane-bound tubules and vesicles. Early endosomes lie just beneath the plasma membrane and are reached by the internalized proteins within about a minute. By comparison, late endosomes are closer to the nucleus and are reached within 5–10 minutes.

The early endosomes provide the main location for sorting proteins on the endocytic pathway. The interior of the endosome is acidic (pH < 6), which is important in determining the fate of proteins taken up by endocytosis. For example, the fate of a receptor–ligand complex depends on its response to the acidic environment of the endosome. Exposure to a low pH environment changes the conformation of the external domain of receptors, causing the ligand to be released and/or changing the structure of the ligand (e.g. transferrin). But the receptor must not become irreversibly denatured by the acidic environment, and the presence of multiple disulfide bridges in the external domain may play an important role in maintaining stability.

Transport to the lysosomes is the default pathway and applies to any material that does not possess a signal specifically directing it elsewhere. The lysosomes contain the cellular supply of hydrolytic enzymes, which are responsible for degradation of the macromolecules. Like the endosome, the lysosomal lumen is acidic (pH ~ 5). There are two routes to the lysosomes. Proteins internalized from the plasma membrane may be directed via the early endosome to the late endosome. Newly synthesized proteins may be directed from the *trans* Golgi via the late endosome, as already described. The relationship between the various types of endosome and lysosome is not clear. Vesicles may be used to transport proteins along the pathways from one structure to the next, or early endosomes may mature into late endosomes, which in turn mature into lysosomes. Regardless of the sequence, the pathway is unidirectional and many proteins that have left the early endosome for the late endosome will end up in the lysosomes.

12.6.2 Uncoupling and receptor recycling

Receptors that have been directed to the early endosome generally behave in one of two ways. They may return to the plasma membrane by vesicular transport or they may be transported to the lysosomes, where they are degraded. Rapid recycling of receptors in general occurs for receptors that bring ligand into the cell, whereas receptors involved in signal transduction are usually degraded. Note that these are generalizations and specific receptors may take different routes through the cell.

Two possible fates for a receptor–ligand complex in which the receptor may return to the plasma membrane are:

1   The receptor and ligand both recycle.

The transferrin receptor provides the classic example of this pathway (see Figure 12.12). A transferrin receptor recycles every 15–20 minutes and has a half-life of about 30 hours.

2   The receptor recycles to the surface in coated vesicles while the ligand is degraded.

This pathway is used by receptors that transport ligand into cells at high rates. A receptor recycles every 1–20 minutes and can undertake about 100 cycles during its lifetime of around 20 hours.

The classic example of this latter pathway is the LDL receptor, whose ligand is the plasma low-density lipoprotein apolipoproteins E and B (collectively known as LDLs). For example, Apo-B is a large protein ($M_r \sim 500\,000$) that carries cholesterol and cholesterol esters. The LDL is released from its receptor in the endosome and the receptor recycles to the surface to be used again. The LDL, having released cholesterol for use by the cell, is sent on to the lysosomes, where it is degraded. This represents the major route for removing cholesterol from the circulation, and people with mutations in the gene encoding the LDL receptor accumulate large amounts of plasma cholesterol, which causes the disease known as familial hypercholesterolemia. In fact, characterization of the internalization defect provided evidence that entry into coated pits is needed for receptor-mediated endocytosis of LDL. In cells from human patients with such defects in the LDL receptor, the receptors gather in small clusters over the plasma membrane and cannot enter the coated pits. The mutations responsible for this type of defect all affect the cytoplasmic domain of the receptor that mediates endocytosis.

Two possible fates for a receptor–ligand complex in which the receptor does not return to the plasma membrane are:

1   The receptor and ligand are both degraded.

The epidermal growth factor (EGF) receptor binds its ligand (a small polypeptide), and is internalized. Although EGF and its receptor appear to dissociate at low pH, they are both carried to the lysosomes, where they are degraded (see Figure 12.12).

2   The receptor and ligand are transported elsewhere.

This pathway is seen in some polarized cells in which the receptor–ligand complex is taken up at one cell surface, and then released at another (e.g. the transport of IgA, see Figure 12.14). Other pathways have been described for specific receptors, including recycling between the cell membrane, endosomes and the Golgi network.

12.6.3 Phagocytosis

> This section looks at some of the cellular mechanisms involved in the phagocytosis of pathogenic microbes and viruses. The important role of phagocytes in defence against infection, and the function of antigen presentation, are discussed more fully in S320, Book 3 *Immunology*, Chapter 2.

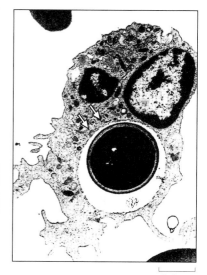

2.5 μm

Figure 12.37
Electron micrograph of a phagocyte (a neutrophil) that has internalized a yeast cell. The yeast cell is enclosed within a membrane-bound phagosome, and lysosomes (arrowed) are fusing with the phagosome to form a phagolysosome.

Phagocytosis in vertebrates and invertebrates is conducted primarily by specialized cells such as macrophages, monocytes and neutrophils, which internalize large pathogens such as bacteria and yeast, or large debris, such as the remnants of dead cells or arterial deposits of fat. Material that has been internalized by phagocytosis forms a phagocytic vacuole (**phagosome**) and will eventually be degraded when lysosomes fuse with the phagosome to form a **phagolysosome**, releasing their digestive enzymes into the vacuole (Figure 12.37). However, the way that a phagocyte responds to phagocytosed material depends very much on the nature of the material and the way in which it is recognized before internalization. For example, bacteria are recognized by the phagocyte as potentially dangerous and they trigger the cell to direct cytotoxic molecules against the internalized bacteria, before digestion in the phagolysosome. Phagocytosis by this pathway activates the phagocyte, which releases cytokines that signal local inflammation. In contrast, debris from cells that have died as part of the normal process of cell turnover, are phagocytosed and degraded, but do not induce the release of cytotoxic molecules, nor do they induce inflammation.

Let us look first at the phagocytosis of apoptotic cells. A molecule that is essential for the successful endocytosis of dying cells is phosphatidylserine.

- ○ Where is phosphatidylserine normally located in the membrane? (Revise Section 6.3.3 if you are unsure.)
- ● It is located on the inner leaflet of the plasma membrane (see Figure 6.18).

Exposure of phosphatidylserine occurs on the outer leaflet of the plasma membrane when cells die by apoptosis. Macrophages have a conserved receptor for phosphatidylserine as well as a number of 'scavenger receptors', which can bind to a variety of other cellular debris. These receptors promote the uptake of dead cells, but crucially, phagocytosis of such debris is associated with the release of cytokines that suppress inflammation. Since apoptosis is a normal physiological process, there is no requirement for the macrophage to signal an inflammatory reaction.

Contrast this with the phagocytosis of pathogens, which are recognized by binding to Fc receptors (antibody receptors) and C3b receptors. (Antibody and C3b are immune system molecules that specifically bind to foreign material.) Some classes of Fc receptors have intracellular domains, which become phosphorylated when the receptor is ligated with antibody. As a consequence, material phagocytosed by these receptors activates the cell and causes it to generate reactive oxidative compounds (e.g. hydrogen peroxide) in the phagosome (Figure 12.38).

Phagocytosis activates GTPases of the Rho family, which cause reorganization of the cytoskeleton as the cell extends processes around the receptor-bound material. The precise way in which this occurs depends on the receptors to which the material has been bound. For example, binding to the Fc receptor will activate a signalling cascade involving activation of Cdc42 and Rac, which causes actin assembly and the formation of cell-surface extensions that close up around the antibody-coated pathogen to engulf it. In other cases, spacious phagosomes may form where the cell extends pseudopodia that eventually fall back on the membrane to enclose the particle and a volume of extracellular fluid. Different receptors appear to trigger phagocytosis by related mechanisms but involving different GTPases.

12.6.4 Lysosomes

Lysosomes are membrane-bound organelles responsible for intracellular digestion of substances derived from both inside and outside the cell. Within their membrane an acidic interior (pH ~ 5) is maintained by the action of proton pumps in the membrane. The lysosomes contain a class of enzymes, hydrolases, that catalyse hydrolysis of covalent bonds in proteins, lipids, carbohydrates and nucleic acids.

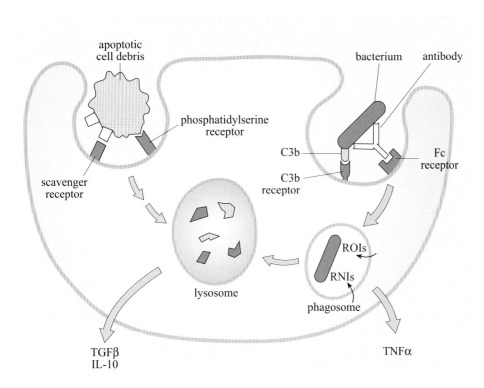

Figure 12.38
Phagocytosis of apoptotic cell debris (left) and pathogens (right) activates different responses in a macrophage. Apoptotic cells taken up by scavenger receptors and a proposed phosphatidylserine receptor are directed to lysosomes, and cause the cell to release cytokines TGFβ and IL-10 which tend to damp down inflammatory reactions. Pathogens such as a bacterium are tagged by antibody and C3b which bind to receptors, which promote internalization, but also induce the secretion of reactive oxygen intermediates (ROIs) and reactive nitrogen intermediates (RNIs) into the phagosomes, to damage or kill the pathogen. This process induces the release of proinflammatory cytokines, such as tumour necrosis factor (TNFα). Killed pathogens are directed to the lysosome for degradation.

The lysosomal hydrolases break down complex molecules into simpler, low molecular mass compounds that can be reused. The enzyme content of lysosomes varies in different tissues according to the needs of the tissue.

Lysosomes are not just involved in breaking down material arriving via endocytosis, but also degrade intracellular debris, such as defective organelles and macromolecules. Molecules destined to be degraded are tagged (most frequently by ubiquitination) and then taken up by lysosomes, or are first encapsulated within endosomes that fuse with lysosomes. This process is called **autophagy**. Products of lysosomal degradation are released from lysosomes into the cytosol and are re-used by the cell. Material that cannot be digested accumulates in vesicles called residual bodies, whose contents are removed from the cell by exocytosis. Some residual bodies contain high concentrations of heterogenous pigmented substances, including polyunsaturated fatty acids and proteins, called lipofucsin or 'age pigment'. Under particular conditions some lysosomal enzymes are secreted from the cell for the digestion of extracellular material in connective tissue.

◯ What do you suppose is the consequence of a genetic deficiency in individual lysosomal enzymes?

⬤ People who are genetically deficient in lysosomal enzymes are unable to break down particular macromolecules that have been directed to the lysosome for recycling. The macromolecules accumulate in the cell, or they may be released to accumulate in the extracellular space.

The deficiencies result in so-called 'lysosomal storage diseases'. What accumulates depends on which type of enzyme is deficient. For example, the lack of some endoglycosidases leads to the accumulation of heparan sulfate-containing

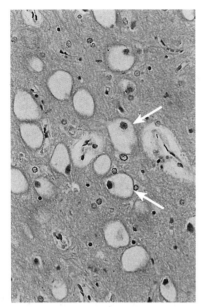

glycoproteins. As a consequence the undegraded molecules accumulate in tissues and cause damage, particularly in the brain where they produce loss of neurons and progressive dementia. Most of these conditions are rare but extremely serious, and affected individuals often die in childhood (Figure 12.39).

12.6.5 Special endosomal compartments

Different cell types may have specialized endosomal compartments related to their specific functions. In this section we are going to look at just one example of this, the pathway of antigen processing and presentation that occurs in a number of different types of leukocyte, including B cells, the lymphocytes that make antibodies.

> The importance of antigen processing and presentation in immune defence is discussed in some detail in S320, Book 3 *Immunology*, Section 2.9. The following section is concerned with the cell biology of the process, but includes just a brief introduction to place it in its physiological context.

In order to synthesize antibodies, B cells interact with another class of lymphocyte, a T helper cell. To do this the B cell has to degrade foreign material that it has internalized and present antigen fragments to the T cell. These steps, called **antigen processing** and **antigen presentation**, play a central role in the induction of the immune response. As you read the following paragraphs, refer to Figure 12.40.

Figure 12.39
A section of brain tissue, stained with haematoxylin and eosin, from a patient who died of type-A Niemann–Pick disease, an autosomal recessive condition that causes progressive neural damage in children. In this disease, the enzyme responsible for one of the steps in the breakdown of sphingomyelin is absent, causing accumulation of sphingolipids. Note the numerous abnormal distended neurons (arrows).

Figure 12.40
Pathways of antigen presentation in a B cell. Antigen is bound to the surface antibody on the B cell, internalized and directed to a compartment where it is degraded by lysosomal enzymes, and moves to the MIIC compartment. MHC class II molecules, with an associated invariant chain, move from the *trans* Golgi network to the MIIC compartment. The invariant chain is removed by proteolysis, and a chaperone molecule (DM) is involved in loading the MHC class II molecule with a peptide. The complex is moved to the cell surface to be presented to a T cell.

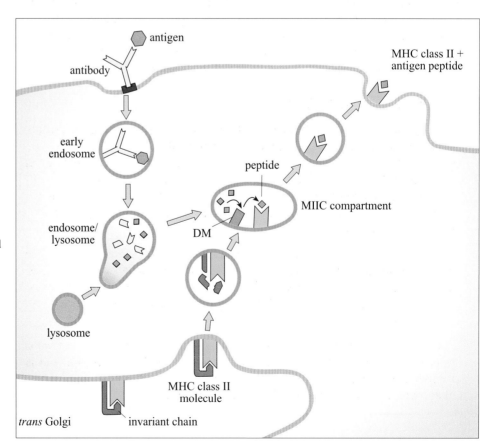

The T cell recognizes small peptide fragments that are non-covalently bound to molecules encoded within the major histocompatibility complex (MHC class II molecules).

Now let us look at the steps in antigen processing and presentation that occur in the B cell, and specifically at the intracellular trafficking pathways. B cells have antibody on their surface, which acts as their receptor for antigen. Antigens that become bound to the surface antibody are endocytosed and passed through the early and late endosomal compartments, and thence to a lysosomal compartment, where they are partly degraded. Partial proteolysis generates polypeptide fragments, which are diverted to an acidic endosomal compartment called the **MIIC compartment**. Figure 12.41 shows the multilamellar appearance of an MIIC compartment in a B cell.

Meanwhile, in the ER, the B cell synthesizes MHC class II molecules, with the associated invariant chain. These are directed to the *trans* Golgi network where they are sorted for delivery to endosomes by a signal sequence that is located in the cytoplasmic tail of the invariant chain. While in transit from the Golgi to the endocytic pathway, the invariant chain is degraded by endosomal proteases. From the *trans* Golgi network, the MHC class II molecules move to the MIIC compartment, where they intersect the pathway taken by polypeptide fragments coming from the lysosomes. Cleavage of the invariant chain causes it to dissociate from the MHC class II molecule, thus exposing its peptide binding site. A type of chaperone (DM in Figure 12.40) located in the compartment now loads the binding site with peptide fragments coming from the lysosomes. The MHC–peptide complex is sent to the cell surface, for potential recognition by a passing T cell.

100 nm

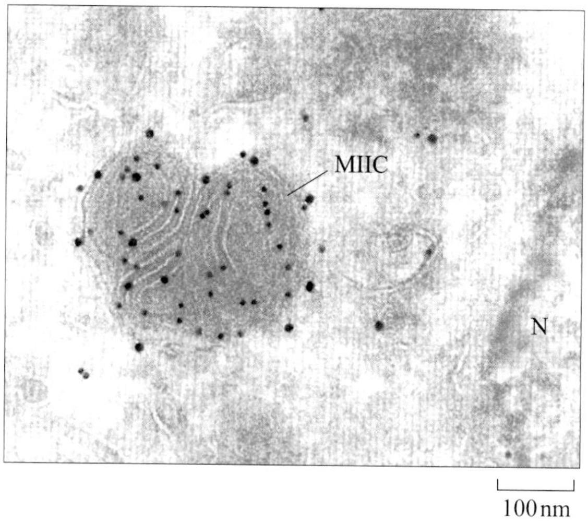

Figure 12.41   The MIIC compartment in a B cell in an ultrathin section. MHC class II molecules are identified by immuno-gold staining with 10 nm gold particles. The molecular chaperone (DM) which loads the peptide fragments onto the MHC class II molecules is identified with 15 nm gold particles. The two molecules colocalize in the MIIC compartment. (N = nucleus).

Summary of Section 12.6

1   Endocytosed material can be taken up by macropinocytosis, via clathrin-coated pits, caveolae or non-coated vesicles. Receptor-mediated uptake is more specific and efficient, and the class of receptor also determines the subsequent intracellular trafficking route. Material taken up by receptor-mediated endocytosis may be dissociated in the endosome, directed to the lysosome or despatched for transcytosis. Monoubiquitination is an important signal for proteins to be endocytosed.

2   The default pathway for endocytosed material is via the early endosome to the late endosome and thence to the lysosome. However some receptors, such as the transferrin receptor, are recycled to the plasma membrane. Other receptors may transfer material across a cell (transcytosis) or to other intracellular compartments.

3   Phagocytosed material is taken up by binding to receptors that direct material to phagosomes that fuse with lysosomes to form phagolysosomes, where it is degraded. The response of the phagocytic cell depends on the nature of the phagocytosed material and on which receptors are ligated.

4   Enzymes within lysosomes degrade material that has been endocytosed, as well as cellular proteins tagged with polyubiquitin, defunct organelles, polynucleotides and lipids. Deficiencies of lysosomal enzymes result in failure to break down macromolecules, and this leads to lysosomal storage diseases.

5   Many cells have specialized endosomal compartments, for example the MIIC compartment in antigen-presenting cells, where antigenic peptides are loaded onto MHC class II molecules.

12.7 Exocytosis

In all eukaryotic cells, proteins that are destined for the plasma membrane or secretion are synthesized in the rough endoplasmic reticulum and enter the Golgi apparatus where they undergo a variety of post-translational modifications, before transfer to the cell surface in secretory vesicles.

◯   Which post-translational modifications of proteins occur in which compartment?

⬤   *N*-glycosylation and *N*-myristoylation occur in the ER. Remodelling of N-glycosyl residues and *O*-glycosylation occur in the Golgi network. Sulfation takes place in the *trans* Golgi network (Section 12.3).

The processes of exocytosis are closely related to those used for importing molecules into the cell. But secretory vesicles not only transport molecules to the plasma membrane, they also provide a mechanism for replenishing and remodelling the plasma membrane with lipids and proteins. The addition of membrane lipids by exocytosis balances the loss of membrane that occurs during endocytosis. Also, membranes in every cell need to be replenished continuously as they become 'aged'.

◯   When introducing the subject of secretion we made a distinction between constitutive and regulated exocytosis or secretion. Based on your understanding of this distinction, say which of the following are constitutive and which are regulated.
1   Release of the hormone adrenalin from cells in the adrenal medulla.
2   Release of the neurotransmitter acetylcholine at the motor end-plate (nerve/muscle junction).
3   Release of the proteolytic enzyme pepsin from gastric epithelium.
4   Release of the cytokine receptor IL-4 to the surface of B cells.
5   Release of the inflammatory mediator serotonin from granules in mast cells.
6   Release of collagen from fibroblasts to form the extracellular matrix.

⬤   They are all examples of regulated secretion except for numbers 4 and 6. Hormones, neurotransmitters, the proteolytic enzymes in the gut and mediators are all secreted at relatively short notice in response to an external stimulus. The release of the IL-4 receptor to the plasma membrane occurs in response to activation of the B cell but is regulated at the level of mRNA transcription; likewise collagen production by fibroblasts. In the case of unregulated secretion, the cell is producing molecules that affect itself or its immediate environment.

In this section we are going to look in detail at one example of regulated secretion, the secretion and release of neurotransmitter from synaptic vesicles, and the way in which this process is triggered. We have already looked at the way in which a synaptic vesicle is coated, and at some of the molecules, such as syntaxin and synaptobrevin, that target it to active zones in the plasma membrane, and effect recovery of the vesicle components. Here we shall continue studying the release of neurotransmitters, but focus on how their release is triggered.

While many neurotransmitters are small molecules (e.g. dopamine and acetylcholine), and are synthesized at the nerve terminal, some are polypeptides, which are synthesized in the rough ER and modified in the Golgi apparatus. However, most neuroactive peptides are not synthesized in the form in which they are eventually secreted, but as a part of a larger inactive precursor protein, or prohormone. Proteolysis of the precursor into smaller fragments, including the active peptides, occurs in the secretory vesicles and in the Golgi apparatus. In some cases, several different neuroactive peptides may be generated from a single precursor. It is possible that there is some advantage in producing small peptides from a large precursor molecule, because such peptides may be too small to carry the necessary signal sequences to send them to their destination; the precursor contains the signals for translation, Golgi processing and intracellular localization, and the final peptides are released only when all these steps have been completed.

After synthesis near the body of the neuron, neuroactive peptides are packed into the vesicles and transported along microtubules in the axon to the release sites, where they are stored until an appropriate stimulus arrives. The distance from the site of synthesis to the point of use at the end of the nerve axon may be considerable. Note that this mechanism to resupply the nerve terminal with neuropeptides and transmitters is a long-term process, distinct from the rapid recycling and reformation of vesicles described in Figure 12.26.

12.7.1 Triggering systems

In neurons, the stimulus for vesicle release is usually a depolarization (action potential) that causes calcium to enter the nerve cell through voltage-gated calcium channels. The rise in intracellular Ca^{2+} concentration, $[Ca^{2+}]$, causes the vesicle to fuse with the plasma membrane and a large amount of neurotransmitter is then released. Although the SNARE complex constitutes the essential fusion machinery of the synaptic vesicles, it is unclear exactly how fusion is triggered by calcium ions. Two elements appear to be important, synaptotagmin and **CaM kinases**, which are a family of kinases whose activity is critically dependent on the local $[Ca^{2+}]$ (see Box 12.5).

☐ Where is synaptotagmin located?

◉ It is present on the membrane of the synaptic vesicle and briefly on the plasma membrane, after the vesicle has fused to release its cargo (see Figure 12.26).

Synaptotagmin is most probably the major calcium sensor that mediates membrane fusion at the synapse. It has a large cytoplasmic calcium-binding domain, and it has been suggested that calcium binding to synaptotagmin induces conformational changes that cause oligomerization (i.e. aggregation of a few molecules) leading it to interact with components of the plasma membrane and thence to the assembly and clustering of the SNARE complex.

In nervous tissue, a member of the CaM kinase family known as CaM kinase II is present at very high concentration. An important property of CaM kinases is their ability to integrate and decode Ca^{2+} pulses. As each action potential reaches the nerve terminal it opens the voltage-gated calcium channels, thus producing a pulse of intracellular Ca^{2+}. An increase in the rate of action potentials produces a corresponding increase in the rate of Ca^{2+} pulses. Because of their molecular memory, the CaM kinases can integrate this signal over time. Moreover, because of the positive feedback in their action the kinase activity of CaM kinases is highly dependent on $[Ca^{2+}]$ – small changes in $[Ca^{2+}]$ produce big changes in kinase activity. One function of CaM kinase II is to phosphorylate synapsin, a protein that controls the interaction of synaptic vesicles with the cytoskeleton and hence whether they are free to bind to the plasma membrane (Figure 12.42). A variety of methods using fluorescent tracers has been used to elucidate the mechanisms of vesicle fusion (Box 12.6).

☐ Calcium-dependent signalling controls secretion in many other cell types. Can you recall another example?

Figure 12.42
Possible mechanisms of Ca^{2+}-dependent fusion of synaptic vesicles. Influx of Ca^{2+} through voltage-gated Ca^{2+} channels activates CaM kinase II, which phosphorylates synapsin. This releases the vesicle from its interaction with microfilaments and allows it to fuse with the plasma membrane, a process that is also mediated by Ca^{2+}, which binds to synaptotagmin and promotes vesicle binding to syntaxin and neurexin.

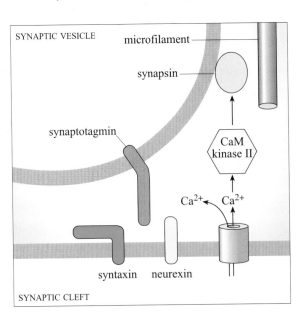

● The rate of release of insulin by β cells in the pancreas is regulated by intracellular $[Ca^{2+}]$ – see Section 12.2.3.

Box 12.6   Investigating exocytosis and endocytosis

Release of neurotransmitters from small synaptic vesicles can be visualized with a fluorescent dye called FM2–10. This dye is not fluorescent in solution but it becomes so after binding to cellular membranes. Thus, when a synaptic terminal is exposed to FM2–10, the external membrane becomes fluorescent. If the neuron is stimulated at this time, the membrane of small synaptic vesicles fuses with the plasma membrane where they encounter the FM2–10. When this vesicular membrane is recycled by endocytosis the synaptic vesicles within the nerve terminal become fluorescent. If the externally added FM2–10 is removed from the medium, the plasma membrane will lose its fluorescence but the internal synaptic vesicles will remain fluorescent. Subsequent stimulation of the nerve terminal thus allows measurement of the rate of fusion of synaptic vesicles at the synaptic junction, as shown in Figure 12.43.

Most studies of neurotransmitter release use electrophysiological measurements of the postsynaptic response to presynaptic events. However, it is also possible to follow presynaptic activity directly by measuring changes in membrane capacitance. When a synaptic vesicle or secretory granule from a non-neuronal cell fuses with the plasma membrane during exocytosis, the surface area of the secreting cell increases. Conversely, the surface area decreases when membrane is retrieved by endocytosis. These changes in the cell surface can be followed by measuring the electrical capacitance of the cell membrane (Figure 12.44).

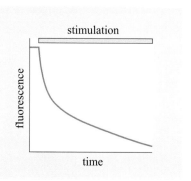

Figure 12.43
Graph demonstrating the change in fluorescence of neuronal cells loaded with FM2–10. Following stimulation the tracer is lost by release into the extracellular medium or by lateral diffusion of the dye in the neuronal membrane.

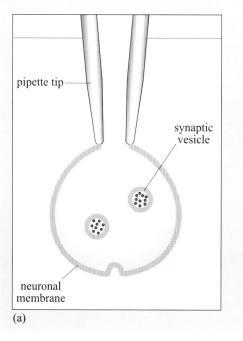

(a)

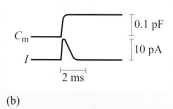

(b)

Figure 12.44
The measurement of membrane capacitance. The starting point is a process in which a small piece of neuronal membrane with its associated synaptic vesicle is held on a pipette tip (a). Following stimulation the vesicles fuse with the membrane, which creates a transient current (I, measured in picoamps, pA) and an increase in the surface area of the membrane, which produces a permanent increase in its capacitance (C_m, measured in picofarads, pF). The trace from such a stimulated preparation is shown in (b).

12.7.2 Regulation of secretion

Up to this point we have made a clear distinction between constitutive secretion and regulated secretion. In reality however the border is a bit more blurred. For example, many molecules are constitutively expressed on the surface of a cell, but their expression is increased in response to a particular stimulus. In other words, surface expression is determined by both constitutive and regulated secretion. Constitutive secretion is regulated primarily at the level of protein synthesis, whereas regulated secretion is controlled at the level of release from intracellular stores.

◯ What is the essential functional difference for the cell in regulating the surface expression of molecules by one mechanism or the other? Think in terms of how long it takes a cell to respond.

● If a cell responds to a stimulus by changing its level of protein synthesis, it will take time before any change is seen in the level of expression at the cell surface (>2 h). But if it responds by releasing molecules from intracellular stores (secretory vesicles), the level of expression on the plasma membrane will increase within seconds.

For this reason, cells that need to respond quickly to a stimulus often retain intracellular stores of molecules that can be rapidly mobilized to the cell surface. In this section, we are going to look briefly at a group of cell surface proteins called **selectins**, which are regulated in this way. Selectins play important roles in blood clotting and in leukocyte migration from the blood into tissues. You will be learning much more about the physiological functions of selectins in Chapter 16: here we shall just look into how a cell regulates their expression.

Selectins are expressed on the plasma membrane of blood platelets and endothelial cells lining blood vessels as well as on leukocytes. They mediate cell-to-cell adhesion. All selectins carry an extracellular lectin domain, which allows them to interact with polymeric carbohydrates present on glycoproteins of other cells. There are three members of the selectin family, E-selectin (Endothelial), P-selectin (Platelet) and L-selectin (Leukocyte) (Figure 12.45), named according to the cells that express them. In practice however, expression of each selectin is not confined to just one cell type, for example both E-selectin and P-selectin are expressed on blood vessel endothelium. The function of P-selectin on endothelium is principally concerned with blood clotting, and the function of E-selectin with leukocyte migration into tissue – a component of inflammation. When an endothelial cell is activated by a suitable stimulus, the surface expression of P-selectin increases within minutes, and the expression of E-selectin increases over 2–8 h.

◯ Which of these two selectins is regulated at the level of protein synthesis and which by regulated secretion? Can you relate the way the cell controls the expression of its selectins to their physiological functions?

● E-selectin expression is enhanced by increasing protein synthesis, which takes several hours, and inflammation is a process that develops over a period of hours or days. P-selectin expression is rapidly increased by release from intracellular stores: blood clotting is, of necessity, a speedy response.

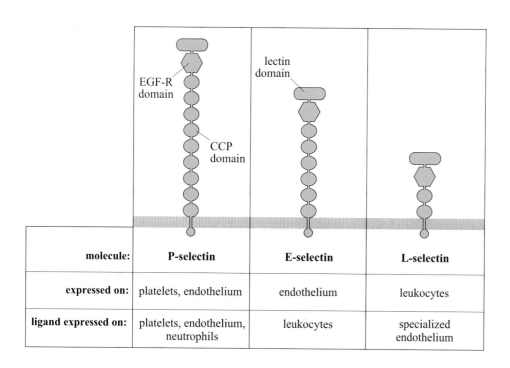

molecule:	P-selectin	E-selectin	L-selectin
expressed on:	platelets, endothelium	endothelium	leukocytes
ligand expressed on:	platelets, endothelium, neutrophils	leukocytes	specialized endothelium

Figure 12.45
Molecules of the selectin family have an N-terminal lectin domain, an epidermal growth factor receptor domain (EGF-R) and a variable number of complement control protein (CCP) domains. They all bind carbohydrate ligands that may be expressed on different cell types, and hence are involved in intercellular adhesion.

There are numerous other examples of proteins whose expression is controlled by both constitutive production and regulated secretion. Moreover, even a protein such as insulin, whose release is controlled by regulated secretion, must be replenished by an appropriate level of protein synthesis.

Summary of Section 12.7

1 Secretion of proteins may be constitutive or regulated. Constitutive secretion replenishes membrane lipids and proteins as part of normal cellular physiology. Cells may also release molecules to remodel their immediate environment, such as the extracellular matrix. Regulated secretion occurs in response to an external stimulus.

2 Secretory vesicles are held near the membrane and released in response to a specific stimulus.

3 In nerve terminals, action potentials cause a rise in intracellular $[Ca^{2+}]$, which activates CaM kinase II to promote release of synaptic vesicles from the cytoskeleton and their fusion with the membrane. Secretion in many other cells is also controlled by intracellular $[Ca^{2+}]$.

4 In many cases the basal expression of surface molecules is controlled by constitutive production and secretion, but release of molecules from intracellular stores can produce a rapid increase in surface expression if required.

Experimental investigation 2

Go to the Study Skills file: *Experimental investigation 2*. This activity explains the technique of immuno-electron microscopy, which is then used to investigate the cellular localization of two proteins. In the second part of the experiment, you will examine how these proteins traffic through different intracellular compartments following stimulation of the cells in tissue culture.

Learning outcomes for Chapter 12

When you have studied this chapter, you should be able to:

12.1   Define and use each of the terms printed in **bold** in the text.

12.2   Describe the characteristics of different intracellular compartments with respect to their structure, location and composition within a mammalian cell.

12.3   Describe the traffic pathways between the endoplasmic reticulum, the Golgi apparatus, the endosomal compartments, and the basolateral and apical regions of the plasma membrane.

12.4   Give examples of regulated and unregulated secretion, the mechanisms controlling the processes, and their functional significance.

12.5   Give examples of endocytosis, the mechanisms involved and their functional significance.

12.6   Describe the components of the cytoskeleton and their role in intracellular transport.

12.7   Describe the main classes of motor protein and their functions within the cell.

12.8   Understand the role of compartmentalization in organizing different intracellular regions for distinct biochemical interactions and cell functions, which are specific for each type of cell.

12.9   Design and interpret the results of an experiment to investigate the subcellular localization of a receptor protein, based on the technique of immuno-electron microscopy.

Questions for Chapter 12

Question 12.1

List the successive steps involved in the endocytosis of transferrin and its transport from the cell surface to an early endosome. (Many of these steps are similar to those occurring in other transport pathways.) Relate these steps to the functions of the proteins listed below, and indicate where they are most likely to fit into the overall process.

AP2, ARF, clathrin, dynamin, epsin, kinesin, GGA-protein, Rab5A, tubulin, transferrin receptor, t-SNARE, v-SNARE.

Question 12.2

Outline the traffic pathway taken by a protein hormone, such as insulin, and give an example of how regulated secretion is controlled.

Question 12.3

In what circumstances can the minus end of a microfilament grow more quickly than the plus end?

Question 12.4

Drugs, such as vincristine, that bind to tubulin αβ heterodimers are used to inhibit the growth of rapidly dividing cells and are used to treat tumours. Why would a drug with this action selectively target dividing cells, in comparison with non-dividing cells such as neurons, which contain extensive microtubule networks?

Question 12.5

If one produced a genetically engineered version of a secreted enzyme, which had the amino acids –KDEL added to the C-terminus, what would you expect to happen to this protein, when expressed within a cell?

Question 12.6

Give three functional similarities and one difference between kinesins and dyneins.

Reference

Alberts, B., Johnson, A., Lewis, J., Raff, M., Roberts, K. and Walter, P. (eds) (2002) *The Molecular Biology of the Cell*, 4th edn, Part IV, Chapters 10–13 and 16, Garland Science, Taylor and Francis Group.

Further sources

Altschuler, Y., Hodson, C. and Milgram, S. (2003) The apical compartment: trafficking pathways, regulators and scaffolding proteins, *Current Opinion in Cell Biology*, **15**, pp. 423–429.

Conner, S. D. and Schmid, S.L. (2003) Regulated portals of entry into the cell, *Nature* **422**, pp. 37–44.

Ford, M., Mills, I., Peter, B., Vallis, Y., Praefcke, G., Evans P. and McMahon, H. (2002) Curvature of clathrin-coated pits driven by epsin, *Nature*, **419**, pp. 361–366.

Jarousse, N. and Kelly, R. (2001) Endocytotic mechanisms in synapses, *Current Opinion in Cell Biology*, **13**, pp. 461–469.

Kandel, E., Schwartz, J. H. and Jessel, T. (2000) *Principles of Neuroscience*, Part III, Chapters 10–16, MacGraw Hill.

Pollard, T. D. and Earnshaw, C. (2002) *Cell Biology*, Chapters 17–24, Elsevier Science.

Solemina, M. and Gerdes, H.-H. (2003) Secretory granules, *Trends in Cell Biology*, **13**, pp. 399–402.

Szule, J. and Coorssen, J. (2003) Revisiting the role of SNAREs in exocytosis and membrane fusion, *Biochimica et Biophysica Acta*, **1641**, pp. 121–135.

Troub, L. M. (2001) Endocytosis: molecules, membranes and movement, *Cell*, **10**, pp. 272–274.

Vincent, J.-P. (2003) Membranes, trafficking and signalling during animal development, *Cell*, **112**, pp. 745–74.

13 SIGNAL TRANSDUCTION

13.1 General principles of signal transduction

Even the simplest organisms can detect and respond to events in their ever-changing environment. Similarly, within a multicellular organism, cells are surrounded by an extracellular environment from which signals are received and responded to. We have studied some cellular responses such as cell division in previous chapters; others such as cell death, differentiation and movement will be discussed in detail in later chapters. Extracellular events are decoded and transmitted to relevant parts of individual cells by way of a series of activation/deactivation steps involving many intracellular molecules. This relay of information along molecular pathways is called **signal transduction**; it is sometimes also simply referred to as 'signalling'.

The fundamental principles of signalling can be illustrated by a simple example in the yeast *S. cerevisiae* (Figure 13.1). In order to sexually reproduce, a yeast cell needs to be able to make physical contact with another yeast cell. First, it has to 'call' to yeast cells of the opposite mating type. It does this by secreting a 'mating factor' peptide, an extracellular signal, which can also be called an 'intercellular signal'. Yeast mating factor binds to specific cell surface receptors on cells of the opposite mating type, and the signal is relayed into the target cell via a chain of interacting intracellular signalling molecules, which switch from an inactive (Figure 13.2a) to an active state (Figure 13.2b). Signalling molecules are said to be **upstream** or **downstream** of other components of the pathway (this terminology should not be confused with that used to describe the structure of genes in relation to transcription). Ultimately, signalling molecules activate target effector proteins (an **effector** in this context is a molecule that carries out the cellular response(s) of

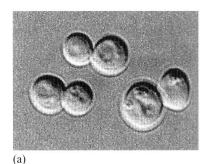

(a)

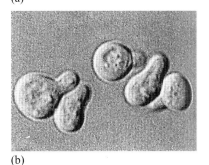

(b)

Figure 13.1
An example of a cellular response to the activation of a signalling pathway by an extracellular molecule.
(a) Resting yeast cells.
(b) Yeast cells respond to mating factor by extending cellular protrusions towards the cell that releases the mating factor.

Figure 13.2
A model of a hypothetical signalling pathway such as the one that operates in yeast. (a) The intracellular signalling molecules (green) and target proteins (blue) are present, but the signalling pathway is not activated. (b) An extracellular signalling molecule has bound to a receptor (usually spanning the plasma membrane) and activated a series of intracellular signalling molecules, which activate target molecules and effect changes in metabolism, the cytoskeleton and gene expression, etc., within the cell.

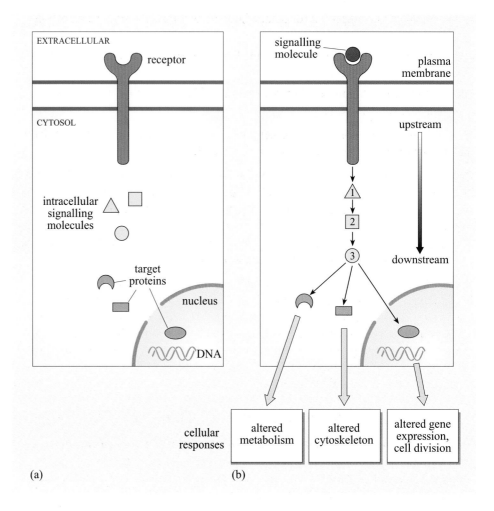

(a) (b)

the signalling pathway). In the yeast, signal transduction to mating factor ultimately stops the target cell proliferating, and induces morphological changes which result in the formation of protrusions towards the cell that releases the mating factor (Figure 13.1b). The morphological changes are a response to the signal. The two cells can then make physical contact with each other, and mating can ensue.

☐ Which signal pathway molecule(s) can be said to be upstream and downstream of molecule 2 in Figure 13.2b?

⬤ The receptor and intracellular signalling molecule 1 are upstream; both intracellular signalling molecule 3 and the target proteins are downstream.

Signalling in multicellular organisms is a complex process, in which many millions of highly specialized cells may need to act in a coordinated fashion. Cells may need to respond to several signals at once, and different cells may need to respond to the same signal in different ways. All this is made possible because the mechanism for detection of a signal is not directly coupled to the response, but is separated by a chain of signalling events, such as that shown in outline in Figure 13.2b. This principle allows signalling systems to be highly *flexible*. Examples of this flexibility are:

▶ the same type of receptor can be coupled to different signalling pathways in different cell types;

- the signal can be amplified (or damped down) as it travels along the signalling pathway;
- it can switch on multiple pathways, leading to several cellular responses in diverse regions of the cell;
- information can be processed from several different receptors at once to produce an integrated response.

Most of this is made possible by protein–protein interactions and protein regulatory mechanisms such as those described in Chapter 3.

Despite this complexity, the basic model of signal transduction set out in Figure 13.2 holds true for most intracellular signalling pathways across species, and often the signalling molecules themselves are highly conserved. For example, there is a high degree of homology between the major proteins in the yeast mating factor signalling pathway and the human mitogen-activated protein (MAP) kinase growth signalling pathway (discussed later in this chapter and in Chapter 19).

A mitogen is an extracellular molecule that induces mitosis in cells.

In this chapter, we shall guide you through the signalling network, firstly by introducing you to the kinds of molecules involved in signal transduction and the general principles employed by cells. Then we shall go into greater detail to show you exactly how the key molecular players operate including receptors and intracellular signalling molecules. In the final section, we shall consider specific examples of signal transduction pathways regulating cellular responses involved in glucose metabolism in different cell types.

13.1.1 Extracellular signals can act locally or at a distance

First we shall consider the general types of *inter*cellular signalling mechanism within multicellular organisms (Figure 13.3). Broadly speaking, cells may interact with each other directly, requiring cell–cell contact, or indirectly, via molecules secreted by one cell, which are then carried away to target cells.

Cell–cell contact-dependent signalling

In some instances, cells may communicate directly with their immediate neighbour through gap junctions (Figure 13.3a (i); also explained in Book 1, p. 287). Communication via gap junctions partially bypasses the signalling model we have outlined above in Figure 13.2. Gap junctions connect the cytoplasm of neighbouring cells via protein channels, which allow the passage of ions and small molecules (such as amino acids) between them (as an example, gap junctions allow the coordinated contraction of cardiac muscle cells).

Alternatively, cells can interact in a 'classic' signalling manner, through cell surface molecules, in a so-called **contact-dependent** way (Figure 13.3a (ii)). Here the signalling molecule is not secreted, but is bound to the plasma membrane of the signalling cell (or may even form part of the extracellular matrix), and interacts directly with the receptor exposed on the surface of the target cell. This type of signalling is particularly important between immune cells, where it forms the basis of antigen presentation and the initiation of the immune response, and also during development, when tissues are forming and communication between cells and their neighbours is paramount in deciding between cell fates such as proliferation, migration, death or differentiation.

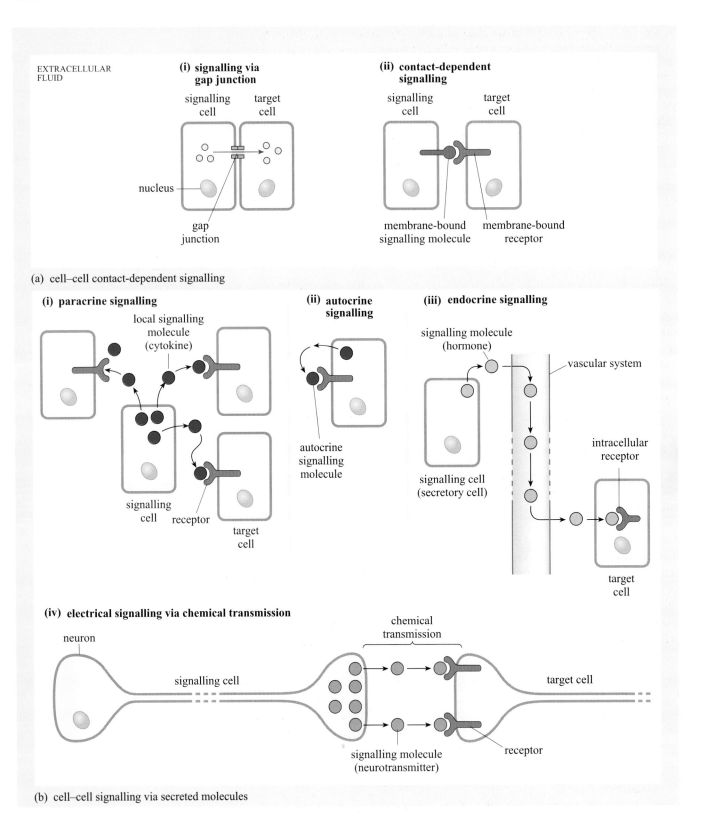

EXTRACELLULAR FLUID

(i) signalling via gap junction

signalling cell   target cell

nucleus

gap junction

(ii) contact-dependent signalling

signalling cell   target cell

membrane-bound signalling molecule   membrane-bound receptor

(a) cell–cell contact-dependent signalling

(i) paracrine signalling

local signalling molecule (cytokine)

signalling cell   receptor

target cell

(ii) autocrine signalling

autocrine signalling molecule

(iii) endocrine signalling

signalling molecule (hormone)

vascular system

signalling cell (secretory cell)

intracellular receptor

target cell

(iv) electrical signalling via chemical transmission

neuron

signalling cell

chemical transmission

target cell

signalling molecule (neurotransmitter)   receptor

(b) cell–cell signalling via secreted molecules

Figure 13.3   The major types of signalling mechanisms found in multicellular organisms. (a) Signalling that depends on contact between cells: (i) via gap junctions; (ii) via cell surface molecules, in which both the ligand and the receptor are located on the plasma membrane of the signalling cell and the target cell. (b) Signalling that depends on secreted molecules (which are mainly water-soluble). (i) Paracrine signalling, in which signalling molecules (cytokines) are released and act locally on nearby cells. (ii) Autocrine signalling, in which signalling molecules are released and then act on the cell that produced them. (iii) Endocrine signalling, in which signalling molecules (hormones) are released from specialized cells and carried in the vascular system (bloodstream) to act on target cells at some distance from the site of release; depending on the nature of the ligand, the receptor can be on the membrane or be intracellular (as shown here). (iv) Electrical signalling, in which the signalling cell transmits information in the form of changes in membrane potential along the length of the cell; the electrical signal is transferred from the signalling cell (here a neuron) to the target cell, either in chemical form (as a neurotransmitter) or via gap junctions.

Cell–cell signalling via secreted molecules

Extracellular signalling molecules are all fairly small, and are easily conveyed to the site of action; they are structurally very diverse. The classification and individual names of these mainly water-soluble mediators often reflect their first discovered action rather than their structure. So, for example, growth factors direct cell survival, growth and proliferation, and interleukins stimulate immune cells (leukocytes). However, to complicate matters further, they often have different effects on different cells, and so sometimes their names can appear confusing. **Signalling via secreted signalling molecules** can be paracrine (acting on neighbouring cells), autocrine (acting on the cell that secretes the signalling molecule), endocrine (acting on cells that are remote from the secreting cell) or electrical (between two neurons or between a neuron and a target cell).

(i) In **paracrine signalling** (Figure 13.3b (i)) water-soluble signal molecules called cytokines diffuse through the extracellular fluid and act locally on nearby cells. This will usually result in a signal concentration gradient, with the cells in the local area responding differentially to the extracellular signalling molecule according to the concentration they are exposed to (this is an important strategy in development). In order to keep the effect contained, signalling molecules involved in paracrine signalling are usually rapidly taken up by cells or degraded by extracellular enzymes. An example of paracrine signalling involves the gaseous molecule nitric oxide (NO), which, among other effects, acts by relaxing smooth muscle cells around blood vessels, resulting in increased blood flow. As the NO molecule is small (and diffuses readily) and short-lived (so only having time to produce local effects), it fulfils the requirements for a paracrine signalling molecule perfectly.

(ii) **Autocrine signalling** (Figure 13.3b (ii)) is an interesting variant of paracrine signalling. In this scenario, the secreted signal acts back on the same cell or group of cells it was secreted from. In development, autocrine signalling reinforces a particular developmental commitment of a cell type (Chapter 17). Autocrine signalling can promote inappropriate proliferation, as may be the case in tumour cells (Chapter 19).

(iii) **Endocrine signalling** (Figure 13.3b (iii)) is a kind of signalling in which signals are transmitted over larger distances, for example from one organ, such as the brain, to another, such as the adrenal gland. For long-distance signalling, diffusion through the extracellular fluid is obviously inadequate. In such cases, signalling molecules may be transported in the blood. Secretory cells that produce signalling molecules are called **endocrine cells**, and are often found in specialized endocrine organs. Blood-borne signalling molecules were the first to be discovered and are collectively known as **hormones** (see margin note), though they are chemically very diverse.

The word 'hormone' was first used by ancient Greeks to describe the vital principle flowing in the body. The term was then resurrected by the English physiologists W. Bayliss and E. Starling, who in 1902 discovered 'secretin', the first known hormone, which is a substance produced in the small intestine that stimulates secretion by the pancreas.

They include steroid hormones (such as the sex hormones and cortisol), some peptide hormones such as insulin, and modified amines that can also act as neurotransmitters (see below) such as noradrenalin. Steroid hormones are biosynthesized from cholesterol. Because they are water-insoluble, they are transported in the blood by specific carrier proteins and are quite stable (their half-lives can be measured in hours or days). This is in contrast to water-soluble signalling molecules, which are much more prone to degradation by extracellular enzymes. Hence they tend to be short lived and are involved in short-term paracrine signalling.

(iv) **Electrical signalling** (Figure 13.3b (iv)) via chemical transmission (also called **synaptic signalling**) is a faster and more specific form of cell–cell signalling. Nerve cells, or neurons, can convey signals across considerable distances to the next neuron in the neuronal network within milliseconds. By contrast, blood-borne messages can only operate as fast as blood circulates, but reach many more cellular targets in different tissues. The transfer of information from one neuron to the next is mediated by complex structures called synapses, which are essentially formed by a presynaptic terminal (neuron 1), a synaptic cleft (the tiny gap between the two neurons) and a postsynaptic membrane (neuron 2). When electrical signals reach the end of a neuronal axon (the thin tube-like part of neurons), molecules released from the axon can cross the physical gap between cells and bind to receptors in the target cell. These signalling molecules are collectively called **neurotransmitters**. Again, these are a diverse group of compounds, including amino acids such as glutamate, nucleotides such as ATP, and CoA derivatives such as acetylcholine.

☐ In addition to its role as a neurotransmitter, can you recall what other roles ATP may have in cells?

⬤ ATP is used in phosphorylation reactions (Chapter 3), as an energy currency (Chapter 4) and as a building block for nucleic acid synthesis (Chapter 5). ATP is only one example by which localization and compartmentalization enables the same molecule to be used effectively for diverse purposes. You will encounter other examples later in this chapter.

13.1.2 Most receptors are on the cell surface

Water-soluble signalling molecules cannot cross the membrane lipid bilayer, but bind to specific receptors embedded in the plasma membrane. The receptors have an extracellular domain that binds the signalling molecule, a hydrophobic transmembrane domain and an intracellular domain.

☐ What other name could be used to describe an extracellular signalling molecule?

⬤ A ligand (Chapter 3).

Binding of a ligand induces a conformational change in the receptor, in particular that of its intracellular region. It is this conformational change that activates a relay of intracellular signalling molecules, ultimately bringing about the appropriate cellular response represented in Figure 13.2.

Receptors can be classified structurally into single-pass transmembrane receptors (with one extracellular, one transmembrane and one intracellular region) and multipass transmembrane receptors (with multiple transmembrane regions and a number of extracellular and intracellular loops; Section 6.4.3). However, in terms of their signal transduction characteristics, it is easier to distinguish four groups of receptors (Figure 13.4).

1   *Receptors that also serve as the effector* For example, one type of acetylcholine receptor is also an ion channel, and belongs to a family of receptors called **ion-channel receptors**. In response to acetylcholine, these receptors allow the passage of specific ions, thereby effecting changes in the membrane potential of a cell. Acetylcholine receptors are extremely important in the transmission of electrical signals between excitable cells.

2   *7-helix transmembrane receptors* (**7TM**; Section 6.4.3) 7TM receptors possess seven membrane-spanning regions, an N-terminal extracellular region and a C-terminal intracellular tail. The mechanism of activation of most 7TM receptors involves coupling to G proteins (Section 3.6.2), and in this case they are also called **G protein-coupled receptors (GPCRs)**. Adrenalin receptors are examples of GPCRs.

3   *Receptors whose intracellular tail contains an enzymatic domain,* which are known as **receptors with intrinsic enzymatic activity (RIEA)** This group includes the receptor tyrosine kinases, involved in the response to many growth factors.

4   *Receptors that require association with cytosolic or membrane-bound proteins with enzymatic activity for signalling* These receptors do not have intrinsic enzymatic activity, and have been referred to as **enzyme-associated receptors** or **recruiter receptors** (although, strictly speaking, both GPCRs and receptors with intrinsic enzymatic activity also function by recruiting cytosolic signalling molecules, as you will see in Section 13.3.2).

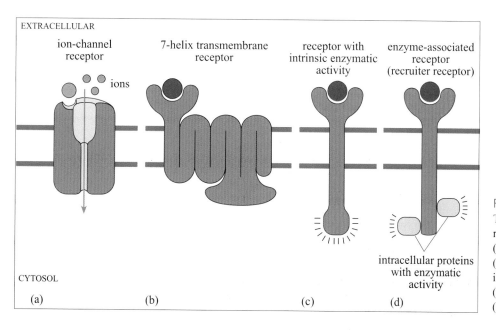

Figure 13.4
The four major classes of membrane receptors: (a) ion-channel receptors; (b) 7-helix transmembrane receptors (7TM receptors); (c) receptors with intrinsic enzymatic activity (RIEA); (d) enzyme-associated receptors (recruiter receptors).

From an evolutionary perspective (Figure 13.5), 7TM receptors are of ancient origin and to date have been found in all eukaryotic genomes that have been sequenced, including yeast (a type of 7TM receptor mediates the yeast mating response described in Section 13.1 and Figure 13.1). Receptors with intrinsic enzymatic activity and many recruiter receptors are found in *C. elegans*, *D. melanogaster* and chordates but not yeast, whereas some recruiter receptors, such as T cell receptors that mediate immune responses, are specific to vertebrates (others such as cytokine receptors are specific to chordates, including all vertebrates and some invertebrates such as the sea-squirt).

In addition to the four groups of cell-surface receptors shown in Figure 13.4, another group of receptors function as DNA-binding molecules, and thus regulate gene transcription (these are called **receptors with intrinsic transcriptional activity**; do not confuse with RIEAs). Some of these receptors (such as Notch, discussed in Chapter 17) are on the cell surface, but most are intracellular (Section 13.3.4), and require ready access of the ligand to the intracellular compartment.

○ What sort of ligand might act on an intracellular receptor?

● Signalling molecules that can readily diffuse through the cell membrane. These include lipid-soluble compounds such as steroid hormones, and small diffusible molecules such as NO.

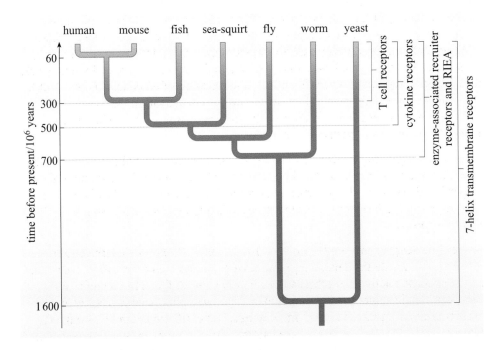

Figure 13.5
Evolutionary origins of plasma membrane receptors. Receptor families are presented in order of their presumed appearance during evolution. (RIEA = receptors with intrinsic enzymatic activity.)

13.1.3 Cellular responses are diverse

Cellular responses can be extremely rapid – for example, the opening of ion channels to effect a change in the membrane potential or the contraction of muscle fibres, which occur within milliseconds of signal reception, or may take minutes, such as whole cell movement, synthesis of new proteins or changes in metabolic activity.

There are also longer-term responses, which may be on the scale of hours or even days, such as cell division (Chapter 8) and programmed cell death (Chapter 14). Often several types of response may occur following a single stimulus, in a coordinated manner, and over different timescales.

Within a multicellular organism, a given cell is exposed to many different extracellular signals at any one time. The cell's ultimate response depends on the appropriate integration of these signals and on what cell type it is (for example, only a muscle cell can contract). So, for instance, signal 1 will induce a cell to proliferate but only in the presence of signal 2; in the absence of signal 2, signal 1 will induce the same cell to differentiate. The same signals may produce different responses in different cell types. In the example above, signal 1 might induce cell death in a second cell type. Different cellular responses to an extracellular signal are due at least partly to the specific receptors and intracellular signalling molecules that are active in different cell types. So, not only is the context of the signal vitally important in determining the response but also the type of target cell.

13.1.4 Signal transduction mechanisms

Signalling information has to be transmitted from the receptor in the plasma membrane across the cytoplasm to the nucleus (if gene transcription is the response), the cytoskeleton (if cell movement, or another change to cell morphology, is the response), or various other subcellular compartments. The transmission of a signal must occur in a time-frame appropriate for the cellular response. So, signal transduction needs to take place over both space and time. We have already described a simple signalling model (Figure 13.2), where a chain of intracellular mediators successively activates the next in the chain until the target is reached. In reality, of course, it is rarely a simple chain, but a branching network, allowing for integration, diversification and modulation of responses (Figure 13.6). The branched molecular network of activation (and deactivation) of signalling molecules linking receptor activation to the intracellular targets is referred to as a **signal transduction pathway** (or cascade).

Intracellular signalling molecules have particular properties that allow control of the speed, duration and target of the signal, and may be categorized according to these properties. Broadly speaking, intracellular signalling molecules can be divided into two groups on the basis of molecular characteristics, *second messengers* and *signalling proteins*.

Second messengers are small readily diffusible intracellular mediators, whose concentration inside the cell changes rapidly on receptor activation; in this manner, they regulate the activity of other target signalling molecules. The calcium ion, Ca^{2+}, is a classic example of a second messenger, being released in large quantities in response to a signal (so amplifying the signal) and diffusing rapidly through the cytosol. Ca^{2+} ions can therefore broadcast the signal quickly to several distant parts of the cell. For example, Ca^{2+} ions mediate and coordinate contraction of skeletal muscle cells (Figure 13.7). In general, if a rapid, generalized response is necessary, a second messenger is likely be prominent in the signalling pathway.

Other water-soluble second messengers such as cAMP and cGMP act similarly to Ca^{2+}, by diffusing through the cytosol, whereas second messengers such as diacylglycerol (DAG) are lipid-soluble, and diffuse along the inside of the plasma membrane, in which are anchored various other key signalling proteins.

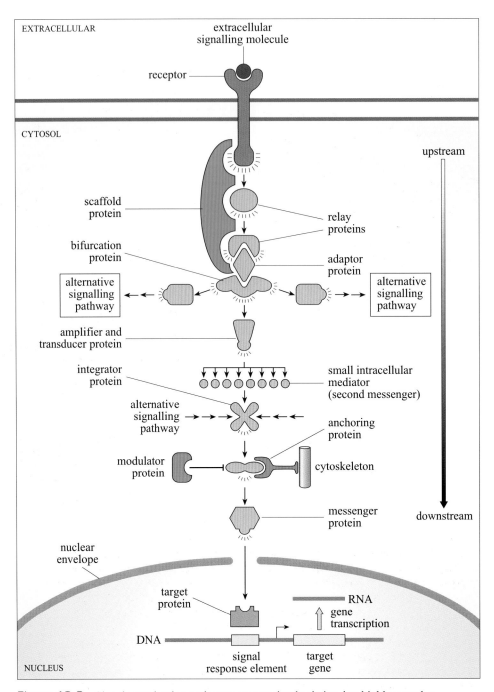

Figure 13.6   Signal transduction pathways are not simple chains, but highly complex, branching pathways, involving many different types of signalling proteins (including scaffold proteins, relay proteins, bifurcation proteins, adaptor proteins, amplifier and transducer proteins, integrator proteins, modulator proteins, messenger proteins and target proteins) and small intracellular mediators known as second messengers. This figure illustrates all the types of interaction involving signalling proteins and second messengers, leading to cellular responses, in this case expression of a target gene and/or changes in the cytoskeleton (via the anchoring protein). A typical signalling pathway will involve many of these components.

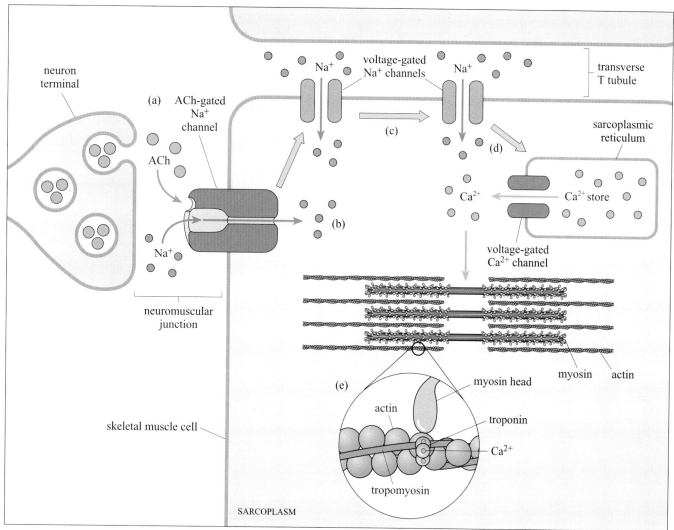

Figure 13.7 Calcium ions help to synchronize the rapid contraction of skeletal muscle cells.
(a) Acetylcholine (ACh, shown in pink) is released from the neuron terminal, and binds to
ACh-gated Na^+ channels on the surface of the muscle cell. (b) These receptors are ion channels,
and so promote local depolarization (an increase in membrane potential caused by the entry
of sodium ions). (c) Depolarization is propagated in the muscle cell (yellow arrows) by
voltage-gated Na^+ channels, which allow further Na^+ ion entry. (d) This more general
depolarization triggers the very rapid release of Ca^{2+} ions into the sarcoplasm (muscle
cytoplasm) through voltage-gated Ca^{2+} channels from stores in the sarcoplasmic reticulum;
the Ca^{2+} ions spread through the muscle cell. (e) The increase of Ca^{2+} concentration throughout
the sarcoplasm enables the rapid and synchronous contraction of the muscle filaments.
Ca^{2+} achieves this by binding to an inhibitory protein complex of tropomyosin and troponin,
which under resting conditions prevents actin and myosin filaments from interacting. (See also
S204 Book 3 Volume II, Section 7.5.3)

How membrane potentials are
maintained and electrical impulses are
generated is described in S204 Book 3,
Box 6.1, Section 6.4.2.

Second messengers were the first intracellular signalling molecules to be identified; they were so named because hormones or other extracellular signalling molecules were considered the 'first messengers'. However, the term 'second messenger' seems somewhat outdated, since a signalling pathway can easily involve a sequence of eight or more different messengers, and the 'second messenger' in question could well actually be acting as, say, the fifth messenger.

Signalling proteins are the large intracellular signalling molecules that generally, but not exclusively, function by activating the next signalling protein in the signal transduction cascade, or by modifying the concentration of second messengers.

○ From what you have learnt about proteins in Chapter 3, cite the attributes relevant to signal transduction which signalling proteins might have compared with small second messengers such as Ca^{2+}.

● Proteins are much larger and generally less mobile than small water-soluble second messengers, so they are not so useful for the rapid dissemination and amplification of a signal. However, proteins are capable of interacting in a highly specific manner with other proteins, they exhibit binding specificity for ligands and for recognition motifs on other molecules, and their activity can be regulated, for example by allosteric regulation and by phosphorylation. They are therefore able to perform rather more sophisticated signalling roles than water-soluble second messengers.

Attempts have been made to group intracellular signalling proteins according to their function, but you will soon see that there are plenty that have more than one function, making classification into functional groupings difficult. Nevertheless, these descriptions give a flavour of the variety of possible signalling functions. Later in this chapter we shall discuss many examples from these groups.

▶ *Relay proteins* simply pass the signal on to the next member of the chain.

▶ *Messenger proteins* carry the signal from one part of the cell to another. For example, activation may cause translocation of the protein from the cytosol to the nucleus.

▶ *Amplifier proteins* are capable of either activating many downstream signalling proteins or generating large numbers of second messenger molecules; they tend to be enzymes such as adenylyl cyclase, which synthesizes cAMP, or ion channels such as Ca^{2+} channels, which open to release Ca^{2+} ions from intracellular stores.

▶ *Transducer proteins* change the signal into a different form. Voltage-gated Ca^{2+} channels are examples of signalling proteins, which fall into two of these functional categories, since in addition to their role as an amplifier protein, they detect a change in membrane potential, and transduce it into an increase in the concentration of a second messenger.

▶ *Bifurcation proteins* branch the signal to different signalling pathways.

▶ *Integrator proteins* receive two or more signals from different pathways, and integrate their input into a common signalling pathway.

▶ *Modulator proteins* regulate the activity of a signalling protein.

Other proteins are involved purely in the correct placement of some signalling molecules:

▶ *Anchoring proteins* tether members of the signalling pathway in particular subcellular locations, such as the plasma membrane or the cytoskeleton, thereby ensuring that the signal is being relayed to the right place.

▶ *Adaptor proteins* link one signalling protein with the next at the correct time, without signalling themselves.

▶ *Scaffold proteins* are proteins that bind several signalling proteins, and may also tether them, forming a much more efficient functional complex. Scaffold proteins may therefore share attributes of both anchoring and adaptor proteins.

13.1.5 Signalling proteins can act as molecular switches

How does a signalling molecule actually convey a signal? With second messengers, it is easy to understand: they are produced or released in large quantities, diffuse to their target, to which they usually bind, bringing about a functional change, after which they are degraded or stored within a subcellular compartment (such as endoplasmic reticulum). With signalling proteins it is less obvious. Protein concentrations cannot fluctuate rapidly, and protein molecules cannot easily move within the cell. As you learnt in Chapter 3, the conformation of many proteins is related to their activity, and is subject to regulatory mechanisms.

◻ What are the mechanisms by which proteins can be switched from one conformation to another?

⬤ One way of modulating a protein's activity is by allosteric regulation, whereby binding of a small ligand induces a conformational change in the protein. Another way is by addition of a negatively charged phosphate group, either by phosphorylation of an amino acid residue by a protein kinase or by binding of a GTP molecule instead of a GDP (G proteins).

Although allosteric regulation by binding small molecules is a widespread regulatory mechanism for the activity of many proteins, including receptors and structural, motor and signalling proteins, the addition or loss of phosphate groups usually drives most functional changes in the sequence of activation/deactivation steps that form a typical intracellular signalling pathway. In reality, many intracellular signalling proteins act as **molecular switches**. What often happens is that the proteins can be temporarily modified, converting them from an inactive (non-signalling) form to an active (signalling) form (Figure 13.2), or vice versa. Usually the upstream signal induces a change in the protein's conformation, which enables it to carry out its downstream signalling function. The reason why such molecules are sometimes referred to as molecular switches is because they are either 'on' or 'off'. These proteins can be grouped according to how they are switched on/off, rather than their subsequent mode of action. As outlined above and in Figure 13.8, signalling molecular switches mainly belong to two categories.

One group of proteins often encountered in signalling are those that are modified by phosphorylation of an amino acid residue by an upstream kinase (Figure 13.8a). The phosphate is derived from the terminal (γ) phosphate of ATP, and added covalently to a tyrosine, serine or threonine residue by a protein kinase. Phosphorylation usually, but not necessarily, activates a protein. Sometimes, however, it may cause a conformational change that inactivates the protein.

Figure 13.8

Molecular switches used in signalling pathways. There is a remarkable similarity between the two systems, phosphorylation and GTP binding. In both, the protein switches between the active and the inactive conformation by the addition/removal of a phosphate group. (a) In the case of proteins that are phosphorylated, the phosphate is derived from the terminal phosphate of ATP, and then added covalently to a tyrosine, serine or threonine residue by a kinase. It is subsequently removed by a phosphatase, generating P_i (inorganic phosphate). (b) In the case of a G protein, the extra phosphate is added by substituting GTP in the place of GDP, often with the help of guanine nucleotide exchange factors (GEFs). The GTP is hydrolysed back to GDP (again, releasing P_i) by either intrinsic or accessory (via GTPase activating proteins, GAPs) GTPase activity.

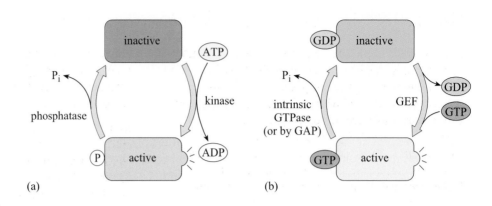

The phosphate group is subsequently removed by a phosphatase, generating P_i (inorganic phosphate), and the protein reverts to its original form. The length of time that the protein remains in its phosphorylated state before being dephosphorylated can be important in determining the signalling outcome. If phosphorylation induces activation, the longer a signalling protein is active, the more downstream signalling molecules it can activate (or the longer that second messengers are synthesized or released by an active signalling protein, the higher the concentrations that they achieve). It is important to note here that many phosphorylated signalling proteins are protein kinases themselves, whose activation results in a series of phosphorylation cascades, as you will see in Section 13.3.5 (see also Box 13.1).

The second main group of signalling molecular switch proteins are the GTP-binding proteins, known as G proteins (Figure 13.8b). In this case, the on/off state characterized by the addition/loss of a phosphate group is not mediated by covalent binding of a phosphate group, but by the binding of a GTP molecule and its hydrolysis to GDP.

◯ What is the basic mechanism of G protein regulation involving Ras as the G protein (Chapter 3)?

⬤ Ras protein is the classic example of a G protein. It has an important role in cell signalling. G proteins such as Ras bind GTP, in which conformation they are active. However, as they have intrinsic GTPase activity, they are only active for a limited time, because the bound GTP becomes hydrolysed to GDP. The protein adopts a different conformation when it is bound to GDP, rendering it inactive. GAPs (GTPase activating proteins) are regulatory proteins that enhance the GTPase activity of the protein, hence helping inactivation, whereas GEFs (guanine nucleotide exchange factors) accelerate dissociation of GDP, allowing it to be replaced by GTP, and promoting activation.

In the same way that the rate of dephosphorylation of a phosphorylated protein determines how long it remains active, the length of time that a GTP-binding protein remains active (and hence the number of downstream molecules it can activate) is determined by the rate of GTPase activity. As described in Chapter 3, their activity is controlled by regulatory proteins called GEFs and GAPs. In a sense, GEFs play a similar role to protein kinases and GAPs are comparable to protein phosphatases. In their active form, G proteins also cause a cascade of phosphorylation events, ultimately resulting in a cellular response.

Box 13.1 Identification of phosphorylated residues in signalling proteins

For many years, phosphopeptide and phosphoamino acid mapping has been a useful method used for identifying protein phosphorylation sites. Cells are metabolically labelled with radioactive P_i, and protein extracts are subjected to polyacrylamide gel electrophoresis (SDS–PAGE; see Chapter 3 and *Experimental investigation 1*) and Western-blotted onto a special membrane. The protein of interest is then isolated, hydrolysed into peptide fragments by proteases or into individual amino acids by hydrochloric acid, and are then separated by two-dimensional thin-layer chromatography on cellulose plates. The extent of phosphorylation of tyrosine, threonine and serine residues is finally established by autoradiography. Another technique, first developed in the 1980s, involves the use of monoclonal anti-phosphotyrosine antibodies, which specifically recognize phosphorylated tyrosine residues in many proteins. For investigation of signal transduction mechanisms, this was an essential tool for studying the activity of tyrosine kinases and phosphatases. The antibody can either be used to probe Western-blotted proteins (Figure 13.9) or, in a more refined technique, can be used to immunoprecipitate the phosphoproteins before separating them by SDS–PAGE.

However, these techniques require the use of populations of single cell types, as these antibodies would not differentiate between cell types in mixed cell populations.

More recently, other polyclonal and monoclonal antibodies targeted to phosphorylated residues (serine, threonine and/or tyrosine) within a specific amino acid sequence of a protein have been developed. For example, there are antibodies that recognize phosphorylated Tyr 527 of Src, and others that recognize Tyr 416 of Src, providing a rapid and easy experimental methodology for the study of Src activation. The use of antibodies specific for phosphorylated amino acid residues has allowed the study of signalling protein activation *in vivo* on tissue sections using immunocytochemical techniques. Cocktails of 30 or more of these antibodies can also be used in combination to simultaneously detect the activation state of several signalling pathways by probing proteins separated in 2-D gels. How these techniques are used experimentally will be explored further in *Experimental investigation 3*, to which you are directed at the end of this chapter.

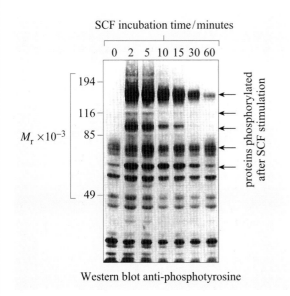

Western blot anti-phosphotyrosine

Figure 13.9

Western blot of phosphotyrosine-containing proteins. In this example, cells (a cell line called CMK) were incubated in a culture medium called 'starving medium', which lacked growth supplements. They were then stimulated with a growth factor called 'stem cell factor' (SCF) and harvested after the indicated incubation times. Whole-cell lysates were separated on an SDS–PAGE gel, blotted onto a membrane, and probed with an anti-phosphotyrosine monoclonal antibody. The blot shows that in resting cells there are some proteins with phosphorylated tyrosines, but that within 2 minutes of SCF stimulation, several proteins have become either *further* tyrosine phosphorylated (characterized by the enlarged bands in treated cells (bottom two arrows)) or *newly* phosphorylated (top three arrows), the effect mostly wearing off within an hour. SCF binds to a receptor tyrosine kinase called 'c-Kit', which is probably both directly and indirectly responsible for the phosphorylations seen here. (Data from Jhun *et al.*, 1995.)

Note: Do not confuse stem cell factor (SCF) with the SCF complex that triggers degradation of cyclins (Section 8.3.3).

Molecular switches can be a lot more sophisticated than a single on/off function. As you learnt in Chapter 3, a protein can be phosphorylated at multiple sites, which may have different effects on its activity.

○ In Chapter 3 you learnt about the regulation of the kinase Src. Summarize the main features of this regulation.

● The inactive conformation of Src is stabilized by intramolecular interactions between the SH2 and SH3 domains, and specific sequences within the kinase domain. When the SH2 and SH3 domains bind to other proteins, the phosphate on Tyr 527 becomes exposed and is removed by a phosphatase, whereas Tyr 416 can be phosphorylated. As a result, Src becomes activated.

A signalling protein such as Src therefore requires several events to happen in order to adopt its fully active conformation. This type of signalling protein can therefore integrate many different signals such that the signalling outcome is determined by the summation of signalling inputs. Therefore, they behave as specific signal integrators.

13.1.6 Localization of signalling proteins

Since signalling proteins cannot diffuse as rapidly as small second messengers, they need be close to their downstream target in order to be able to function. Where they are located with respect to both their subcellular position and their immediate neighbours is therefore vitally important. The plasma membrane is usually the initial location, and proteins can be attached to the plasma membrane in various ways (discussed in Chapters 3, 6 and 11; see also Figure 13.10). Many have hydrophobic regions that are inserted into the membrane as the polypeptide is being synthesized (for example, transmembrane receptors).

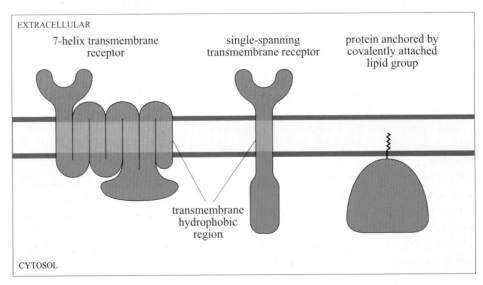

Figure 13.10 Membrane localization of signalling proteins. Most membrane-bound receptors have hydrophobic regions (seven for 7TM receptors or one for single-spanning transmembrane receptors such as receptor tyrosine kinases), which are inserted into the membrane during synthesis. Alternatively, some proteins (notably G proteins) undergo post-translational modification, acquiring a lipid group involving prenylation or fatty acylation, which tethers the protein to the cytosolic face of the membrane.

○   What *post*-translational modifications could serve to anchor a signalling protein to the cytosolic side of the plasma membrane?

⬤   Covalent addition of a lipid group, prenylation or fatty acylation, tethers proteins to the internal surface of the plasma membrane. The Ras family of G proteins is an example of this type of protein.

The area of the cell membrane near a receptor can become crowded with signalling molecules. Very often, several signalling pathways will need to be activated following binding of the ligand to the membrane receptor, since the cellular response may require multiple changes in cell behaviour (such as a change in cell shape, altered metabolism or changes in gene expression). Many signalling molecules, leading to different signal transduction pathways, will be packed together around the cytoplasmic domain of the receptor, and it is unclear how unwanted signalling outcomes are avoided and how signal specificity is maintained.

One mechanism involves the signalling molecules being arranged on a protein scaffold, such that the proteins are ordered in the correct signalling sequences or, in other words, as a *preassembled signalling complex* (Figure 13.11a). This scheme requires one of the signalling components to be able to detach itself from the complex and distribute the signal to other parts of the cell. A similar strategy congregates receptors together with many signalling proteins into specific areas in the plasma membrane such as cholesterol- and glycosphingolipid-rich lipid rafts (Section 6.5), which may then be considered as plasma membrane signal initiator units.

Alternatively, complexes can form transiently, following receptor activation. In this case, the intracellular signalling proteins only assemble once the receptor has bound its extracellular signal molecule (ligand). A common mechanism involves the autophosphorylation of key amino acid residues in the cytoplasmic domain of the receptor after ligand binding (see p. 100). The signalling proteins then recognize and dock onto particular phosphorylated amino acids (Figure 13.11b). We shall see specific examples of this in Section 13.3.

At some point, the signal has to be transmitted over a significant distance and between cellular compartments within the cell in order to reach its targets. How does the signal ultimately escape from the cytosolic side of the plasma membrane? As pointed out earlier, one mechanism involves the deployment of small, diffusible second messengers, which also results in amplification of the signal throughout the cell. However, this system lacks specificity in the subcellular target. Alternatively, signalling proteins themselves can be directed specifically to another part of the cell. In order to achieve this, their 'on switch' (when they are activated by an upstream signalling molecule) must somehow enable them to be transported. For example, when the signalling enzyme MAP kinase is phosphorylated on tyrosine and threonine residues by its upstream kinase, it translocates from the cytoplasm into the nucleus, where it phosphorylates specific transcription factors and so alters the pattern of gene expression. (The MAP kinase pathway is considered in more detail in Section 13.3.5.)

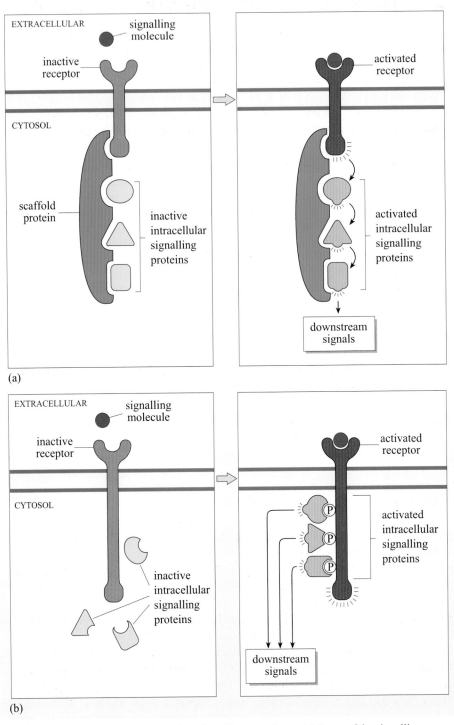

Figure 13.11   Preformed and transient signalling complexes. (a) Some of the signalling proteins are preassembled on a scaffold protein, and are activated sequentially following a signal. (b) Transient assembly of the signalling complex following receptor activation involves the autophosphorylation of the activated receptor at multiple sites, after which the downstream signalling proteins dock at these sites and become activated.

13.1.7 Protein–protein interactions in signal transduction

Many signalling proteins have both a catalytic domain and sometimes several binding domains (as described in Chapter 3). Some only have binding domains, enabling their proteins to act as adaptor, scaffold or anchoring proteins to bring other proteins together. Because of this multiplicity of binding domains, signalling proteins can potentially combine to form complexes with many other proteins; these complexes may be either transient (e.g. in response to stimulation by a growth factor), or stable (to target a protein to an appropriate location). However, protein–protein interactions are not random, as the specific interactions between binding domains and their recognition sites will determine the precise route(s) that a signal transduction pathway will take.

◯ What were the binding domains in signalling proteins introduced in Chapter 3, and what are their binding motifs?

⬤ You may have considered the following (Book 1, Table 3.5, p. 112):

▶ Src homology 2 (SH2) and phosphotyrosine binding (PTB) domains, which bind phosphorylated tyrosine residues.

▶ Pleckstrin homology (PH) domains, which bind phosphorylated inositol phospholipids.

▶ Src homology 3 (SH3) domains, which bind proline-rich motifs.

▶ PDZ domains, which bind specific motifs (involving about five amino acid residues), and are common in scaffold proteins.

Figure 13.12 shows a hypothetical signalling cascade, drawn to illustrate how different protein domains have specific functions that result in an ordered network of consecutive protein–protein interactions – in other words, in a signal transduction pathway. Receptor activation by an extracellular signalling molecule leads to the phosphorylation of tyrosine residues on the receptor and of inositol phospholipids on the cytosolic face of the plasma membrane (Section 6.2.2), thereby creating temporary docking sites for an array of SH2- and PH-containing signalling proteins. A cytosolic signalling protein (shown as signalling protein X) contains three different binding domains plus a catalytic kinase domain. On stimulation by an extracellular signalling molecule, signalling protein X translocates to the plasma membrane by virtue of interactions between its SH2 domain and a phosphorylated tyrosine on the receptor protein (sometimes referred as **phosphotyrosine** or **pY**), and between its PH domain and phosphorylated inositol phospholipids in the cytosolic leaflet of the lipid bilayer. This translocation results in a change of conformation in protein X, which unfolds a PTB domain, allowing it to bind a phosphorylated tyrosine in protein Y. The kinase domain in signalling protein X then phosphorylates signalling protein Y on another tyrosine, which subsequently binds to the SH2 domain of an adaptor protein. The SH3 domain in the adaptor protein binds to a proline-rich motif on signalling protein Z. This interaction brings protein Z close to protein Y, such that protein Z is phosphorylated at a tyrosine residue. The signal is then relayed downstream by the activated protein Z.

Figure 13.13 shows the diversity and flexibility of protein-binding domains in some examples of signalling proteins (discussed later in this chapter).

Figure 13.12

A hypothetical signalling pathway, highlighting the interactions between binding domains and their recognition motifs in signalling proteins. Note that different protein binding domains have been listed next to their respective binding motifs in the key.

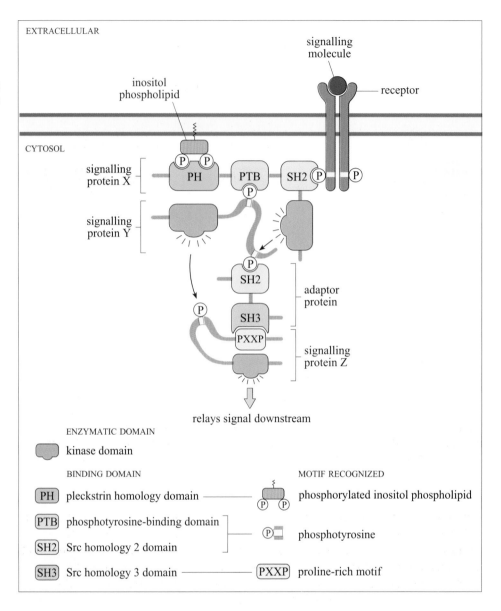

Protein domains can often be identified from their amino acid sequence, and their function deduced from similar, better characterized, proteins. Hence, when a new signalling molecule is identified, it is now often possible to predict, in general terms, from its sequence what it is likely to bind to, and what type of binding domains the signalling molecule contains. It is important to note that whereas the function of a binding domain may sometimes be predicted by the sequence (SH2 domains always bind phosphorylated tyrosines), protein–protein interactions are highly specific — that is, not *all* phosphorylated tyrosines are recognized by a particular SH2 domain.

The selectivity of recognition of a motif by a binding domain such as SH2 is conferred by the amino acid sequence adjacent to the phosphorylated residue. We shall illustrate this principle with the SH2 domain of a protein you encountered in Chapter 3, the tyrosine kinase Src, which has both SH2 and SH3 domains, and a kinase domain (Figure 13.14a). The core structural elements of its SH2 domain

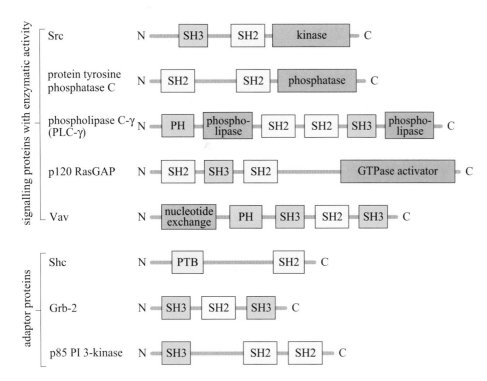

Figure 13.13   Some examples of signalling proteins with different binding domains.
In addition to their enzymatic domains, signalling proteins contain binding domains (SH2,
SH3, PTB, PH, etc.), which allow interactions with other proteins. Adaptor proteins contain
binding domains (but not enzymatic domains), hence bringing different signalling proteins in
close proximity. All the proteins in this figure (with the exception of Vav) are described later in
the chapter.

comprise a central hydrophobic antiparallel β sheet, flanked by two short α helices
(Figure 13.14b), which together form a compact flattened hemisphere with two
surface pockets. The SH2 domain binds the phosphotyrosine-containing polypeptide
substrate via these surface pockets (Figure 13.15). One pocket (phosphotyrosine
pocket) represents the binding site for phosphotyrosine, whereas the specificity
pocket allows interaction with residues that are distinct from the phosphotyrosine,
in particular the third residue on the C-terminal side of the phosphotyrosine. So, for
example, the SH2 domain of Src recognizes the sequence pYXXI, where X is a
hydrophilic amino acid, I is isoleucine and pY is phosphorylated tyrosine. Note that
all proteins that contain this sequence of amino acids are putative binding partners
for the SH2 domain of Src, including the C-terminal phosphotyrosine (pY 527) of
Src itself.

You will be able to study the interactions between SH2 domains and their binding
motifs in more detail in *Molecular modelling 7*.

The SH3 domain has a characteristic fold consisting of five β strands, arranged as
two tightly packed antiparallel β sheets (Figure 13.14c). The surface of the SH3
domain bears a flat, hydrophobic ligand-binding pocket, which consists of three
shallow grooves defined by aromatic amino acid residues, which determine
specificity. In all cases, the region bound by the SH3 domain is proline-rich, and
contains the sequence PXXP as a conserved binding motif (where X in this
case is any amino acid).

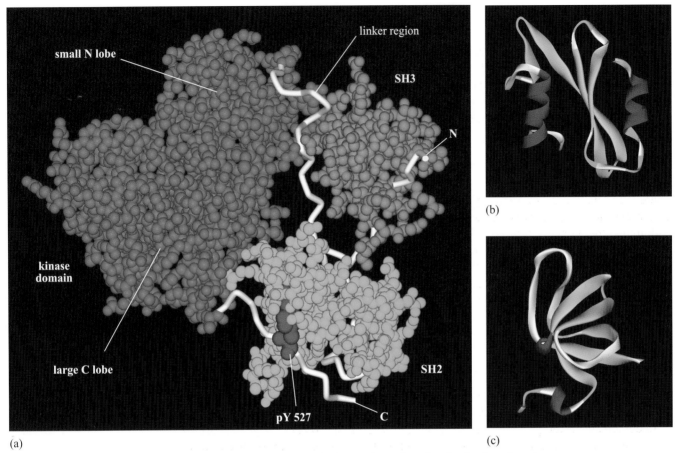

(a)

(b)

(c)

Figure 13.14   (a) The structure of human Src in its compact, inactive conformation, showing its three domains. The SH3 domain has a loose association with the 'linker' region, which has some structural similarity to a polyproline chain. The SH2 domain binds to the C-terminal phosphotyrosine, pY 527. (b) The core structural elements of Src's SH2 domain comprise a central hydrophobic antiparallel β sheet, flanked by two short α helices. (c) The SH3 domain consists of two tightly packed antiparallel β sheets. (Based on pdb file 1fmk.)

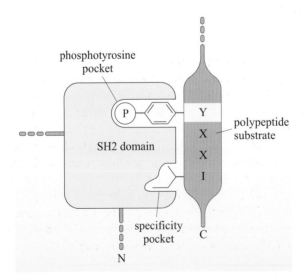

Figure 13.15
Recognition of phosphotyrosine and adjacent amino acids in peptide substrates by the SH2 domain of Src. Selectivity of recognition by SH2 domains is determined by the sequence of amino acids, particularly the third residue (here isoleucine, I) on the C-terminal side of the phosphorylated tyrosine. X is a hydrophilic amino acid residue.

Molecular modelling 7

Go to the Study Skills file: *Molecular Modelling 7*. This activity uses ViewerLite™ to investigate the specificity-determining interactions between protein-binding domains and their respective ligands. It will help you to understand the importance of residues adjacent to phosphotyrosine for the recognition of substrate peptides by SH2 domains.

There are various ways of assaying whether signalling proteins interact with each other through their binding domains. Many of these techniques such as co-immunoprecipitation, yeast two-hybrid screening, proteomics and FRET have already been described in Section 3.8.2 or in Chapter 6. Box 13.2 describes another technique used to analyse protein–protein interactions that you will use in *Experimental investigation 3* at the end of this chapter.

Box 13.2 Use of fusion proteins for pull-down assays in the study of signalling protein domain interactions

Individual domains often retain their function when isolated from their parent protein, and they can be genetically engineered to be fused with other proteins/peptides. Recombinant fusion proteins consist of two proteins: (a) a protein or peptide sequence used as a tag to facilitate protein isolation; and (b) the 'bait' protein, used as a means of indirectly 'pulling down' interacting proteins. One very useful example of this technique is the use of glutathione *S*-transferase (GST) fusion proteins; they consist of GST (tag) fused to a protein or part of a protein of interest (bait).

GST pull-down assays are explained in more detail in *Experimental investigation 3*. Fusion proteins are discussed in S204 Book 4, Section 6.4.9, pp. 273–4.

Using recombinant DNA technology, the DNA encoding the domain of interest is inserted into a plasmid vector just downstream of, and in the same translation reading frame (ORF) as the gene for GST. Under optimized conditions, certain strains of bacteria are induced to take up the plasmid and grown in selection media. Expression of the fusion protein is then chemically induced in transformed bacteria, which are subsequently lysed in a detergent solution. GST is used as the fusion partner because it binds glutathione, a property that can be exploited to purify the fusion protein by affinity chromatography (Chapter 3). Free glutathione can be used to elute the fusion protein from the column. The GST can then be cleaved from the protein being investigated, if not further required. This gentle technique produces fusion protein of sufficient quantity and quality for use in, for example, binding assays and enzyme activity assays. Figures 13.16 and 13.17 show one example of its use.

Figure 13.16

Production of a GST–SH2 fusion protein. (1) The coding sequence of the SH2 domain of a protein is inserted into a plasmid in the same translation reading frame as GST, and under the transcriptional control of a conditional promoter (which initiates transcription if a particular transcriptional activator is added to the culture medium). The plasmid also contains an antibiotic resistance gene to select transformed bacteria (2). Expression of the GST fusion protein is induced in transformed *E. coli*. The bacteria are then lysed in a detergent solution that contains all the intracellular bacterial proteins and the GST fusion protein. (3) The bacterial lysate is added to a chromatographic column containing agarose beads coated with glutathione. (4) The column is first washed to get rid of bacterial proteins. (5) The column is then washed with excess free glutathione, which binds to the recombinant GST–SH2 fusion protein and elutes it from the column.

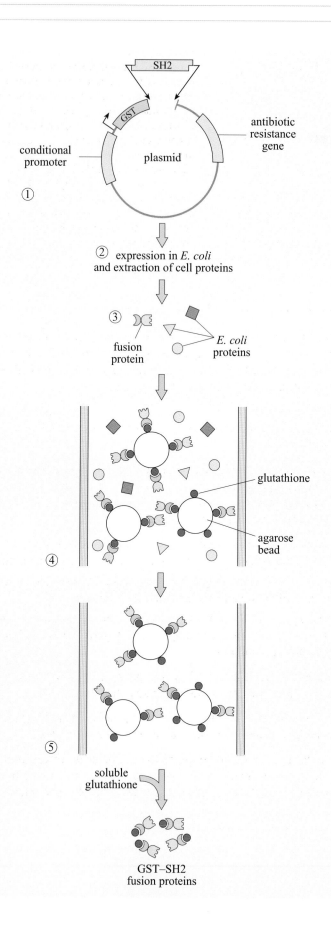

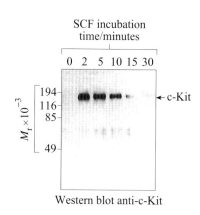

SCF incubation
time/minutes

0 2 5 10 15 30

$M_r \times 10^{-3}$
194
116
85

49

← c-Kit

Western blot anti-c-Kit

Figure 13.17
A GST–SH2 fusion protein, in which the SH2 domain is derived from a tyrosine kinase called CHK, was expressed as in Figure 13.16. The fusion protein was incubated with a lysate of CMK cells (see experiment in Box 13.1, Figure 13.9), the GST–SH2 fusion protein, together with proteins bound to the SH2 domain, was purified by affinity chromatography to a glutathione–agarose column, and separated by denaturing SDS–PAGE. The gel was then Western blotted and probed with an anti-c-Kit antibody. c-Kit can be seen to rapidly, but transiently, associate with the GST–SH2 fusion protein. (Data from Jhun *et al.*, 1995.)

Summary of Section 13.1

1   In a basic model of signal transduction, a signalling molecule binds to a specific receptor, and this activates a sequence (or web) of intracellular signalling molecules that spread the information to relevant parts of the cell, activating target molecules, which effect a cellular response.

2   Signalling between cells can be contact dependent or via secreted signalling molecules. The latter comprise paracrine, autocrine, endocrine or electrical signalling.

3   There are four types of cell surface receptors: ion channel receptors, 7-helix transmembrane receptors, receptors with intrinsic enzymatic activity, and enzyme-associated (recruiter) receptors. Receptors with intrinsic transcriptional activity are mostly intracellular.

4   Two basic categories of signalling molecules intervene in signal transduction, according to the spatial and temporal requirements of the signalling pathway.

  (a) Small diffusible signalling molecules ('second messengers') enable rapid signal amplification and a widespread cellular response.

  (b) Signalling proteins fulfil many roles (by virtue of protein–protein interaction and protein regulation), including signal integration, modulation, transduction and anchoring functions.

5   G proteins and proteins activated by phosphorylation on tyrosine, serine and/or threonine residues can act as molecular switches.

6   The subcellular location of the signalling protein is critical to its function, and this is aided by transient or preassembled signalling complexes.

7   Specific binding of signalling proteins to each other is critical for the effective transduction of the signal. Binding domains allow transient binding to specific (often phosphorylated) amino acid sequences or to phospholipids.

13.2 Receptors and their ligands

Every receptor has to be able to recognize its particular ligand in a specific manner, and become activated by it in such a way that it transmits the signal to the cell. We shall deal with receptor specificity and activation mechanisms. Then we shall see how the same principles of specificity and activation also apply to intracellular receptors.

13.2.1 Receptor specificity

Binding of an extracellular signal to its receptor involves the same type of interactions as those between an enzyme and its substrate, a topic that was described in Chapter 3. Receptor specificity depends on the binding affinity between the ligand and the binding site on the receptor. The dissociation constant (K_D) describes the affinity between receptors and their ligands.

○ From Chapter 2, would you expect a receptor with a high K_D for a ligand to have strong or weak ligand binding?

● Weak. The higher the value of K_D, the lower the affinity of a receptor for its ligand.

As we saw in Chapter 3 and earlier in this chapter, proteins can be thought of as consisting of various domains, and the different combinations of structural motifs in the extracellular regions of receptors will confer the specificity of a receptor for its ligand. Ligand binding may involve multiple sites of contact between the ligand and different domains of the receptor. It is possible that some interactions between the ligand and its receptor may be important for binding, whereas others may be necessary for signal transfer. An example of a ligand that binds to a 7TM receptor is C5a, a chemoattractant cytokine (called a 'chemokine'). The interaction is an association of the C5a N-terminus with a pocket within the receptor, involving its extracellular loops 2 and 3, and the N-terminus. This interaction is not in itself sufficient for receptor activation. For this to occur, the C-terminus of C5a must bind to other sites in the bundle formed by the receptor's seven α-helical membrane-spanning segments.

Ligands are classified as either receptor *agonists* or *antagonists*, depending on the outcome of interactions between ligand and receptor. **Agonists** usually work by binding to the ligand binding site and promoting its active conformation. **Antagonists** bind to the receptor, but do not promote the switch to the active conformation. In addition, it is not always the case that one ligand binds specifically and uniquely to one particular receptor. A single receptor may be able to bind several different ligands, and a single ligand may be able to bind to several receptors.

Here we shall describe two clinically important and well-known examples of receptor–ligand interactions – **acetylcholine**, a ligand for two structurally different classes of receptors, and **adrenalin**, which, together with **noradrenalin**, binds to a number of closely related receptors. (Adrenaline and noradrenaline are also known as epinephrine and norepinephrine, respectively.) We shall return to these receptor signalling pathways throughout the rest of the chapter to illustrate further general principles of signal transduction.

Acetylcholine (ACh) is a neurotransmitter that is released from neuron presynaptic terminals. At the neuromuscular junction, neuron terminals contact a specialized region of skeletal muscle (called the 'motor end-plate'), where acetylcholine functions as a primary neurotransmitter by stimulating muscle contraction (see Figure 13.7).

In addition, acetylcholine also acts as a neurotransmitter in the heart, where its release slows down the contraction rate. However, ACh receptors (sometimes collectively termed 'cholinergic receptors') are structurally and functionally distinct in these two different tissues, and consequently have completely different sets of agonists and antagonists (in both tissues, ACh receptors normally bind to acetylcholine, their endogenous ligand; Figure 13.18).

In skeletal muscle, the ACh receptors are ion-channel receptors (Figure 13.18 and Section 13.2.2), and are also known as **nicotinic receptors**. The skeletal muscle subtype of the nicotinic receptor can bind two naturally occurring powerful toxins, the polypeptide α-bungarotoxin (found in the venom of the krait snake) and the alkaloid tubocurarine (found in curare, a poison extracted from the bark of certain trees in South America, and used in the arrows of some tribes). These toxins act as antagonists, and bind reversibly, but with higher affinity to the nicotinic receptor than acetylcholine itself. For example, the K_D of α-bungarotoxin is 10^{-12} to 10^{-9} mol l^{-1}, whereas acetylcholine binds with relatively moderate affinity to nicotinic receptors; its K_D is 10^{-7} mol l^{-1}. As a result, they prevent the action of ACh by binding to and blocking its receptor without activating it, resulting in paralysis and eventually death.

Nicotinic receptors were given this name because they are activated by the tobacco plant alkaloid, nicotine.

Cardiac muscle contains the other type of ACh receptor, which is a G protein-coupled 7TM receptor (GPCR). This, and the several related subtypes expressed in other neural locations, are usually called **muscarinic receptors**. Atropine is a naturally occurring antagonist of muscarinic receptors, and is derived from the berries of deadly nightshade, *Atropa belladonna* (so called because extracts of it were applied to the eyes by women in the Renaissance period, which resulted in a 'doe-eyed' beauty). One of the downstream consequences of binding of acetylcholine to muscarinic receptors in cardiac muscle cells is the opening of K$^+$ ion channels, which causes membrane hyperpolarization and a decrease in the heart's contraction rate.

Muscarinic receptors were given this name because they were found to be activated by muscarine, a compound found in certain poisonous mushrooms.

Because the muscarinic and nicotinic receptors are not structurally related, there is no overlap between their major agonists and antagonists; nicotine, α-bungarotoxin and tubocurarine have no effect on muscarinic receptors, whereas muscarine and atropine have no effect on nicotinic receptors. How, then, can acetylcholine be a common agonist and bind to two completely different groups of receptors, if their other agonists and antagonists are restricted to binding to just one type each? The answer lies in the flexibility of the acetylcholine molecule. Most of the agonists and antagonists have relatively rigid ring structures, whereas acetylcholine is able to adopt different conformations (Figure 13.18, top), which may help it adjust to the different binding sites in the two receptors.

Adrenalin is the classic 'fight or flight' hormone, having effects on multiple tissues that help put together an appropriate coordinated response to a situation of danger. Actions as varied as increased heart rate, dilation of relevant blood vessels (especially those in skeletal muscle) and constriction of other blood vessels (especially in the skin and digestive tract), and mobilization of metabolic fuels (such as glycogen in liver and skeletal muscle, and stored fat in adipose tissue) are all part of this response.

These effects are mediated by two classes of structurally related GPCRs, the α and β adrenergic receptors, which have the subtypes $α^1$ and $α^2$, and $β^1$, $β^2$ and $β^3$, each with different tissue distributions (Figure 13.19). Figure 13.20 shows the range of effects of α and β adrenergic receptors in various tissues and organs.

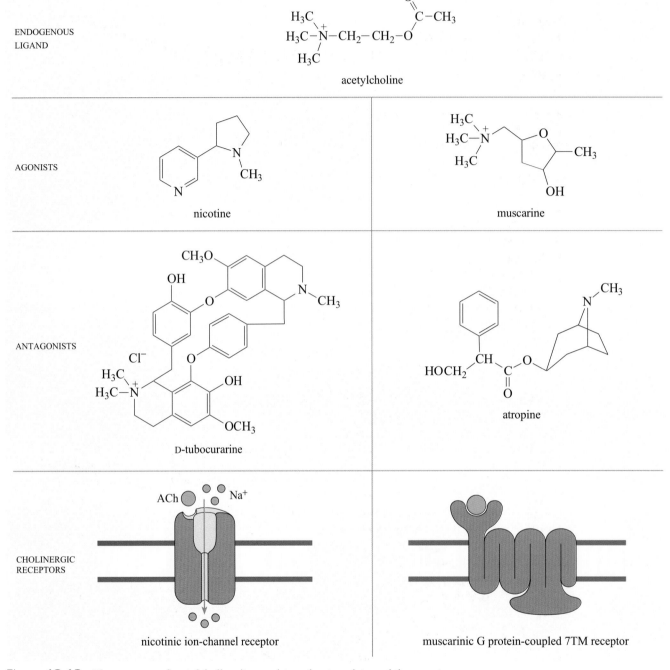

ENDOGENOUS LIGAND

acetylcholine

AGONISTS

nicotine

muscarine

ANTAGONISTS

D-tubocurarine

atropine

CHOLINERGIC RECEPTORS

ACh   Na⁺

nicotinic ion-channel receptor

muscarinic G protein-coupled 7TM receptor

Figure 13.18   The structure of acetylcholine, its agonists and antagonists, and the receptors it binds to. Acetylcholine activates two types of receptors (with very different structures and functions): ion-channel nicotinic receptors and muscarinic G protein-coupled 7TM receptors, which are shown schematically. Nicotine acts as an agonist and D-tubocurarine as an antagonist of nicotinic receptors. Muscarine acts as an agonist and atropine as an antagonist of muscarinic receptors. Note the structural similarity between acetylcholine, the endogenous ligand, and the different agonists and antagonists of cholinergic receptors. The receptors are shown schematically here. More detail on the mechanism of activation of a nicotinic receptor and of a muscarinic receptor is given in Figure 13.21 and in Table 13.1, respectively.

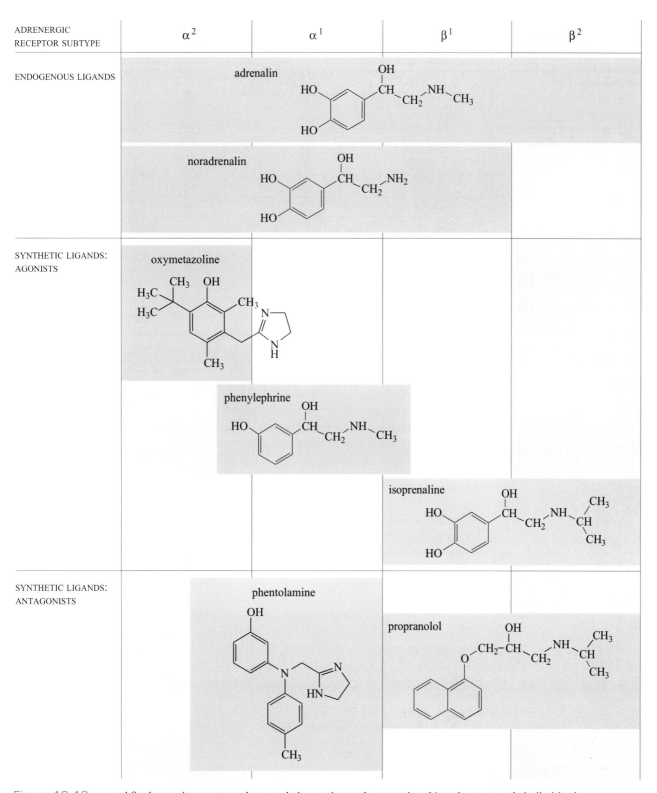

Figure 13.19   α and β adrenergic receptor subtypes, their agonists and antagonists. Note the structural similarities between the endogenous ligands, adrenalin and noradrenalin, and the different synthetic agonists and antagonists of adrenergic receptors. The purple squares within columns indicate the receptor subtype(s) each compound binds to (in the case of partial agonist and antagonist actions, receptor subtype columns have been filled in incompletely).

RECEPTOR SUBTYPE	α^2	α^1	β^1	β^2
ARTERIOLAR SMOOTH MUSCLE	vasoconstriction (in tissues/organs other than skeletal muscle and liver)			vasodilation (in skeletal muscle and liver)
HEART				increased heart rate
SKELETAL MUSCLE				glycogenolysis
LIVER		glycogenolysis		glycogenolysis
ADIPOSE TISSUE	inhibition of lipolysis		lipolysis	
PANCREAS	inhibition of insulin secretion			insulin secretion

Figure 13.20

The range of effects associated with activation of adrenergic receptors of each receptor subtype in various tissues and organs. The purple squares within columns indicate the receptor subtype(s) that mediate the effect on a particular tissue or organ.

For example, the smooth muscle surrounding arteries in the digestive tract contains predominantly α receptors, which mediate vasoconstriction, and the smooth muscle surrounding arteries in skeletal muscle contain predominantly β receptors, which mediate vasodilation. Note also that the β^2 adrenergic receptor increases heart rate, whereas the α^2 adrenergic receptor reduces it.

The classification of adrenergic receptors is based on their interactions with various synthetic agonists and antagonists, which probably reflects the receptor structures. In the simplest example, both α receptors are stimulated by the agonist phenylephrine, and β receptors are exclusively stimulated by the agonist isoprenaline. On the other hand, phentolamine acts as an antagonist of α receptors, whereas propanolol acts as an antagonist of β receptors. Adrenalin itself, of course, can bind all the receptor subtypes, but the structurally related noradrenalin (which is also released into the circulation), has a more restricted binding profile and much more limited effects.

13.2.2 Receptor activation

Receptors may be activated by conformational change (for example, ion-channel receptors such as nicotinic receptors, and 7TM receptors such as muscarinic receptors and adrenergic receptors), by formation of dimers (such as receptors with intrinsic enzymatic activity and recruiter receptors) or by proteolysis (for example, the Notch receptor described in Chapter 17). We shall now consider how each cell surface receptor class described in Section 13.1.2 is activated.

Ion-channel receptors

Nicotinic cholinergic receptors are probably the best studied of all receptors, firstly because they are present throughout skeletal muscle, and secondly because there are plenty of natural and synthetic toxins that bind specifically to this receptor. Furthermore, the technique of patch-clamp electrophysiology has made possible the detailed characterization of the properties of individual ion channels (Figure 13.21a).

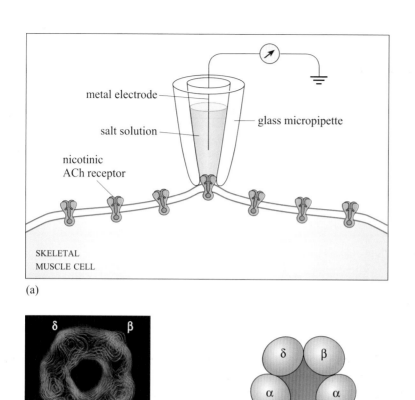

(a)

(b)

2 nm

(c)

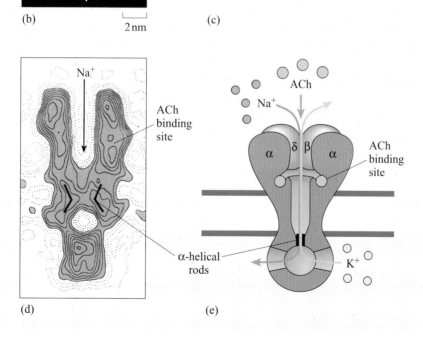

(d)

(e)

Figure 13.21
(a) The technique of patch-clamp recording. A small fire-polished glass micropipette is pressed against the plasma membrane of a skeletal muscle cell, forming a tight seal. The voltage of the plasma membrane is fixed, and the current through individual ion channels is then measured using a metal electrode inserted in the glass micropipette in an electrolyte salt solution. The technique of patch clamping is discussed in detail in S204 Book 3 and Box 6.1. (b) and (d) Structure of the nicotinic acetylcholine receptor in the form of electron-density contour maps; (c) and (e) diagrammatic representations of the receptor. (b) and (c) show the barrel shape of the receptor 'from above', comprising five subunits around a central pore. (d) and (e) show the receptor in cross-section. There are binding sites for two acetylcholine molecules, one on the channel side of each a subunit. Further down, the pore is shaped by a ring of bent a-helical rods (indicated as bars), forming a gate ((d) is shown in the closed position). On binding of acetylcholine, the receptor undergoes a conformational change, which opens the gate (as in (e)), allowing the entry of Na$^+$ ions into the cell and the exit of K$^+$ ions.

Nicotinic receptors are composed of five subunits (two α subunits together with one each of the β, γ and δ subunits), which assemble to form a pore in the membrane (Figure 13.21b–e). The pore can switch between an open and a closed state on binding of two molecules of acetylcholine to the two α subunits at sites within the channel (Figure 13.21). Although the channel alternates between an open and a closed state, binding of acetylcholine increases the probability of the channel being in its open state. When the channel is open, sodium ions flow into the muscle cell, using concentration and voltage gradients. The influx of positive charge due to the Na^+ ions inside the cell tends to locally neutralize the negative charge inside the cell (called 'depolarization'). The channel is also permeable to K^+ ions, which exit the cell. However, the overall effect of the movement of ions causes the net charge inside the cell with respect to the outside to become more positive, and this is ultimately responsible for skeletal muscle contraction (Figure 13.7).

Seven-helix transmembrane (7TM) receptors

Although in unicellular organisms such as the yeast *S. cerevisiae* there are only two classes of 7TM receptors, the pheromone and glucose receptors, multicellular organisms have many more, accounting for up to 5% of all genes in *C. elegans* and 2% of genes in the human and *Drosophila* genomes. 7TM proteins have been classified into four classes, A, B, C (Table 13.1) and Frizzled (Chapter 17). Between them, they can bind a huge range of ligands including simple ions, nucleotides, lipids, steroids, modified amino acids, peptides and glycoprotein hormones at a variety of binding sites, and even photons can activate certain 7TM receptors. An example of the binding of a ligand (adrenalin) to its 7TM receptor is shown in Figure 13.22. As a result of this wide range of ligands, the mechanisms of activation of 7TM receptors are also extremely diverse. They may include, for example, proteolytic cleavage of the N-terminus, and subsequent binding of the new peptide fragment to the central core or ligand binding to the N-terminus or to the central core. However, in all cases the end result is a change in the conformation of the 7TM receptor (Table 13.1).

☐ Can you recall any examples of 7TM receptors?

⬤ Muscarinic cholinergic receptors and adrenergic receptors.

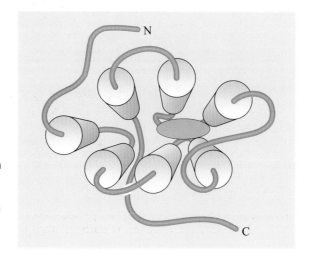

Figure 13.22
A view from the extracellular side of an adrenergic receptor, with an adrenalin molecule (purple ellipse) occupying the binding site, which is located in the core region between the membrane-spanning segments.

Table 13.1 The classes of 7TM receptors and their ligands according to the way in which they bind and activate their receptor.*

Class	Receptors	Ligands	Activation mechanism
A		photons (although strictly speaking photons are not ligands)	photons interact with the 7TM core
		common low M_r hormones, amines (e.g. acetylcholine, adrenalin), nucleotides, eicosanoids	ligands bind in the core region of the 7-transmembrane helices
		proteinases (e.g. thrombin, trypsin)	cleavage of N-terminus generates an auto-ligand, which binds to cysteine-rich domain in new N-terminal segment
		glycoprotein hormones (e.g. TSH, LH, FSH)	ligands make several contacts with the N-terminal segment and the external loops
B		peptide hormones (e.g. secretin, glucagon)	short peptide ligands bind partially in the core region and to the external loops
C		Ca^{2+}, glutamate, $GABA_B$	ligands induce an extensive reorganization of an extended N-terminal segment

* Activation of the A, B and C classes of 7TM receptors involves coupling to G proteins, whereas that of the Frizzled class of receptors (not shown) involves activation of another protein called 'Dishevelled' and interactions with co-receptors (see Chapter 17).

In the case of GPCRs, ligand binding influences the equilibrium between the active and inactive conformation of the receptor in favour of the active conformation, altering the interaction of the cytosolic loops of the protein with a trimeric G protein (which may be already associated with the receptor in a preformed complex). In turn, this brings about activation of the G protein (described in Section 13.3.1).

○ What is the fundamental difference between signalling through nicotinic and muscarinic ACh receptors?

● Nicotinic receptors do not employ a signal transduction pathway to effect their action: the binding of the ligand directly opens a Na^+ ion channel linked to the receptor, and causes membrane depolarization, resulting in the contraction of skeletal muscle cells. Muscarinic ACh receptors, being GPCRs, activate signal transduction pathways via G proteins.

Receptors with intrinsic enzymatic activity

Receptors with intrinsic enzymatic activity are the second biggest group of receptors after the GPCRs. They include four types according to the form of enzymatic activity of the intracellular domain (Figure 13.23a).

▶ **Receptor tyrosine kinases (RTKs)** On activation, the kinase domain phosphorylates tyrosine amino acid residues. There are seven classes of RTK with different extracellular domains (Figure 13.23b).

▶ **Receptor serine–threonine kinases** On activation, the kinase domain phosphorylates serine and/or threonine amino acid residues.

▶ **Receptor tyrosine phosphatases** The intrinsic tyrosine phosphatase activity of the enzymatic domain is suppressed on activation.

▶ **Receptor guanylyl cyclases** The enzymatic domain generates the second messenger cGMP from GTP following activation.

The basic model of activation for receptors with intrinsic enzymatic activity is that ligand binding induces dimerization (in some cases oligomerization) of the receptor, which brings together the cytoplasmic enzymatic domains and leads to a change in enzymatic activity. Dimerization may occur between different receptors that bind the same ligand (heterodimerization), or between the same type of receptor chains (homodimerization), or either. RTKs, RTPs and guanylyl cyclase receptors generally form homodimers (an exception being the epidermal growth factor (EGF) receptor tyrosine kinase), whereas receptor serine–threonine kinases generally form heterodimers. In some cases, oligomerization of several receptors is required for activation.

Figure 13.23   (a) The four classes of receptors with intrinsic enzymatic activity. Note that the kinase domains can phosphorylate residues located on the other receptor chain (autophosphorylation) or on other signalling proteins (as shown here). Note that receptors with intrinsic enzymatic activity have been represented in their active state, that is, following the formation of dimers by the extracellular signalling molecule. (b) The seven subfamilies of receptor tyrosine kinases (RTK). The functional role of most of the cysteine-rich, immunoglublulin-like, and fibronectin-like extracellular domains are not known. Only one member of each subfamily is indicated. Note that the PDGF, FGF and VEGF receptors have a split tyrosine kinase domain; the PDGF receptor is shown in more detail in Figure 13.25. (EGF = epidermal growth factor; NGF = nerve growth factor; PDGF = platelet-derived growth factor; FGF = fibroblast growth factor; VEGF = vascular endothelial growth factor; Eph = ephrin.)

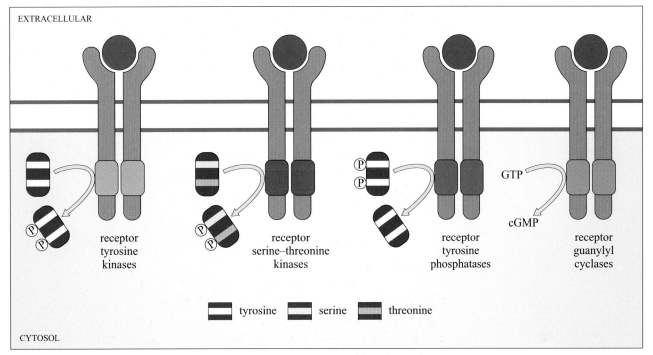

(a)

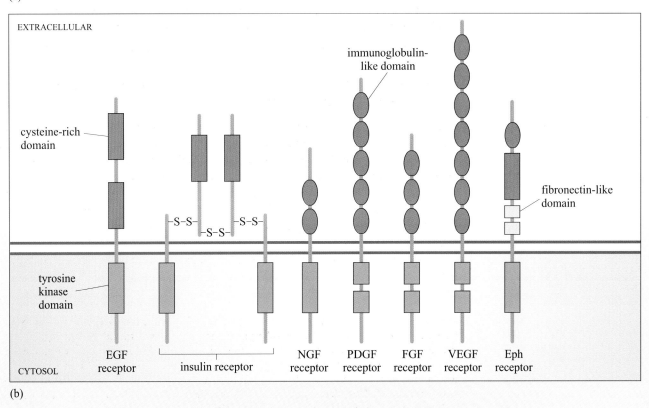

(b)

We shall now describe the general mechanism of activation of RTKs in more detail. There are several strategies by which an extracellular signal may achieve RTK dimerization leading to activation of the receptor:

▶ Ligands such as EGF, which is a monomer, have two binding sites for each receptor unit.

▶ Platelet-derived growth factor (PDGF) is a covalently linked dimer, in which one subunit binds to one PDGF receptor chain, and the other subunit binds to another PDGF receptor chain (Figure 13.24).

▶ Fibroblast growth factor (FGF) binds to proteoglycans (located on the cell surface or on the extracellular matrix) and induces clustering of FGF receptors.

▶ Ephrins are bound to the plasma membrane of the signalling cell in clusters, and thereby induce association of their receptors (called Eph receptors) on the target cells following cell–cell contact.

▶ The insulin receptor is a tetramer prior to binding insulin: on insulin binding, activation occurs by rearrangement of the different receptor chains that brings the kinase domains in close proximity.

Although there can be a great deal of variation in the extracellular domains of RTKs (Figure 13.23b) and in the ways the extracellular signal binds to its receptor, the basic mechanism of receptor activation still applies (Figure 13.24). Association between receptors results in cross-phosphorylation of the kinase domain on each intracellular tail of the RTK, a process called **autophosphorylation**. This results in an increase in its intrinsic kinase activity, which causes phosphorylation of tyrosines in other parts of the cytoplasmic domain (and/or other proteins). Autophosphorylation generates docking sites on the receptor for downstream signalling proteins that contain SH2 domains.

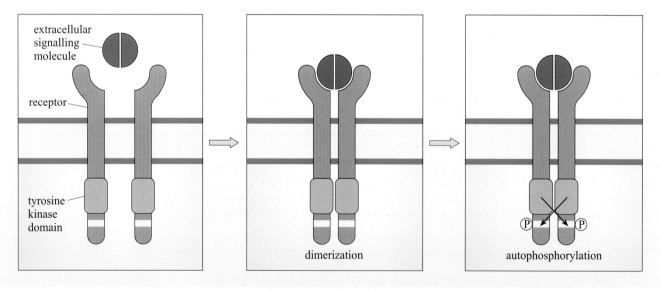

Figure 13.24　RTKs are activated by autophosphorylation of their intracellular kinase domains following dimerization in response to binding the extracellular signal (in this example, a dimer such as PDGF).

Many proteins can bind to phosphotyrosine (pY) residues, but these interactions are influenced by nearby amino acid side-chains (see previous section). For example, the PDGF receptor has specific phosphotyrosine sites, which can bind the regulatory (p85) subunit of phosphatidylinositol 3-kinase (PI 3-kinase), a GTPase-activating protein (p120 RasGAP) and phospholipase C-γ (PLC-γ), among others (Figure 13.25). The insulin receptor extends its docking potential by associating with a large protein, insulin receptor substrate 1 (IRS-1), which has many tyrosine residues that can be phosphorylated by the insulin receptor (Section 13.4). These proteins are called 'docking proteins' and may be activated by being directly phosphorylated by the RTK, or by interactions with other docking proteins or plasma membrane molecules. Some docking proteins are adaptor proteins that merely serve to bring other signalling molecules into place. The overall effect of this system is the recruitment of many different signalling pathways, allowing the modulation of many cellular processes.

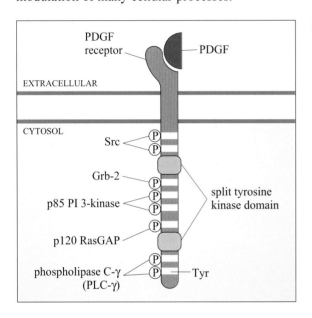

Figure 13.25
Some of the binding (docking) sites on the activated PDGF receptor for SH2-containing proteins. (The domain structure of these proteins is shown in Figure 13.13.) Note that these are not the only autophosphorylation sites on the PDGF receptor. Additional phosphorylated tyrosines are docking sites for other SH2-containing proteins (not shown). For simplicity, only one PDGF receptor chain and one PDGF monomer are shown here.

Recruiter receptors

Enzyme-associated or recruiter receptors also form dimers (or oligomers) on activation by their ligand, in a similar way to receptors with intrinsic enzymatic activity. Dimerization facilitates an interaction between the cell surface receptor (which lacks a catalytic domain) and cytosolic proteins with enzymatic activity. In the case of receptors that associate with tyrosine kinases (called 'tyrosine kinase-associated receptors', the most common in this group), it is the non-covalently linked cytoplasmic tyrosine kinase which is autophosphorylated following receptor dimerization. Sometimes homo- or heterodimerization is not sufficient for receptor activation, and activation may follow oligomerization (clustering of several receptors on the membrane) or require membrane-bound co-receptors (structurally unrelated receptors necessary for signal transfer), which may even be RTKs. The end result of the multiplicity of activation combinations for these receptors is that it allows a refinement of signal specificity and diversity, as different downstream effectors are recruited depending on the ligand–receptor complex.

The **Src** family of tyrosine kinases are the biggest group of kinases that are recruited by tyrosine kinase-associated receptors. One example is Lck (Figure 13.26). In immune reactions, lymphocyte activation brings together T cell receptors (Figure 13.5) and other receptors (called 'CD4' or 'CD8' depending on the activated lymphocyte), which are associated with Lck. Clustering of receptors on the cell surface then results in the tyrosine phosphorylation of the T cell receptor by Lck and activation of downstream signalling pathways. Lck is also very adaptable. As well as associating with CD4 and CD8 receptors, it can also be recruited by means of its SH2 domains to other activated tyrosine kinase (or associated) receptors, thereby strengthening and propagating the signal.

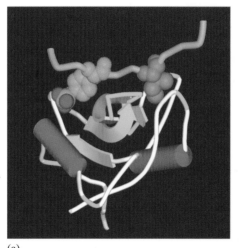 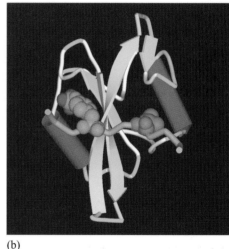

(a)   (b)

Figure 13.26   Structure of the SH2 domain of the Src-related kinase Lck, when it is bound to a substrate peptide containing the recognition motif pYEEI. (a) and (b) represent different viewing angles of the same SH2 domain. The substrate peptide backbone is shown as a pink ribbon. The critical amino acid residues are shown in detail as space-filling structures, phosphotyrosine in orange (with attached phosphate groups in red), and isoleucine in blue. (Based on pdb file 1lcj.)

13.2.3 Receptor inactivation

As with all signalling components, receptors need to be switched off as well as on. Receptor inactivation can operate in several ways including removal of the ligand by degradation or sequestration, and desensitization of the target cell.

Binding of a ligand to its receptor is a reversible process, as the ligand will ultimately dissociate from the receptor and may be degraded. Acetylcholine is a good example of a signal regulated in this way; it is degraded by the enzyme cholinesterase within milliseconds of its release from neuron terminals.

Ligand removal may also occur by sequestration following binding to proteins other than its normal receptor (these may be decoy receptors or extracellular proteins). 'Decoy receptors' are cell surface receptors that bind the ligand but do not convey the signal onward in the pathway (for example, truncated RTKs that lack the intracellular kinase domain). Similarly, soluble extracellular proteins containing ligand-binding domains may also sequester the ligand. In both cases, the effect of the extracellular signal is neutralized prior to receptor binding.

If the ligand cannot be degraded or sequestered, the target cell may, after prolonged activation, become desensitized. Desensitization can occur in several ways, the principal ones being inactivation of the receptor (blocking its interaction with downstream signalling components), sequestering the receptor into endocytic vesicles (from which it can be recycled back onto the plasma membrane), or ultimately degrading the receptor in lysosomes. These mechanisms of receptor desensitization usually function in sequence, and progression from one stage to another can depend on factors such as ligand concentration. Activated GPCRs can be desensitized when they are phosphorylated by different protein kinases. The phosphorylated receptor then binds to a cytosolic protein called *arrestin*, forming a complex that both blocks any interaction with downstream signalling molecules and couples the receptor to clathrin-coated pits (Section 12.3.1), inducing receptor-mediated endocytosis. Another example of desensitization induced by binding of a cytosolic protein to the receptor is provided by c-Cbl. It binds to phosphotyrosine residues of certain activated RTKs via its SH2 domains, thereby promoting the association of the receptor–Cbl complex with ubiquitin. The receptors are then sequestered and degraded via the ubiquitin–proteasome pathway (Chapter 11).

13.2.4 Intracellular receptors

Signal receptors are usually located at the cell surface. However, it is important to remember that there are some groups of receptors that do not fit into the general signal transduction model set out in Figure 13.2. These are intracellular receptors, which bind small or lipophilic molecules such as steroid hormones, which can cross the cell membrane. The signalling pathways activated by these receptors seem quite simple compared with the other pathways we shall be dealing with, but the same principles of ligand binding, conformational change, signal amplification, translocation and so on described earlier still apply.

One important family of intracellular receptors are the **nuclear receptors** (also known as 'nuclear hormone receptors'), which includes receptors for steroid hormones, thyroid hormones, retinoids and vitamin D. Although the ligands differ in their structural type, all nuclear receptors are structurally similar. They are good examples of receptors with intrinsic transcriptional activity (Section 13.1.2), comprising a transcription-activating domain, a DNA-binding domain and a ligand-binding domain. Their ligands are all small and hydrophobic, and so they can diffuse readily through the plasma membrane. The receptors are usually held in an inactive conformation by inhibitory proteins (often chaperones/heat-shock proteins). Binding of the ligand induces a conformational change that causes the inhibitory protein to dissociate from the receptor (Figure 13.27). The receptor may then translocate to the nucleus if it was in the cytoplasm, or it may already be in the nucleus; either way, the receptor–ligand complex is now able to bind to specific DNA sequences by means of its DNA-binding domain. Binding to DNA can also be facilitated by association of the receptor–ligand complex with other proteins (referred to as 'coactivator proteins'). The DNA sequence to which the receptor–ligand complex binds is a promoter region of the target genes; in the case of hormones, it is called a '**hormone response element (HRE)**'.

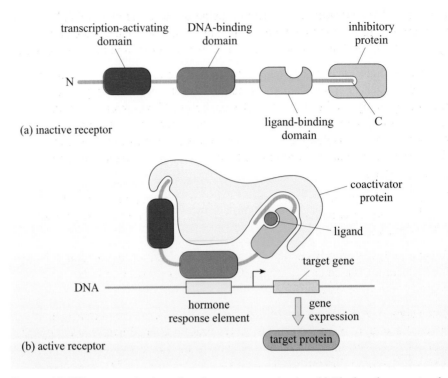

Figure 13.27   The mechanism of nuclear receptor activation. (a) The inactive receptor, bound to an inhibitory protein. (b) In the receptor, ligand binding induces the ligand-binding domain to shut tight around the ligand, allowing the inhibitory protein to leave the complex. This allows the binding of a coactivator protein and consequent binding to a hormone response element in the DNA sequence, and initiating gene transcription.

Summary of Section 13.2

1   Receptors comprise a limited number of structural motifs, which determine binding affinity and specificity of receptor–ligand complexes. Some ligands bind to several receptors and some receptors bind to several ligands.

2   Acetylcholine is a good example of a ligand with two structurally different kinds of receptor. Nicotinic receptors are ion channels, which are found predominantly in skeletal muscle, and are stimulated by nicotine. Nicotinic receptor antagonists include the toxins α-bungarotoxin and tubocurarine. Acetylcholine binds at two sites within the channel. Muscarinic receptors, in contrast, are 7TM G protein-coupled receptors, found (for example) in cardiac muscle. Muscarine acts as an agonist, whereas atropine acts as an antagonist. Acetylcholine binds in the core region (Table 13.1) of the transmembrane helical segments.

3   Adrenalin, however, has a range of structurally related 7TM G protein-coupled receptors, with different tissue distributions and different affinities for numerous agonists and antagonists. Adrenalin, like acetylcholine, binds in the core region of the receptor, though other GPCRs can be activated in a variety of ways.

4   Mechanisms for receptor activation are varied and include conformational changes (ion-channel receptors and 7TM), homo- or heterodimerization (receptors with intrinsic enzymatic activity and recruiter receptors) or even proteolysis.

5   For most 7TM receptors (the exception being the Frizzled class of 7TM receptors), conformational change on ligand binding activates associated cytoplasmic G proteins. Hence, they are called 'G protein-coupled receptors'.

6   Receptors with intrinsic enzymatic activity include receptor tyrosine kinases, receptor serine–threonine kinases, receptor tyrosine phosphatases, and receptor guanylyl cyclases. Most RTKs are activated by dimerization on ligand binding, leading to autophosphorylation of the cytoplasmic portion of the receptor. Phosphorylated tyrosine residues serve as docking sites for SH2-containing signalling proteins, which also recognize sequence-specific flanking motifs.

7   Dimerization of recruiter receptors facilitates the interaction between the membrane-bound receptor and cytosolic proteins with intrinsic enzymatic activity such as kinases.

8   Receptors can be inactivated by removal of the ligand, or by receptor desensitization, which can be by inactivation, by sequestration or by degradation of the receptor.

9   Some signalling molecules can diffuse across the plasma membrane, and so have intracellular, rather than cell surface receptors. Small hydrophobic ligands such as steroid hormones bind to members of the nuclear receptor group, which undergo conformational change and bind to specific DNA sequences, stimulating transcription of target genes.

13.3 Intracellular signalling components

We are now ready to describe in detail the major intracellular signalling pathways responsible for relaying the signal from the surface receptor to evoke a cellular response. This section will deal with signalling molecules that operate at the cytosolic leaflet of the plasma membrane (**trimeric G proteins**, monomeric G proteins and lipid-modifying enzymes), second messengers (such as Ca^{2+}, cAMP, cGMP), protein kinases and phosphatases, and finally transcription factors.

13.3.1 Trimeric G proteins

G proteins are attached to the cytosolic face of the plasma membrane, where they serve as relay proteins between the receptors and their target signalling proteins.

☐ From Chapter 3, what is the difference between a monomeric and a trimeric G protein?

⬤ Trimeric G proteins interact with 7TM receptors and are all heterotrimeric, having structurally different α, β and γ subunits. Monomeric G proteins are the small G proteins, such as Ras, which are structurally related to the α subunit of trimeric G proteins.

The three-dimensional structure of trimeric G proteins in their inactive form is shown in Figure 13.28 (see also Section 3.6.2).

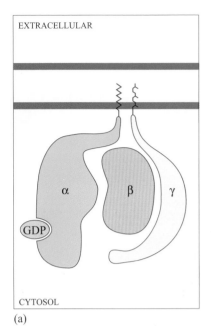

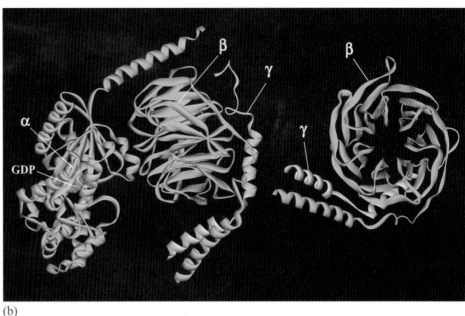

(a)   (b)

Figure 13.28   (a) Schematic diagram of a trimeric G protein, bound to GDP, associated with the plasma membrane. (b) Three-dimensional structure of the α, β and γ subunits of a trimeric G protein. The α subunit (left, cyan) has a molecule of GDP bound, and the N-terminal helix is at the top right. The β and γ subunits (β green, γ yellow) are in close apposition forming a complex. The hydrophobic attachments that are responsible for the association of the three subunits are not shown. They involve the N-terminus of the α subunit and the C-terminus of the γ subunit. The separate βγ complex on the right has been rotated about a vertical axis. (Based on pdb file 1gp2.)

Ligand binding induces a conformational change in the 7TM receptor, which results in the release of GDP and binding of GTP to the α subunit (Figure 13.29). As a result, the α subunit also changes conformation and becomes activated. This conformational change results in the dissociation of the α subunit from the βγ complex, which also becomes activated, although it does not change conformation itself. The α subunit primarily, and also the βγ complex to a lesser extent, regulate the activity of downstream effector proteins located on the plasma membrane. There are many different α subunits, which can be classified according to sequence similarity, and to which upstream and downstream proteins they interact with (see Table 13.2 for the most important ones). In fact, the G protein complex is often categorized by the type of α subunit it is formed from; hence you will come across Gα$_s$, Gα$_i$, Gα$_q$, etc. For example, Gα$_s$ stimulates adenylyl cyclase, whereas Gα$_i$ inhibits it, and Gα$_q$ activates PLC-β (see Table 13.2). There are also different βγ subunits, some of which have been shown to have their own effector function. More generally, though, βγ subunits are thought to stabilize the inactive state of the α subunit.

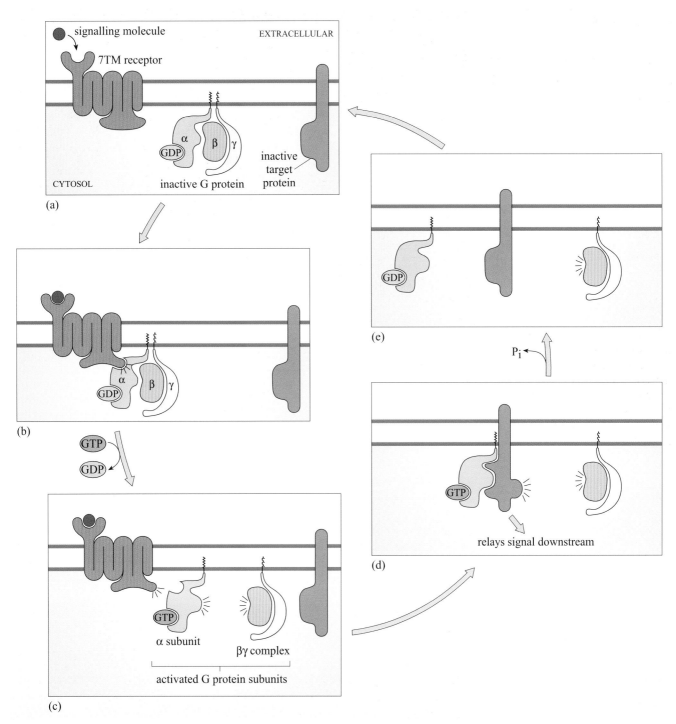

Figure 13.29   Signalling through G protein-coupled receptors (GPCRs). (a) All components of the signalling pathway are shown in their inactive form. (b) The change in conformation of the 7TM receptor on ligand binding brings about the binding of the trimeric G protein. (c) GTP binds and activates the α subunit, which becomes dissociated from the βγ complex. (d) The α subunit binds and activates target proteins, which also act as effectors and propagate the signal. (e) Inactivation of the α subunit via GTPase activity (intrinsic or accessory) results in dissociation from the target protein (which itself becomes inactivated) and formation of the inactive trimeric G protein complex by association with a βγ complex (a).

Table 13.2   The major membrane protein targets of trimeric G proteins*

Target effector protein	G protein subunit type	Interfering toxin†	Section where discussed
ion channels	regulated by $G\alpha_s$, $G\alpha_i$, $G\alpha_0$ and $\beta\gamma$ (for example, $G\alpha_i$ and $G\alpha_0$ coupled to muscarinic ACh receptor activates K^+ channels)		13.2.2
adenylyl cyclase	activated by $G\alpha_s$ inhibited by $G\alpha_i$	cholera toxin pertussis toxin	13.3.3
cGMP phosphodiesterase	activated by $G\alpha_t$ (transducin) in photoreceptors		not discussed further
phospholipase C-β	activated by $G\alpha_q$ and $G\alpha_0$		13.3.2 and 13.3.3
phospholipase A_2	activated by a $\beta\gamma$ complex		not discussed further
PI 3-kinase	activated by a $\beta\gamma$ complex		Chapter 16
small GTPases	$G\alpha_{12/13}$		not discussed further

*You do not have to remember all the target effector proteins, $G\alpha$ protein subunits or interfering toxins at this point.

†Cholera toxin and pertussis toxin (from the *Bordetella pertussis* bacterium, which causes whooping cough) both interfere with the action of G protein α subunits. Cholera toxin locks $G\alpha_s$ subunits into an active form and pertussis toxin interferes with $G\alpha_i$ subunits by inhibiting them, making these toxins useful laboratory tools for determining which signalling pathways are activated by GPCRs.

G proteins usually remain active for only a short time, which depends mainly on the rate of hydrolysis of GTP to GDP (Figure 13.29). The intrinsic GTPase activity of the α subunit is quite inefficient by itself. For many cell signalling processes where a rapid turnover rate is necessary (for example, transduction of a photoreceptor activated by visual stimuli), the intrinsic GTPase activity of the α subunit is usually aided by binding of a second protein that enhances the rate of G protein inactivation. This may be either its target protein, ensuring that the α subunit remains active for just as long as it takes to make contact with the target, or a GTPase activating protein (GAP, Section 13.1.5).

13.3.2 Lipid-modifying enzymes

The internal surface of the plasma membrane provides a useful environment for spreading signals received by surface receptors around the cell. Several specialist enzymes are activated by membrane-bound receptors, creating large numbers of small lipid-soluble second messenger molecules, which can diffuse easily through the membrane. These enzymes all use **phosphatidylinositol (PI)** and its derivatives as their substrates. PI itself is a derivative of glycerol: the OH group on carbon atom 1 has been replaced with an inositol ring linked via a phosphate group, and the OH groups on carbon atoms 2 and 3 have been replaced by two fatty acyl chains, one saturated and one unsaturated (Figure 13.30a).

☐   What class of membrane lipids do phosphatidylinositols belong to?

⬤   Glycerophospholipids (Section 6.2.2).

The fatty acyl chains are embedded in the cytosolic leaflet of the plasma membrane, leaving the inositol ring projecting into the cytosol. Carbon atoms 3, 4 and 5 of the inositol ring can be phosphorylated by lipid kinases (Figure 13.30). The best-studied enzymes employing these substrates are the **phospholipase C** family, which cleave the fatty acyl chains from the inositol ring, and **phosphatidylinositol 3-kinase (PI 3-kinase),** which phosphorylates carbon atom 3 of the inositol ring. These products then serve as second messengers. We shall now briefly explain the action of these enzymes, and then go on to describe the roles of the second messengers they generate.

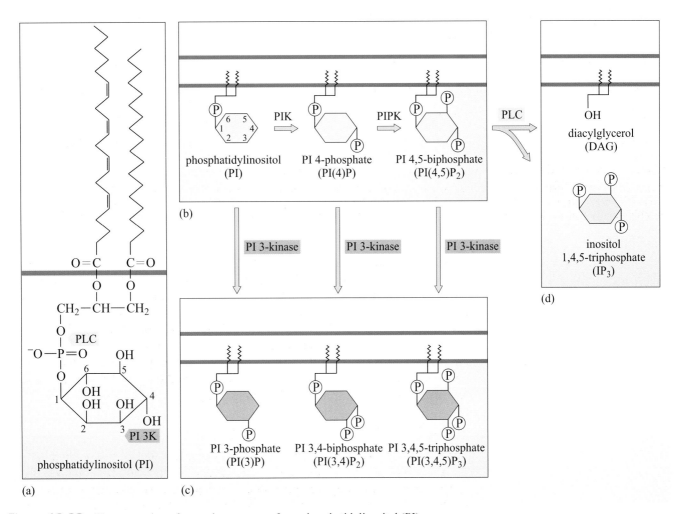

Figure 13.30   The generation of second messengers from phosphatidylinositol (PI).
(a) The structure of phosphatidylinositol (PI), which is the parent molecule for several key second messengers. Arrows indicate modifications by PLC and PI 3-kinase (denoted as PI 3K on figure). (b) PI (shown in green) can be phosphorylated on its inositol ring by lipid kinases including phosphatidylinositol kinase and phosphatidylinositol phosphate kinase (denoted as PIK and PIPK on figure). (c) Each of these intermediate products can be further phosphorylated by PI 3-kinase to produce the second messengers PI(3)P, PI(3,4)P$_2$ and PI(3,4,5)P$_3$ (shown in purple). It is the phosphorylation of the 3 position which is critical for the second messenger function, as will be seen later. (d) Alternatively, the intermediate product PI(4,5)P$_2$ can be cleaved by phospholipase C (PLC) at the position indicated by the blue arrow in part (a) to produce the second messengers diacylglycerol (DAG) and inositol 1,4,5-triphosphate (IP$_3$, blue). (Note that IP$_3$ is the only second messenger product of this system that does not remain membrane bound.)

Phosphatidylinositol 3-kinase (PI 3-kinase)

Members of this family of lipid kinases usually have two subunits: one is a catalytic subunit with a lipid kinase domain and the other is a regulatory subunit, which contains two SH2 domains and a SH3 domain (p 85 PI 3-kinase in Figure 13.13).

○ What will the SH2 domains of the regulatory subunit enable PI 3-kinase to do?

● They will enable PI 3-kinase to bind to proteins containing a phosphorylated tyrosine residue within a specific motif. In this way, PI 3-kinase is targeted to the membrane when required, by binding to phosphotyrosine residues on activated RTKs.

The preferred substrate of PI 3-kinase is $PI(4,5)P_2$. However, this kinase also phosphorylates PI and PI(4)P. It is the phosphorylation at the 3 position by PI 3-kinase that makes the molecule active in a signalling context. Thus, the two main products, **phosphatidylinositol 3,4-biphosphate** $(PI(3,4)P_2)$ and **phosphatidylinositol 3,4,5-triphosphate** $(PI(3,4,5)P_3)$, are both active signalling molecules because they are recognized by PH domains in other proteins (Figure 13.31). In contrast, PI(3)P is not an active second messenger.

○ What distinguishes $PI(3,4)P_2$, $PI(3,4,5)P_3$ and $PI(4,5)P_2$ from each other? Which are substrates for PI 3-kinase?

● These molecules differ in their phosphorylation state. $PI(3,4)P_2$ is phosphorylated on carbons 3 and 4, $PI(3,4,5)P_3$ on carbons 3, 4 and 5, and $PI(4,5)P_2$ on carbons 4 and 5. Only $PI(4,5)P_2$ is a substrate for PI 3-kinase, whereas the two others are products.

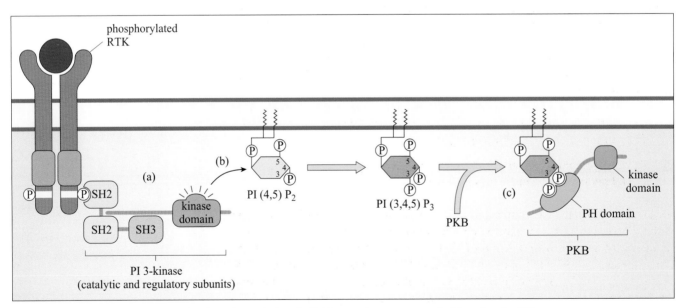

Figure 13.31 PI 3-kinase phosphorylates inositol phospholipids, creating temporary docking sites for PH domain-containing proteins. (a) In this scenario, PI 3-kinase is brought to the membrane following RTK activation, when one of the SH2 domains of its regulatory subunit binds to a phosphotyrosine on the receptor. (b) The catalytic subunit of PI 3-kinase then phosphorylates $PI(4,5)P_2$, generating the second messenger $PI(3,4,5)P_3$, (c) to which PH domain-containing proteins can bind. There are many target proteins with PH domains. The example used here is the serine–threonine kinase PKB (also called Akt), which will be discussed in Chapter 14.

☐ How does the activity of PI 3-kinase influence the localization of signalling proteins?

⬤ By virtue of its catalytic activity, PI 3-kinase generates $PI(3,4)P_2$ and $PI(3,4,5)P_3$, which serve as plasma membrane docking sites for PH-containing proteins.

Proteins differ in their affinity for binding to either $PI(3,4)P_2$ or $PI(3,4,5)P_3$, depending on the interacting PH domain. One signalling enzyme that utilizes the membrane docking sites generated by PI 3-kinase is protein kinase B (PKB, also known as Akt), which thereby becomes an accessible substrate for an upstream kinase, PDK1 (not shown in Figure 13.31). PKB is a serine–threonine kinase, principally involved in mediating survival signals (Chapter 14). Another important target is phospholipase C (PLC), which binds to PI 3-kinase substrates at the membrane via its PH domain (see below). The docking sites for PH domains are, as with all signalling components, temporary; specific inositol phospholipid phosphatases ultimately remove the phosphate from the 3 position of the inositol ring. The role of one of these lipid phosphatases called PTEN in tumour progression will be discussed in Chapter 19.

Phospholipase C (PLC)

Members of this family of enzymes contain two catalytic domains and several protein binding domains (Figure 13.13). The PH domain can temporarily tether phospholipase C to the membrane by attachment mainly to $PI(3,4)P_2$.

We shall discuss two main isoforms of PLC: PLC-β, which is activated by a subset of trimeric G proteins ($G\alpha_q$ and $G\alpha_0$), and PLC-γ, which, in contrast, associates with phosphotyrosines on activated RTKs (such as the PDGF and insulin receptors) by means of its SH2 domains. The substrate of both PLC-γ and PLC-β is $PI(4,5)P_2$, which is cleaved by PLC to produce two second messengers: **1,2-diacylglycerol (DAG)** consists of linked fatty acyl chains, and so remains in the plasma membrane; **inositol 1,4,5-triphosphate (IP$_3$)** consists of the phosphorylated inositol ring, which because it is water-soluble is able to diffuse through the cytosol.

☐ Why is IP_3 released from the plasma membrane? You may want to look back at the structure of IP_3 (shown in Figure 13.30).

⬤ IP_3 is hydrophilic and lacks the hydrophobic fatty acyl chains that anchor inositol phospholipids in the plasma membrane.

IP_3 binds to IP_3-gated calcium channels on the ER membrane, causing Ca^{2+} stored in the ER to flood into the cytosol. This activates many proteins, but most notably (in this scenario) the **protein kinase C** family (**PKC**, so called because of their Ca^{2+} dependence). Binding of calcium causes PKC to translocate to the membrane (Section 13.3.3). Full activation of PKC is complicated and depends on the isoform involved, but generally DAG binds to, and helps to activate, protein kinase C. Thus, the two products of PLC activity are acting in a coordinated fashion on the same protein (Figure 13.32).

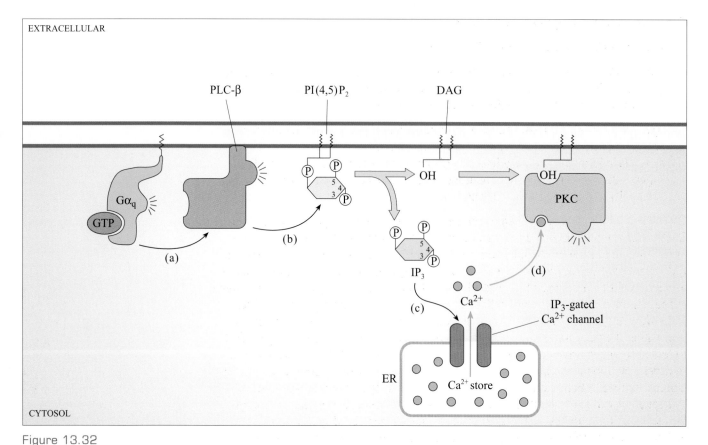

Figure 13.32

Both products of PLC result in the activation of protein kinase C (PKC). (a) In this scenario, PLC-β is activated by a $G\alpha_q$ protein. (c) PLC-β then cleaves $PI(4,5)P_2$ into DAG and IP_3. (c) IP_3 diffuses through the cytosol and binds to IP_3-gated calcium channels. (d) The calcium ions that are released into the cytosol, together with the DAG produced by PLC-β and phosphatidylserine (not shown) on the plasma membrane, act in concert to activate protein kinase C (PKC).

13.3.3 Second messengers

In the previous section, we have discussed the principles of second messengers (Section 13.1.4) and, in particular, those produced by PLC (IP_3 and DAG) and PI3 kinase ($PI(3,4)P_2$ and $PI(3,4,5)P_3$). We shall now consider the roles and mechanisms of action of the other chief mediators, which are **Ca^{2+} ions**, cAMP and cGMP. These are water-soluble second messengers.

☐ Of the second messengers produced by PLC and PI 3-kinase, which ones are hydrophobic?

◼ PI 3-kinase products $PI(3,4)P_2$ and $PI(3,4,5)P_3$ and the PLC product DAG are hydrophobic. They contain fatty acyl chains that anchor them to the plasma membrane.

Calcium ions

The Ca^{2+} concentration is normally low in the cytosol ($\sim 10^{-7}$ mol l^{-1}) compared with the extracellular space ($\sim 10^{-3}$ mol l^{-1}; Section 2.4.4). There are several mechanisms for achieving this. The most widespread are ATP-dependent Ca^{2+} efflux pumps on the plasma membrane, which pump Ca^{2+} ions out of the cell. Muscle and nerve cells, where oscillations in intracellular Ca^{2+} concentration often occur, employ an additional Na^+-driven Ca^{2+} exchanger. There are also pumps driving cytosolic Ca^{2+} into the endoplasmic reticulum, so that it acts as a Ca^{2+} store. When Ca^{2+} channels are transiently opened by a signalling protein, Ca^{2+} floods down the concentration gradient into the cytosol. The result is a rapid 10–20-fold increase in the cytosolic Ca^{2+} concentration in the cytosol, which in turn activates numerous different Ca^{2+}-dependent proteins, such as PKC.

There are three main types of Ca^{2+} channel:

(a) *IP$_3$-gated Ca^{2+} channels* on the ER (Section 13.3.2).

(b) *Voltage-dependent Ca^{2+} channels* in the plasma membrane, which open when the membrane is depolarized. These are used, for example, at neuron terminals, where Ca^{2+} release stimulates secretion of neurotransmitters.

(c) *Ryanodine receptors* closely associated with receptors on the plasma membrane, which respond to changes in membrane potential, and release Ca^{2+} from the sarcoplasmic reticulum in skeletal muscle cells (as described in Section 13.1.4, Figure 13.7) or from the ER in neurons. Their name derives from their sensitivity to the plant alkaloid ryanodine.

Ca^{2+}-sensitive fluorescent indicators can be used to monitor changes in intracellular Ca^{2+}. After stimulation with an extracellular signal, opening of channels and release of Ca^{2+} in the cytosol by the mechanisms described above result in local increases in Ca^{2+} concentration, often circumscribed to small regions of the cell. These increases usually reflect the opening of individual channels or of small groups of channels; these changes in intracellular Ca^{2+} are called 'quarks' or 'blips'. If the signal is persistent and sufficiently strong, the change in the concentration of Ca^{2+} spreads across the cell. Under the fluorescent microscope, it appears as if an initial wave of high Ca^{2+} is followed by other waves propagating through the cytosol, with Ca^{2+} concentrations first rising and then returning to basal levels; these changes are referred to as 'spikes' or 'oscillations', and can be repeated at intervals of seconds or minutes. The frequency of Ca^{2+} oscillations can determine the response. For example, a low frequency of Ca^{2+} spikes may trigger transcription of one set of genes, whereas a higher frequency triggers transcription of a different set. The sensitivity of the cellular response to the frequency of Ca^{2+} oscillations requires a special kind of protein called **calmodulin**.

Calmodulin is abundant, constituting about 1% of total cellular protein. It has no intrinsic catalytic activity, but on binding to Ca^{2+} it is able to modulate the activity of other proteins. It has four Ca^{2+} binding sites (small, helical Ca^{2+}-binding motifs called 'EF hands', which are also present in some other Ca^{2+}-binding proteins); at least two of them must be occupied for it to adopt its active conformation (Figure 13.33).

☐ What term describes the regulation of calmodulin by Ca^{2+}?

⬤ Calmodulin is allosterically regulated by Ca^{2+} ions (Section 3.6.2).

The biggest class of proteins affected by calmodulin is called the **Ca^{2+}/calmodulin-dependent protein kinases (CaM kinases)**, which are serine–threonine kinases. CaM kinase II is found in high quantities in the brain, particularly at synapses. It seems to be involved in some kinds of memory, since mice with mutations in CaM kinase II have specific learning difficulties. On binding Ca^{2+}/calmodulin, CaM kinase II activates itself by autophosphorylation, the degree of activation being dependent on the oscillation frequency of Ca^{2+} concentration.

Many members of the protein kinase C family are Ca^{2+}-binding proteins, but in these proteins Ca^{2+} binds to a larger domain, known as the 'C2 domain'. Ca^{2+} binding changes the net charge of the C2 domain, enabling it to bind negatively charged phospholipids such as DAG in the plasma membrane (see Section 13.4.2 and Figure 13.31). Here, Ca^{2+} is acting as a switch, helping to change the localization of the enzyme.

Figure 13.33
The role of calmodulin in the activation of CaM kinases. (a) The structure of calmodulin. It is basically a dumb-bell shape, comprising two globular domains connected by a single, long, flexible α helix. The binding sites for calcium ions (green) are in the form of two 'EF hands' in each globular domain. (b) (i) CaM kinase II is held in an inactive state by means of its inhibitory domain. Ca^{2+}-bound calmodulin binds to this inhibitory domain, wrapping itself around it by means of its flexible α helix. (ii) This releases and activates the kinase domain, which autophosphorylates the inhibitory domain and can then phosphorylate target proteins. The phosphorylation of the inhibitory domain prolongs the activation of CaM kinase in two ways: it slows the dissociation of calmodulin, and it enables the kinase activity to remain partially active even when the calmodulin has dissociated from the CaM kinase II. The CaM-kinase II requires a phosphatase (not shown) to become completely inactivated.

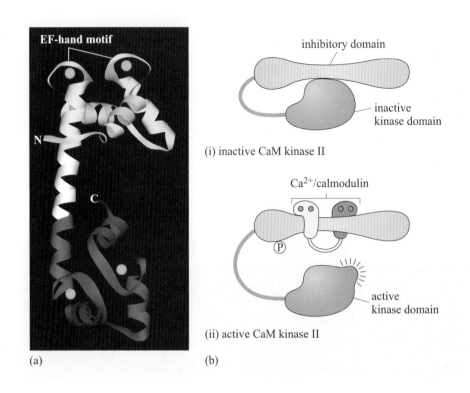

Cyclic AMP

The concentration of **cyclic AMP (cAMP)** in the cytosol increases 20-fold within seconds of an appropriate stimulus. This is achieved by the action of the plasma membrane-embedded protein **adenylyl cyclase**, which synthesizes cAMP from ATP (Figure 13.34). cAMP is short-lived, as with all second messengers, because it is continuously degraded by **cyclic AMP phosphodiesterases** to 5′-AMP. Adenylyl cyclase is activated by stimulatory G proteins ($G\alpha_s$) and inhibited indirectly by inhibitory G proteins ($G\alpha_i$). It is usually the α subunit of the G protein that regulates adenylyl cyclase in this way, though sometimes the βγ complex can have the same effect. Different hormones can induce a similar cAMP response in a particular cell type, leading to similar cellular outcomes. However, different cell types will respond differently to similar cAMP increases, so the same hormone may have different effects on different cells. For example, cAMP mediates the action of adrenalin acting through β-adrenergic receptors (see Figure 13.48), causing glycogen breakdown in skeletal muscle cells, while promoting triglyceride breakdown in fat cells. Most of the downstream signals of cAMP are propagated by **cAMP-dependent protein kinase A (PKA)**, which is a serine–threonine kinase.

PKA has many target proteins, which vary according to cell type. This explains why a hormone can produce the same increase in cAMP concentration in different cells, yet the cellular response to this increase is different for each cell type. PKA consists of two catalytic subunits and two regulatory subunits. The latter have two roles. They bind to PKA-anchoring proteins, thus tethering the enzyme to particular subcellular locations. They can also each bind two cAMP molecules in a cooperative fashion; when bound to more than two cAMP molecules, the regulatory subunits undergo sufficient conformational change for them to dissociate from the catalytic subunits (which remain in the cytosol). As with other signalling proteins with multiple binding sites, such as calmodulin, PKA is allosterically regulated by

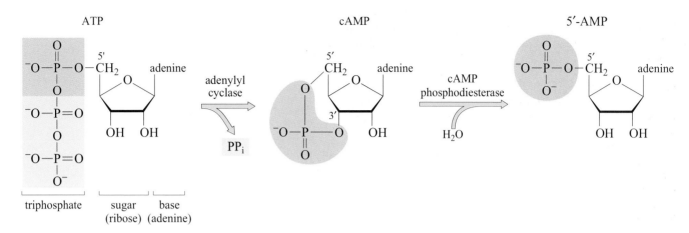

Figure 13.34
The synthesis and degradation of
cAMP. Adenylyl cyclase catalyses
the formation of cAMP from ATP,
removing the terminal two phosphates
from ATP in the process. Removal of
pyrophosphate (PP$_i$) provides the
energy for the cyclization reaction.
cAMP is short-lived because it is
rapidly hydrolysed by cAMP
phosphodiesterase, yielding 5'-AMP.

the second messenger cAMP. The released catalytic units are now active. They
may act in the cytoplasm, for example by phosphorylating enzymes involved in
glycogen metabolism and/or they may migrate to the nucleus, where they can
switch on transcription of genes containing **cAMP response elements (CREs)**
in their promoters. This is achieved by phosphorylating a serine on the nuclear
CRE-binding protein (CREB), which, together with a coactivator, then binds to
the CRE and stimulates transcription of the downstream gene.

Cyclic GMP

Cyclic GMP (cGMP) is a second messenger with many similarities to cAMP. It is
synthesized from GTP by guanylyl cyclase, and degraded to 5'-GMP by cyclic
GMP phosphodiesterases. Some of the targets of cGMP are analogous to those of
cAMP: cGMP-dependent protein kinase (PKG), and cGMP-gated Na$^+$ ion channels.

☐ We have already discussed a type of receptor that employs cGMP for signal
transfer. What type of receptor is it?

⬤ Receptors with intrinsic enzymatic activity with an intracellular guanylyl cyclase
catalytic domain (Figure 13.23a).

13.3.4 Monomeric G proteins

We shall discuss **monomeric G proteins** (also called **small G proteins** or **small
GTPases**) separately from the trimeric G proteins for three reasons: their upstream
activators are different, they tend to have different target proteins, and they
commonly operate within different signalling pathways.

☐ What structural features and activities do monomeric G proteins share with
trimeric G proteins?

⬤ You may have thought of the following:
  (a) Monomeric G proteins are structurally related to the α subunit of
      trimeric G proteins.
  (b) They bind GTP and hydrolyse it to GDP, acting as a molecular switch.
  (c) The rate of GTP hydrolysis can be increased by GAP proteins.
  (d) They are tethered to the internal surface of the plasma membrane by
      means of post-translational lipid modifications (Sections 3.6.2 and 13.1.5).

There are many types of monomeric G proteins, involved in a myriad of cellular processes; examples include Ran, which has a role in the nuclear localization of proteins (Section 11.5.1), Rab, with a role in endocytosis (Section 12.3.3), or the Rho family, which functions in cell adhesion and migration (Chapter 16). The best-studied monomeric G protein is Ras, which we shall consider here in some detail. Ras is structurally similar to the α subunit of trimeric G proteins. In fact, the GTP-binding domain of Gα is known as the Ras domain (Figure 13.35).

Ras forms part of the signal transduction pathway from most RTKs, including the growth factor receptors. As such, it is central to regulation of the growth, proliferation and differentiation of cells, and is involved in the formation of tumours when these pathways become dysfunctional. (Tumorigenesis is covered in Chapter 19.) Ras homologues have been found to regulate vulval development in *C. elegans* and photoreceptor development in *Drosophila*, providing excellent experimental models in which to study its function in development. There are three members of the mammalian Ras family – H-Ras (first discovered in its viral form in Harvey murine sarcoma virus), K-Ras (from Kirsten sarcoma virus) and N-Ras (or neural Ras). There are also more than 70 other small G proteins, which share regions of sequence homology and are involved in a whole variety of cell processes.

Figure 13.35
Ras is structurally related to the α subunit of trimeric G proteins. (a) The Gα subunit contains a Ras domain (purple) and a large helical domain (yellow), which monomeric G proteins such as Ras do not have; this further enhances GTP binding. Each ribbon structure shows a space-filling GDP (orange) at the guanine nucleotide binding site, and the Ras structure also shows where a magnesium ion binds (green sphere). (Based on the pdb files: Gα 1GP2.pdb; Ras 4Q21.) (b) The most highly conserved sequences between Ras and Gα subunits, and their different contributions to GDP/GTP binding. The short conserved sequences, named G1–G5, are involved in binding the guanine nucleotide and magnesium ion. Mutations in G1 and G3 in Ras lead to prolonged activation of the protein, and are associated with cancer (Chapter 19).

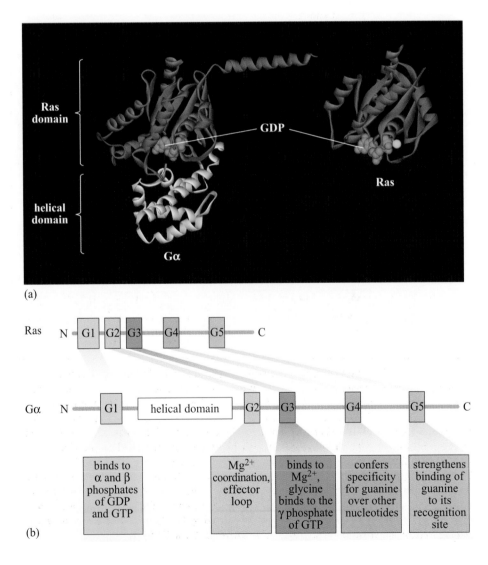

For example, Rho and Rac have been shown to mediate changes to the actin cytoskeleton, leading to stress fibre formation and lamellipodia formation, respectively (Chapter 16).

Ras is activated following stimulation of many RTKs (Figure 13.36). How does this happen? It is a much more indirect process than for trimeric G proteins, where conformational change in the receptor directly induces conformational change and activation of the G protein. Instead, what usually happens is firstly that autophosphorylation of RTKs creates docking sites for SH2-containing proteins. One of these SH2-containing proteins is an adaptor protein called Grb-2 (growth factor receptor-bound protein 2). Grb-2 consists of little more than two SH3 domains flanking an SH2 domain (Figure 13.13). Grb-2 binds to the activated receptor via its SH2 domain. Sometimes the RTK does not contain the correct docking sequences for Grb-2, in which case an intermediary adaptor protein such as Shc (another SH2 protein also in Figure 13.13) is used.

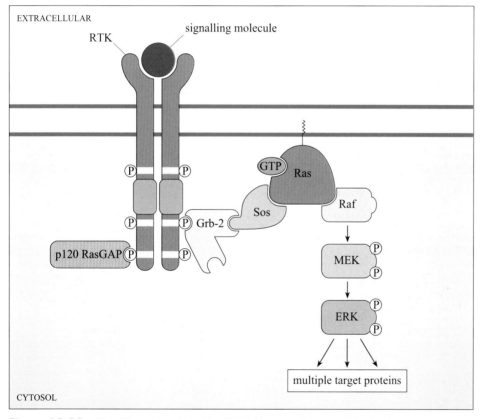

Figure 13.36   Signalling through the Ras/MAP kinase pathway. In this simple scenario, binding of the growth factor to its RTK induces autophosphorylation of the cytoplasmic domain of the dimerized receptor. This creates multiple docking sites for SH2-containing proteins (Figure 13.25), including the adaptor protein Grb-2 and p120 RasGAP. Grb-2 associates with the Ras guanine nucleotide exchange factor (GEF) Sos, by virtue of one of Grb-2's SH3 domains. Thus, Sos is brought to the plasma membrane, where it encourages inactive Ras to exchange its GDP for GTP. The active, GTP-bound Ras is now able to recruit Raf (discussed in Section 13.3.5) to the membrane, where it becomes activated. Raf is then able to phosphorylate MEK in its kinase domain, thus activating it. MEK then phosphorylates the MAP kinase ERK in its kinase domain, which then goes on to phosphorylate a range of target proteins, including transcription factors. Activation of Ras is also modulated by GAPs, docked to the membrane by binding to phosphotyrosines on activated RTKs (here p120 RasGAP).

One of the SH3 domains of Grb-2 bind to a Ras activator protein, which contains the appropriate proline-rich domains. Ras activators are proteins that, by binding to Ras, stimulate Ras to exchange its GDP for a molecule of GTP.

○ What is the name for this class of protein?

● Guanine nucleotide exchange factors, GEFs (Section 13.1.5).

The usual GEF that acts on Ras is called Sos (Figure 13.36). You can thank *Drosophila* researchers for this name! The photoreceptor studied by them is called R7, and the gene for the tyrosine kinase receptor involved in photo-receptor development is called 'sevenless' (because sevenless mutants lack R7 photoreceptors). The GEF was discovered to be downstream of the receptor, and so its gene was called son of sevenless. Because Sos is recruited to the plasma membrane by Grb-2 following receptor activation, it is then in the right place to bind to Ras (which is permanently tethered there) and encourage it to bind GTP. Since GEFs promote GTP binding and RasGAPs promote hydrolysis of GTP to GDP, the overall model is that GEFs switch Ras on, and GAPs switch Ras off (look back at Figure 13.8b). GDP-bound Ras is in an inactive conformation, but when it is bound to GTP, two 'switch' regions (the main one of which is an α helix) are affected, resulting in the adoption of an active conformation (Figure 13.37). These switch regions are implicated in binding to effectors and also to RasGAP.

It is remarkable that such a small and permanently membrane-bound protein as Ras is able to mediate so many profound changes within a cell. However, we can see how it can serve as an integrator of signalling information via GEFs and GAPs. As for its effectors, Ras is known to affect PI 3-kinase, but it achieves most of its effects by activating the first component of a key signal transduction cascade called the MAP kinase pathway (Figure 13.36), which serves to amplify signals and operate over a rather longer time frame than, say, second messenger systems. Moreover, it has many different cellular targets, including transcription factors, which it activates.

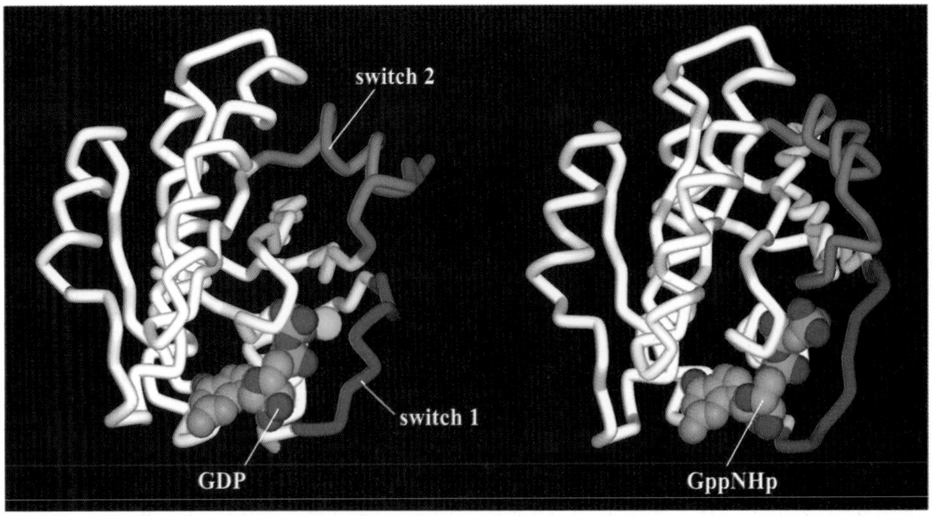

Figure 13.37
The switch regions of Ras.
(a) Ras bound to GDP. This nucleotide is shown as a space-filling structure, with the magnesium ion in green. (Based on pdb file 4q21.)
(b) Ras bound to GppNHp (a non-hydrolysable analogue of GTP also shown as a space-filling structure). When accommodating the larger nucleotide, the switch 1 region appears to stretch and the switch 2 region swivels. (Based on pdb file 5p21.)

(a)

(b)

13.3.5 Protein kinases

Protein kinases phosphorylate proteins either at tyrosine residues (**tyrosine kinases**), or at serine and threonine residues (**serine–threonine kinases**), or on any of these three amino acids (**dual-specificity kinases**). All these activities are employed in signal transduction pathways (histidine kinases also operate in certain plant and bacterial pathways, but not in animals). You should now be familiar with receptor tyrosine kinases, and have seen in some detail how phosphorylation of particular tyrosine residues can create docking sites for SH2-containing proteins (Section 13.2.2). You have also been introduced to the idea that phosphorylating key residues can induce a conformational change that can help to either activate or inactivate the protein, depending on both where the phosphorylation site is on the protein and on what other signals are being received by the protein, as illustrated for Src in Figure 3.29. You have also become familiar with several of the key serine–threonine kinases involved in signalling, such as the PKA, PKC and CaM kinases (Sections 13.3.2 and 13.3.3). There are two further very important groups of kinases that we shall now describe, namely those of the MAP kinase and the JAK–STAT pathways. Then we shall draw all these kinases together into families, and point out common domains and common themes in their mechanism of activation.

The MAP kinase pathway

The **MAP kinase pathway** is so called because the last component of the pathway was originally identified as a kinase activity in EGF-stimulated cells – hence the name 'mitogen-activated protein kinase' (MAP kinase), as it stimulates cell growth and proliferation.

◯ What is the mechanism of activation of the EGF receptor?

⬤ The EGF receptor is an RTK (Figure 13.23b), which becomes activated by dimerization. By contrast with most other RTKs, the EGF receptor does not form homodimers.

It was subsequently found that MAP kinase acts downstream of Ras, and that there are also two intermediary kinases (Raf and MEK in mammals), making it a three-kinase signalling module (Figure 13.36). MAP kinase forms the link between Ras in the plasma membrane and downstream effectors such as transcription factors in the nucleus. As such, it is crucial to signalling from growth factor receptors and other RTKs (and tyrosine kinase-associated receptors).

When Ras is activated, it recruits the serine–threonine kinase Raf to the membrane, where it becomes activated in a poorly understood mechanism involving membrane-bound kinases other than Ras itself (see Box 13.3). Raf is the first of the three kinases in the MAP kinase cascade, and is therefore also known as MAP kinase kinase kinase (abbreviated to MAPKKK). Raf phosphorylates (and thereby activates) the next kinase (a MAP kinase kinase, or MAPKK), which in mammalian cells is called MEK (MAP/ERK kinase). In turn, this phosphorylates MAP kinases (the classic one in mammals being ERK, extracellular signal regulated kinase). In their active state, MAP kinases are able to translocate to the nucleus and are able to phosphorylate numerous nuclear target proteins, leading to such major cellular events as proliferation or differentiation.

Why is there a chain of three kinases rather than just one? This is partially explained by the following principles.

- Firstly, we have to consider signal specificity. MAP kinases are very active proteins with many targets, and so need to be under close regulation. MEK provides this, since the peculiar phosphorylation requirements of MAP kinases (see below) mean that MEK is the only known activator of MAP kinases. Assembling the three-kinase signalling module on a scaffold, as happens in some MAP kinase pathway situations, can also help maintain specificity.

- Secondly, a sequence of kinases gives an opportunity for signal amplification.

- Thirdly, signal duration can radically change the signalling outcome (Section 13.3.7). Indeed, RTKs and Ras are generally inactivated fairly quickly by tyrosine phosphatases and GAPs, respectively, whereas the MAP kinase cascade can remain active for more extended periods of time (Section 13.3.6).

- Finally, the signal needs to be translocated from one part of the cell (the plasma membrane) to another (the nucleus). The MAP kinase pathway does not employ any second messenger molecules to broadcast the signal, but MAP kinase itself is the nearest protein equivalent, translocating to the nucleus once activated.

Box 13.3   Investigating the activity of signalling molecules

The activity of signalling molecules can be altered by site-directed mutagenesis (Section 3.8.1), which has proved very useful in the engineering of constitutively active or inactive versions of kinases. The inactive versions can act in a dominant negative manner within a cell, blocking the downstream pathway, whereas the constitutively active versions can permanently switch on the downstream pathway. These can be very useful tools for investigating signal transduction pathways. The example we shall examine is the mutagenesis of MEK, which is activated by phosphorylation on two nearby serines, Ser 217 and Ser 221, within the activation loop. The experiment, whose results are illustrated in Figure 13.38, shows the consequences of introducing MEK constructs that have been mutated at these residues by site-directed mutagenesis into cells. The effects of these mutations are assessed by determining the activity of its immediate downstream effector, ERK, by an *in vitro* kinase assay.

Replacing serine residues with glutamate residues at positions 217 and 221 creates a constitutively active mutant of MEK, which continuously activates ERK.

- From your knowledge of amino acid structure, suggest why glutamate instead of serine at positions 217 and 221 creates a constitutively active mutant.

- Glutamate is negatively charged, so to some extent it mimics phosphoserine.

Replacing either of these two key serines with alanine creates an interfering mutant of MEK, which blocks the activation of ERK.

- Again, suggest why replacing serine with alanine stops MEK functioning normally.

- Because the alanine side-chain has no —OH group, it cannot be phosphorylated, so MEK cannot become activated and cannot phosphorylate ERK.

The technique used to introduce the mutant MEK constructs into cells is known as 'transfection' (Box 9.3 and Figure 13.39a), a technique for which there are several variants. The principle is to induce tissue culture cells to take up a plasmid expression vector containing the gene to be expressed. Cationic lipids are used to promote uptake of plasmid DNA. In this experiment, a plasmid was used in which the mutant MEK gene was downstream of a promoter (SV40 in this instance). This protocol is suitable for experiments that terminate within a day or two (called 'transient' transfection). When a cell line that permanently expresses the gene is needed, the plasmid must be maintained and replicated within the cells.

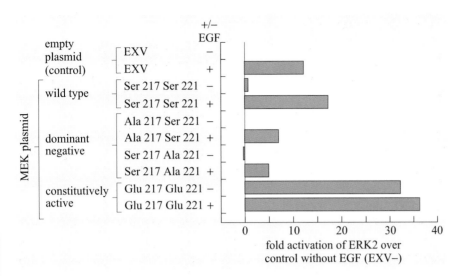

Figure 13.38 The activation of ERK by MEK mutants expressed in a cell line.
Cells were transiently transfected with wild-type MEK and different MEK mutants.
Cells were first growth arrested in starving medium and then stimulated or not with
EGF for 10 minutes (+ or −). They were then compared with control cells that had been
transfected with the empty plasmid (EXV) and stimulated or not with EGF under the same
conditions. Cells were harvested, and ERK was immunoprecipitated (in particular the
ERK2 isoform). ERK kinase activity was assayed *in vitro* by measuring the amount of
^{32}P-labelled ATP incorporated into a peptide ERK substrate. 'Fold activation' represents
the activity of ERK in experimental conditions divided by the activity of ERK in the
control untreated cells (EXV−). The results show that alanine mutants (Ala 217 and
Ala 221) interfere with the EGF stimulation of ERK2, and that the glutamate mutant
(Glu 217 Glu 221) constitutively activates ERK2. (Data from Cowley *et al.*, 1994.)

In this case, the expression vector must have the
appropriate replication sequences and a selectable
marker (such as the resistance gene to an antibiotic
like puromycin), so that transfected cells may be
selected from the untransfected neighbours; this is
known as 'stable transfection' (Figure 13.39b). When
short-term effects need to be observed in individual
cells, or where cells are difficult to transfect,
recombinant DNA (or protein) may be microinjected
(Figure 13.39c).

Figure 13.40 shows the rat PC12 neural cell line
microinjected with MEK mutant DNA. The
constitutively active MEK mutant induces
differentiation of this cell line (as seen by the
outgrowth of neural processes, also known as
'neurites'), similar to that induced by nerve growth
factor (NGF). This evidence supports a role for the
ERK MAP kinase pathway in neural outgrowth in this
cell type.

The activity of a signalling protein can be altered not
only by changing the catalytic activity of its kinase
domain, but also by translocating the signalling
protein to particular subcellular localizations, which
can be critical for their activation and/or ability to
access their targets. This can be investigated
experimentally by 'forcing' the protein of interest
into a particular subcellular localization. The
principle has been successfully exploited, for
example, to investigate the activation of Raf.
The membrane localization signal of K-Ras (the
amino acid sequence Cys–Val–Ile–Met), which is
post-translationally prenylated by addition of a
farnesyl residue, was added to the carbon terminus
of Raf. This modification constitutively localized
Raf to the membrane, resulting in its constitutive
activation. The activated Raf could be further
activated by EGF independently of Ras, which
suggested that Ras acts as a temporary membrane
anchor for Raf (as shown in Figure 13.36), and
that Raf is also activated by other membrane-
associated signals when in the membrane
environment.

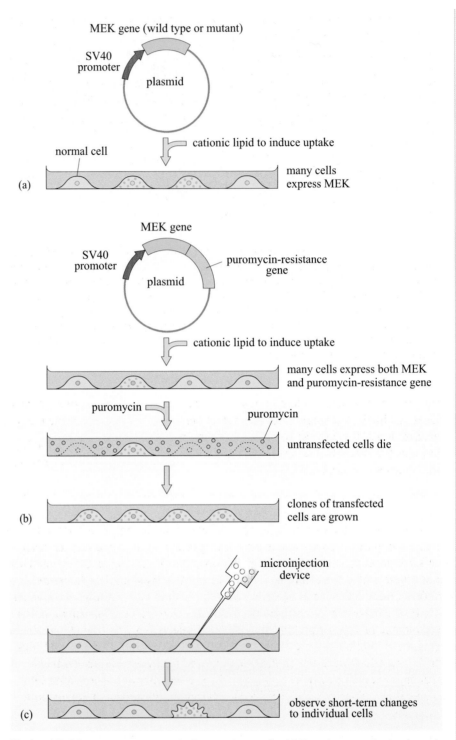

Figure 13.39   Expressing genes in tissue culture cells. (a) Transient transfection is used for bulk gene transfer experiments that last less than a few days. (b) Stable transfection is used for generating stably transfected cell lines for long-term use. (c) Microinjection of recombinant DNA or proteins, for looking at short-term effects on individual cells.

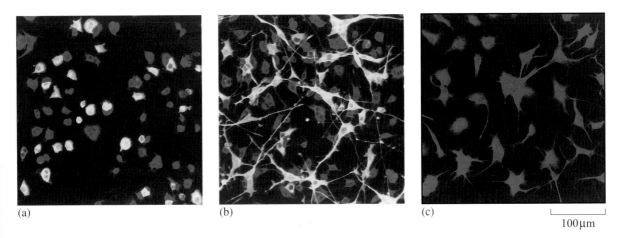

(a) (b) (c)

100 µm

Figure 13.40 Microinjection of DNA encoding constitutively active MEK induces neurite formation in the PC12 neural cell line. In each micrograph, cells that are over-expressing MEK fluoresce green. Actin and tubulin are stained with a red fluorescent dye to show the morphology of non-expressing cells. Note that where green and red fluorescence overlap, the cells are yellow. (a) Wild-type MEK, which does not induce neurite outgrowth when over-expressed. (b) Constitutively active Glu 217 Glu 221 MEK mutant, showing neurite formation in the majority of cells, over-expressing the mutant MEK (green), against a background of morphologically normal uninjected cells, which are not expressing MEK, stained red. (c) Positive control. These cells are not microinjected, but are stimulated with NGF, inducing neurite formation similar to that seen in part (b). (Data from Cowley *et al.*, 1994.)

Proteins may be targeted to a number of cellular locations by this technique. For example, nuclear localization sequences can be added to signalling proteins (such as MAP kinases) to investigate their role in gene transcription.

What signal sequence do you think would target a protein to the nucleus?

A nuclear localization signal (NLS). NLS sequences were described in Section 11.5.1.

Activation of MAP kinases involves specific phosphorylation of residues within the activation loop of the catalytic domain of the protein, in the same way as many other kinases such as Src (the activation loop of Src is explained in Section 3.4.3 and in Figure 3.29). For example, Raf activates MEK by phosphorylating two specific serines within the activation loop (Box 13.3). The activation requirements of MAP kinase are even more specific. It requires activation by phosphorylation of a threonine residue and a tyrosine residue. These two are separated from the threonine receptor by a single amino acid within the activation loop. In ERK this motif is Thr–Glu–Tyr, in which the threonine and tyrosine residues can be phosphorylated *only* by MEK, because MEK is a member of the very unusual dual-specificity kinases, which are able to phosphorylate serine–threonine *and* tyrosine residues.

Activated MAP kinase family members are activators of immediate 'early genes', so called because they are activated within minutes of cell stimulation. Many of these genes encode transcription factors (Section 13.3.7), which then switch on other sets of genes, thereby initiating cellular programs of differentiation or proliferation. There are also cytosolic targets of MAP kinases, which include regulators of protein synthesis. As an example, MAP kinase phosphorylates another kinase called Mnk1, which, in turn, phosphorylates and activates the translation initiation factor 4E (eIF-4E; a member of the initiation factors discussed in Section 11.4.1).

There are several MAP kinase pathways. The pathways employing ERK represent the classic pathway, but there are also two other major mammalian MAP kinase pathways implicated in cellular responses to stress (not discussed here). Moreover, the MAP kinase pathway is conserved across the animal kingdom and even in yeast and plants, as shown in Table 13.3. In particular, the model organisms *C. elegans* and *Drosophila* have provided extremely useful experimental systems for investigating MAP kinase pathways, and for showing that it operates downstream of growth factor receptors and Ras.

Table 13.3   MAP kinase signalling pathways.*

	Mammals	**C. elegans†**	**D. melanogaster**	**S. cerevisiae**		**Plants**
ligand	growth factors	anchor cells	Boss	mating factor	high osmolarity	ethylene
receptor	RTKs	Let-23 (RTK)	Sevenless (RTK)	7TM receptor	osmolarity sensing receptor	histidine kinase receptor
adaptors	Grb-2	Sem-5	Drk			
GTPase regulators	hSos + / GAP −	? + / Gap1 −	Sos + / Gap1 −			
G proteins	Ras	Let-60	Dras	trimeric G protein		
MAP kinase cascade — kinase 1	Raf	Lin-45	Draf	kinase 1	kinase 1	kinase 1
kinase 2	MEK	Mek-2	D-mek	kinase 2	scaffold kinase	kinase 2
kinase 3	ERK	Mpk-1	ERK-A	kinase 3	HOG	kinase 3
target proteins	Jun, Fos, Elk	several transcription factors	Sina	various	various	transcription factors for ethylene response genes
response	cell proliferation	cell fate in vulval development	R7 cell neuronal fate in eye development	mating response	glycerol synthesis in response to change in osmotic equilibrium	ripening, senescence and stress responses

*There is remarkable conservation of MAP kinase signalling pathways, from mammals to plants. In addition to the MAP kinase cascade (blue), there are other striking homologies in several of the pathways, especially between growth factor pathways in mammals, vulval induction in nematodes and eye development in fruit-flies, where the receptors (pink), adaptors, GTPase regulators and G protein homologues (green) are also related. Not all the names of all the signalling proteins here are explained, and they need not be remembered; they are included merely to illustrate the conservation of the pathways.

†The GEF for the Ras homologue in *C. elegans* remains unidentified, and is denoted as '?'.

The JAK–STAT pathway

Another important protein kinase pathway is the **JAK–STAT pathway**. Cytokines (described in Chapter 12 and Section 13.2.1), are frequently used for signalling between cells of the immune system. Cytokine-induced signal transduction cascades are often direct pathways to the nucleus for switching on sets of genes. Janus kinases (JAKs, named after the two-faced Roman god) are a particular group of tyrosine kinases that associate with cytokine receptors. When cytokines such as α-interferon bind to their receptor, JAKs (denoted as JAK1, Tyk2, etc.) associated with different receptor units cross-phosphorylate each other on tyrosine residues (Figure 13.41). The receptors are then phosphorylated by JAKs, creating phosphotyrosine-docking sites for SH2-containing proteins, in this case a specific group of proteins called STATs (signal transducers and activators of transcription).

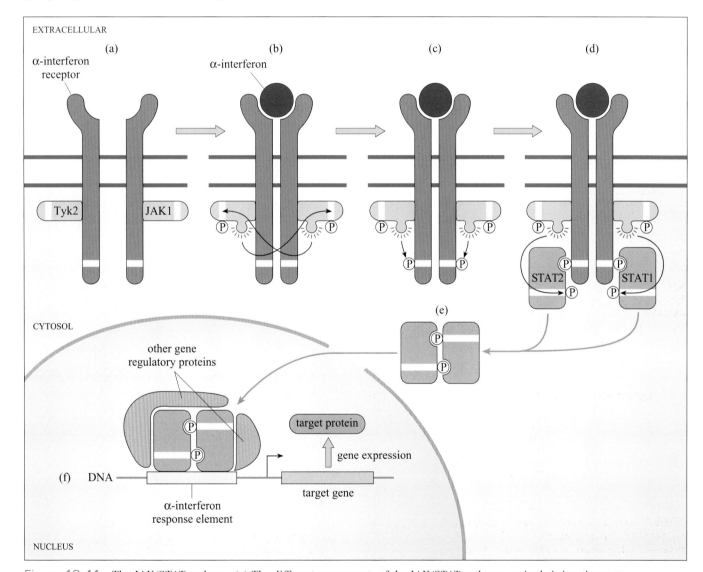

Figure 13.41   The JAK/STAT pathway. (a) The different components of the JAK/STAT pathway are in their inactive state. (b) Cytokines such as α-interferon induce dimerization of their tyrosine kinase-associated receptors. (c) JAKs cross-phosphorylate each other on tyrosine residues. Activated JAKs phosphorylate both α-interferon receptor subunits on tyrosine residues, (d) which then act as docking sites for STAT proteins. (e) STATs become phosphorylated by JAKs, which then allows the formation of STAT dimers via their SH2 domains. (f) STAT dimers translocate to the nucleus and initiate transcription of target genes.

Box 13.4   Detecting protein–protein interactions using the MAPPIT system

The mammalian protein–protein interaction trap (MAPPIT) system uses the same two-hybrid principle described in Section 3.8.2. However, instead of the genes of interest being fused to transcriptional activator domains, they are fused to components of the JAK–STAT signalling pathway (Figure 13.42). Using recombinant DNA technology, the bait protein domain is fused to a mutant erythropoietin (Epo) receptor, which has JAK binding sites but lacks STAT binding sites. The prey protein is fused to a protein fragment that has several potential STAT binding sites. If there is no interaction between bait and prey,

JAKs cross-phosphorylate each other on stimulation with Epo, but STAT is not recruited as there are no available docking sites on the receptor. If there is an interaction between bait and prey, the protein fragment becomes tyrosine-phosphorylated by JAKs on receptor activation, enabling STAT to bind to it. STAT is then in the vicinity of JAK, which can access and phosphorylate the STAT. Then STAT can dimerize, translocate to the nucleus and induce transcription of a reporter gene (Section 3.8.2), which can be easily quantified.

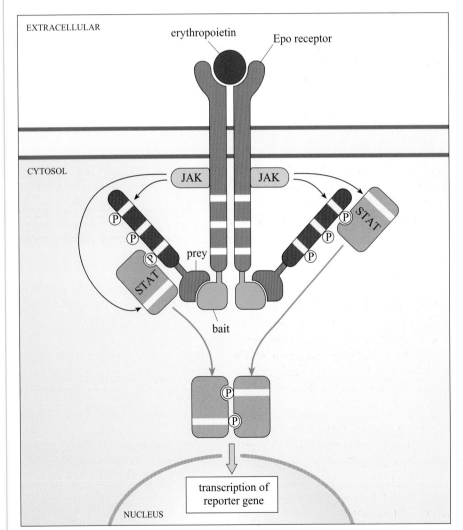

Figure 13.42
The basic principle of a mammalian protein–protein interaction trap (MAPPIT). Absent STAT-binding tyrosine residues in the erythropoietin (Epo) receptor are indicated as white bands whereas present tyrosine residues are represented as yellow bands. A positive interaction between bait and prey proteins results in the phosphorylation of tyrosine residues in the protein fragment by JAK, which then act as docking sites for STAT. The end result is the formation of STAT dimers, which induce transcription of a reporter gene.

In turn, the STATs are phosphorylated by the JAKs, which causes the STATs to dissociate from the receptor and instead bind to each other by means of their SH2 domains. STAT dimers translocate directly to the nucleus, where they bind to other gene regulatory proteins and to response elements in target genes.

○ Can you recall any other signalling pathway that has also has a direct route to the nucleus?

● The nuclear hormone receptor signalling pathway, where the intracellular receptor binds the ligand (for example, a steroid) and translocates to the nucleus, where it binds to hormone response elements (Figure 13.27).

The JAK–STAT pathway has recently become the basis for the development of techniques for the study of protein–protein interactions (Box 13.4).

Now that we have described the major protein kinases, we can look at them all together, and see what features they have in common. Figure 13.43 is a dendrogram showing how the various subgroups of protein kinases in humans are related to each other both functionally and structurally. Despite their different subcellular localizations, activation mechanisms and substrates, protein kinases have remarkable similarity of structure within their kinase domain.

○ Recall the kinase domain of Src from Chapter 3, which illustrates the major features of all protein kinases. From this, suggest the common features of kinase domains.

● The kinase domain comprises two lobes, with the active site in the cleft between them. The smaller lobe binds ATP. The larger lobe has an activation loop protruding from the cleft. This activation loop often needs to be phosphorylated in order to activate the protein (either by an upstream kinase or by autophosphorylation).

13.3.6 Protein phosphatases

Together with inositolphospholipid phosphatases (p. 111), protein phosphatases are key regulators of signal transduction pathways. Like protein kinases, protein phosphatases are either **tyrosine phosphatases** (the majority of protein phosphatases, some of which are shown in Figure 13.44) or **serine–threonine phosphatases** (including the phosphoprotein phosphatase family, designated PP1–6), which will be described in Section 13.4, or, rarely, **dual-specificity phosphatases.**

Phosphatases are required to inactivate signalling proteins that have been activated by phosphorylation. Many tyrosine phosphatases such as SHP-1 and -2 have SH2 domains, and are recruited to the membrane following ligand-stimulated phosphorylation of receptors. For example, the tyrosine phosphatase SHP-1 binds to phosphotyrosines on activated cytokine receptors such as the erythropoietin (Epo) receptor, and is then phosphorylated by JAK2, which activates it. Active SHP-1 can downregulate (damp down) the JAK/STAT signalling pathway by dephosphorylating specific JAKs and STATs. It is therefore acting as a negative regulator.

Another role for phosphatases occurs when they activate a protein that is held in an inactive state by phosphorylation.

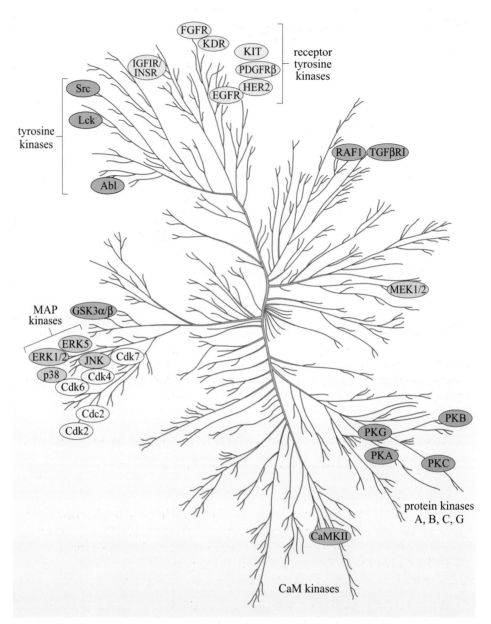

Figure 13.43 Dendrogram representing the relationships between protein kinases. Currently known human protein kinases have been represented according to the sequence similarity of their protein kinase domain. Note, for example, that the kinase domain of the MAP kinase ERK is closely related to that of cyclin-dependent kinases (Chapter 8), but not to that of MEK1/2, its upstream activator. Most, but not all, of the protein kinases discussed in this chapter are shown here. Remember that the lipid kinases, such as PI 3-kinase, are not protein kinases, so are not represented here.

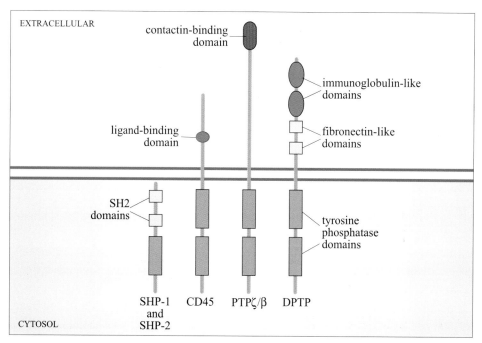

Figure 13.44   Examples of cytosolic (SHP-1 and SHP-2) and receptor tyrosine phosphatases (CD45, PTPζ/β and DPTP). SHP-1 and CD45 are discussed in the text. PTPζ/β and DPTP (a *Drosophila* protein tyrosine phosphatase) are shown here to illustrate the variety of extracellular domains and conservation of cytoplasmic domains.

☐   You have already met an example of a protein regulated in this way. What is it?

⬤   Src, which in its inactive state has an inhibitory phosphate on Tyr 527 (Section 13.1.5).

Lck is a Src family tyrosine kinase (Figure 13.26), which is dephosphorylated and thereby activated by the membrane-bound tyrosine phosphatase CD45. (CD45 plays an essential role in the activation of leukocytes following antigen presentation.) CD45, like many of the PTPs, is a transmembrane protein (Figure 13.44); such proteins are referred to as receptor tyrosine phosphatases (p. 98).

Tyrosine phosphatases are often referred to as protein tyrosine phosphatases, abbreviated PTPs, e.g. DPTP in Figure 13.44.

One of the most well-studied phosphatases is the dual-specificity phosphatase MKP-1, which inactivates MAP kinase. The MKP-1 gene is one of the immediate early genes expressed following MAP kinase activation, being expressed approximately 20 minutes after cell stimulation. As MKP-1 levels rise, MAP kinase is dephosphorylated and inactivated.

☐   What type of regulation is effected by MKP-1 on MAP kinase?

⬤   Feedback inhibition.

Because negative feedback by MKP-1 is a transcription-dependent mechanism, it helps to explain the relatively long duration of MAP kinase activation.

13.3.7 Activation of transcription factors

We have already come across several examples of signalling pathways leading to activation (or inactivation) of transcription factors, which in turn modulate transcription of sets of genes leading to, for example, programs of differentiation or proliferation. You will also meet several other specific examples in subsequent chapters. For now, we shall examine one particular scenario, namely the activation of immediate early genes by MAP kinases, which illustrates some of the principles and details involved.

One of the most important immediate early genes activated by the ERK family of MAP kinases is *fos*. The *fos* gene product is itself an important transcription factor, which helps to activate transcription of genes containing binding sites for the transcription factor complex AP-1 (formed by association of Fos and Jun; Figure 13.45) in their promoters. ERK brings about transcription of *fos* by phosphorylating the nuclear transcription factor known as 'ternary complex factor (TCF)'. This, together with the serum response factor (SRF), binds to the serum response element (SRE) in the promoter of the *fos* gene and increases its transcription rate (Figure 13.45).

It takes about 30 minutes or more for the proteins encoded by immediate early genes such as *fos* to be synthesized. Once Fos protein has been produced, MAP kinases participate in its activation, in a stepwise manner, firstly by phosphorylating two sites in the C-terminal region of Fos. This exposes the ERK-binding motif of Fos. ERK then further phosphorylates Fos at two more sites. It is immediately apparent that if MAP kinase activation is only transient, lasting for less than 30 minutes, Fos cannot be activated. Therefore, we can see how transient MAP kinase activation can lead to a different cellular outcome than sustained MAP kinase activation.

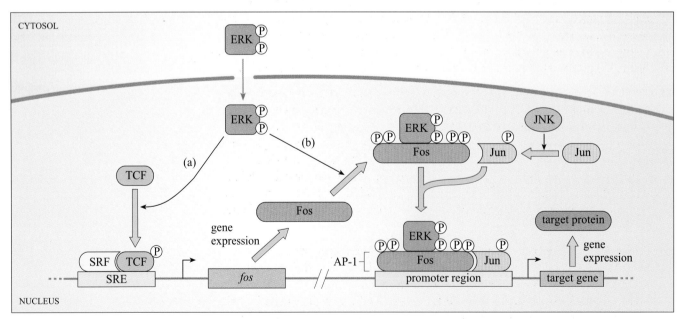

Figure 13.45   Activation of transcription by the MAP kinase pathway (following on from Figure 13.36). (a) Activated ERK translocates to the nucleus and phosphorylates TCF, which, together with SRF activates the expression of immediate early genes containing serum response elements (SRE) in their promoters; *fos* is one of these genes. Transcription and translation take about half an hour. (b) If ERK remains active during this period, it will bind to and activate the newly synthesized Fos protein, which, together with Jun (phosphorylated by another MAP kinase called JNK), make up the transcription factor complex AP-1. This then promotes expression of another set of target genes.

This is illustrated by the neural cell line PC12, which fully differentiates them into neurons only when ERK activation is sustained (for example, by addition of nerve growth factor; Figure 13.40c).

☐ Can you think of an experimental method for the investigation of the relationship between sustained activation of ERK and differentiation of PC12 cells?

⬤ By transfection of PC12 cells with constitutively active mutant forms of MEK and analysing neurite outgrowth (Box 13.3).

Summary of Section 13.3

1   Heterotrimeric G proteins are tethered to the internal surface of the plasma membrane, and are activated by conformational change within 7TM receptors. There are many different α subunits (and a few $\beta\gamma$ subunits), which interact with different receptors and different effectors. The major targets of G proteins include ion channels, adenylyl cyclase (activated by $G\alpha_s$ and inhibited by $G\alpha_i$) and PLC-β (activated by $G\alpha_q$).

2   Phosphatidylinositol (PI) is the precursor of a family of small lipid second messengers. The inositol ring can be further phosphorylated at positions 3, 4, and 5 by lipid kinases. PI 3-kinase specializes in phosphorylating the hydroxyl group at the 3 position, thus generating the active signalling molecules $PI(3,4)P_2$ and $PI(3,4,5)P_3$. The phosphorylated 3 position is recognized as a docking site by PH domain-containing proteins, thus providing a mechanism for signalling proteins to be recruited to the membrane.

3   Phospholipase C enzymes (especially PLC-β, activated by G proteins, and RTK-activated PLC-γ) cleave $PI(4,5)P_2$ to generate diacylglycerol (DAG) and inositol 1,4,5-triphosphate (IP_3). DAG remains embedded in the membrane, where it activates protein kinase C (PKC). IP_3 diffuses through the cytosol, and opens IP_3-gated calcium channels, releasing stored calcium into the cytosol.

4   The Ca^{2+} ion is an important second messenger, which enters the cytosol from the extracellular space through specific channels on the plasma membrane, or is rapidly released from stores into the cytoplasm. Calcium channels include IP_3-gated calcium channels, voltage-dependent calcium channels, or ryanodine receptors in skeletal muscle cells. It activates numerous Ca^{2+}-dependent proteins, including PKC, but many of its effects are mediated via calmodulin, which has four allosteric Ca^{2+} binding sites. Ca^{2+}/calmodulin then binds to and regulates target proteins, especially Ca^{2+}/calmodulin-dependent protein kinases (CaM kinases).

5   Cyclic AMP (cAMP) is another important second messenger, synthesized by adenylyl cyclase (which is activated or inhibited by different G protein subtypes). It can open cAMP-gated ion channels, but it mediates many of its effects through cAMP-dependent protein kinase A (PKA), whose roles include regulating glycogen metabolism, and phosphorylation of a transcription factor that binds to the cAMP response element (CRE).

6   Cyclic GMP is synthesized by guanylyl cyclase. Its targets include cGMP-gated ion channels and a cGMP-dependent kinase (PKG).

7   Ras is the archetypal monomeric, or small, G protein. Ras classically operates downstream of growth factor receptors: Grb-2, an SH2/SH3-containing adaptor protein, binds to phosphotyrosines on the activated RTK, and recruits Sos to the membrane environment; Sos promotes GTP binding by Ras. Activated Ras has more than one target, including PI 3-kinase, but its most important downstream pathway is the MAP kinase pathway. Activated Ras recruits Raf to the membrane, where it is activated and then phosphorylates MEK, which then phosphorylates ERK, a MAP kinase. These have multiple cytoplasmic and transcription factor targets involved in cell growth and division or differentiation.

8   Protein kinase families involved at various points in signalling pathways include receptor tyrosine kinases (for example, the EGF receptor), non-receptor tyrosine kinases (such as Src and JAK), serine–threonine kinases such as PKC, PKA, MAP kinases and the TGF receptor, and rare dual-specificity kinases such as MEK.

9   Protein phosphatases dephosphorylate proteins, and are grouped according to their targets, as are protein kinases. They include protein tyrosine phosphatases, serine–threonine phosphatases, and a few dual-specificity phosphatases.

10 The duration of ERK activity determines activation of different transcription factors (SRF/TCF for immediate early genes; AP-1 for other target genes).

11 The major signalling molecules we have discussed are brought together into five basic pathways in Figure 13.46.

13.4 Glucose metabolism: an example of integration of signalling pathways

We are now in a position to draw together the major concepts and components of signalling, and show how they operate in one well-understood system, namely the regulation of the storage or release of glucose in the human body. From this, you will be able to recognize archetypal pathways represented in specific examples, you will be able to appreciate how the same basic pathways can be stimulated by different hormones in different tissues, and you will see how opposing hormones activate separate pathways that affect the same targets but in opposite ways.

Following a meal, insulin is released into the bloodstream by pancreatic β cells. The overall systemic effects of insulin are to increase uptake of blood glucose into cells, and to promote its storage as glycogen in muscle and liver cells. (Note that glycogen is a polysaccharide consisting of repeated units of glucose used for short-term energy storage by animal cells.) A rise in the concentration of blood glucose, such as that following the consumption of food, stimulates insulin production, which signals through the insulin RTK. The insulin RTK phosphorylates various substrate proteins, which link to several key signalling pathways such as the Ras–MAP kinase pathway. There are, however, two major pathways that control glycogen synthesis and breakdown in animal cells (Figure 13.47).

1   Glygogen synthase kinase-3β (GSK-3β) inhibits glycogen synthase (GS), which is responsible for synthesizing glycogen from uridine diphosphate (UDP)–glucose.

2 Phosphorylase kinase, a serine–threonine kinase of the CaM kinase family, which, in turn, activates the enzyme phosphorylase, responsible for cleaving glucose 1-phosphate units from the glycogen chain.

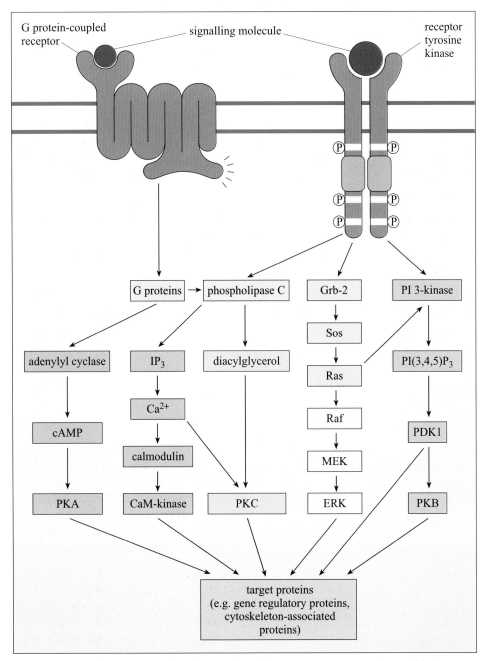

Figure 13.46   A summary of the five major signalling pathways described in this chapter. In this highly simplistic schematic diagram, each of these pathways ends with a kinase, which goes on to phosphorylate a group of target proteins. There are many connections between the pathways, only some of which are shown, for simplicity. Note that the phospholipase C activated by G proteins is PLC-β, whereas PLC-γ is activated by RTKs. The MAP kinase activation pathway shown here corresponds to that found in mammals. Different pathways are distinguished by colour: PKA pathway (lilac); CaM pathway (light brown); PKC pathway (pink); MAP kinase pathway (cream); PI 3-kinase (orange). Other pathways discussed in the text are not illustrated here, and none of the inactivation mechanisms for these pathways are shown.

Figure 13.47
The control of glycogen synthesis by insulin. Several proteins bind, and are phosphorylated by, the activated insulin receptor. Cbl activates a pathway that is implicated in the translocation of the glucose transporter GLUT4 to the membrane, allowing glucose transport into the cell. Meanwhile, IRS-1 serves as a docking protein for PI 3-kinase, which leads to PKB activation. PKB phosphorylates glycogen synthase kinase-3β (GSK-3β), which is thereby inactivated, so relieving its inhibition of glycogen synthase by phosphorylation. Glycogen synthase is therefore activated, and converts UDP–glucose to glycogen. Glycogen synthase is further activated by the phosphatase PP1G, which itself is activated by an insulin-stimulated protein kinase (ISPK). ISPK also activates PP1, so inhibiting glycogen breakdown (note that PP1 dephosphorylates phosphorylase kinase, which activates phosphorylase). The overall result is import of glucose into the cell, which is converted to glycogen by glycogen synthase, and inhibition of glycogen breakdown by phosphorylase. Phosphorylase is so called because in the process of cleaving glucose units from the glycogen chain, it adds a phosphate group to each glucose molecule.

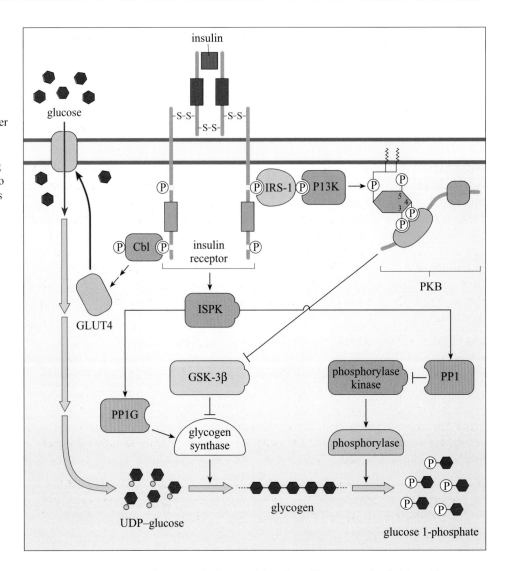

Both regulatory mechanisms are influenced by signalling cascades initiated by the interaction between phosphotyrosine residues on the insulin receptor and *two* signalling molecules:

1   The first is Cbl, which was introduced in Section 13.2.3 as a link between RTKs and ubiquitin in receptor sequestration. In this case, it seems to be the start of a pathway that ends up with translocation of GLUT4 glucose-transporter molecules to the plasma membrane, thus promoting the uptake of glucose into the cell.

2   The second is IRS-1, insulin receptor substrate-1, which is a large protein that binds several SH2-containing proteins, including PI 3-kinase. As described previously (Section 13.3.2), PI 3-kinase creates phosphorylated inositol phospholipid docking sites for PH-containing proteins, including PKB. GSK-3β is inhibited by PKB, so that its inhibitory action on glycogen synthase activity is negated.

At the same time, an insulin-stimulated protein kinase (ISPK, activated by insulin by an unknown mechanism) acts on the serine–threonine phosphatase PP1G to further enhance glycogen synthase activity. ISPK also activates another serine–threonine phosphatase, PP1, which negatively regulates the activity of phosphorylase kinase, and, ultimately, phosphorylase.

So insulin promotes uptake of glucose into tissues by mobilizing glucose transporters, and in liver and skeletal muscle, activates glycogen synthesis by modulating the activity of GSK-3β and GS, and inhibits glycogen breakdown via PP1. In other words, insulin induces gluconeogenesis in liver and skeletal muscle.

Two hormones, adrenalin (secreted from the adrenal medulla in anticipation of muscle activity) and glucagon (released from pancreatic α cells when blood sugar is low) have the opposite effect to insulin; that is, they increase the rate at which glycogen is converted to glucose (glycogenolysis; Figure 13.20). In skeletal muscle, glucose enters the glycolytic pathway to produce ATP, the fuel for muscle contraction. In the liver (which is more responsive to glucagon than to adrenalin), glucose is released into the bloodstream for use by muscle cells. Adrenalin and glucagon act through GPCRs, so their signalling pathways start off quite differently from that of insulin, a RTK. However, they end up (among other things) regulating the activity of the same enzymes involved in glycogen synthesis that insulin itself modulates.

Adrenalin has many effects, but in skeletal muscle it acts through β-adrenergic receptors, which are coupled to $G\alpha_s$ and stimulate adenylyl cyclase activity. This results in cAMP elevation and consequently activation of PKA (Figure 13.48). PKA activates phosphorylase kinase (see (a) in Figure 13.48), which in turn activates the enzyme phosphorylase. (Phosphorylase kinase activation is also promoted by ACh release from neuron terminals; Figure 13.48). PKA also phosphorylates three key proteins to promote glycogen breakdown and inhibit its synthesis as shown by letters (b)–(d) in Figure 13.48:

(b) The serine–threonine phosphatase PP1, which is inhibited as a result (PP1's action is to dephosphorylate, and therefore inhibit, phosphorylase kinase and phosphorylase). Note that PKA phosphorylates (and inactivates) PP1 on different residues than ISPK (which activates PP1).

(c) PP1 inhibitor, which on phosphorylation is activated.

(d) Glycogen synthase, which on phosphorylation is inactivated.

This system provides a good illustration of how a key signalling enzyme (PKA) with multiple substrates can regulate different targets within the same metabolic pathway, all combining to promote one outcome, in this case glycogen breakdown. In at least two cases (glycogen synthase and PP1), it is the *same* enzymes whose activity is ultimately regulated (either negatively or positively) by insulin (via PKB) and adrenalin (via PKA), acting antagonistically.

In the liver, however, adrenalin acts mainly but not exclusively through α-adrenergic receptors, which are coupled to $G\alpha_q$, and activate the PLC/IP$_3$ pathway, which opens IP$_3$-gated Ca^{2+} channels (Figure 13.49), helping to activate phophorylase kinase and promote glycogen breakdown, leading to glucose release into the blood.

Glucagon is a hormone that activates glycogen breakdown, particularly in the liver, resulting in a release of glucose into the blood. In the liver, the control of glycogen breakdown is fundamentally the same as in skeletal muscle, but with particular differences. Whereas skeletal muscle needs to be extremely responsive to adrenalin (for the classic fight or flight response), the function of the liver is to maintain

Figure 13.48

The control of glycogen breakdown in muscle by adrenalin. In skeletal muscle, adrenalin, through its β-adrenergic 7TM receptor, stimulates $G\alpha_s$ protein, which activates adenylyl cyclase to produce cAMP. This activates PKA, which then phosphorylates (and activates) phosphorylase kinase. This then phosphorylates (and activates) the enzyme phosphorylase, which breaks down glycogen to glucose 1-phosphate. Phosphorylase kinase is also partly activated by Ca^{2+} ions, because it is a CaM kinase (Sections 13.3.2 and 13.3.3). Ca^{2+} is released on neural stimulation of the muscle. PKA also phosphorylates three key proteins to promote glycogen breakdown and inhibit its synthesis (see text). Note that the βγ subunits of the G proteins have been omitted for clarity.

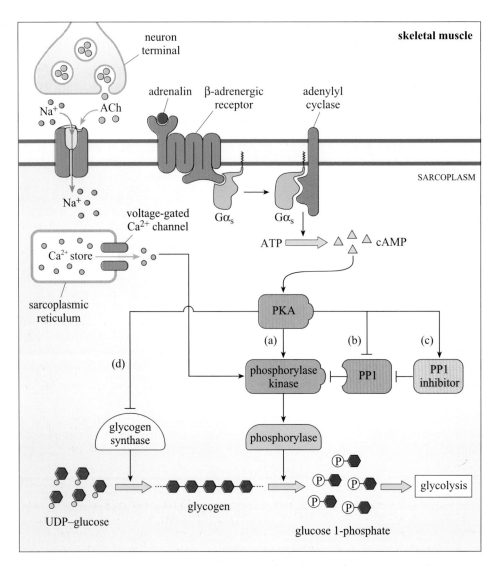

blood sugar levels within a constant, physiological range. Liver cells therefore have many glucagon receptors (Figure 13.49), which are GPCRs coupled to $G\alpha_s$, activating the same basic pathway that adrenalin does in skeletal muscle, via cAMP/PKA. The result is phosphorylation and activation of phosphorylase kinase, thereby promoting glycogen breakdown.

Summary of Section 13.4

1   Glycogen metabolism is controlled by two enzymes, glycogen synthase (mediating glycogen synthesis) and phosphorylase (mediating glycogen breakdown).

2   Three pathways converge in the regulation of glycogen synthase: cAMP/PKA and GSK-3β are negative regulators, whereas ISPK/PP1G positively regulate the activity of glycogen synthase.

3   Insulin and adrenalin have opposite effects on glycogen synthesis: insulin promotes glycogen synthesis by activating ISPK/PP1G and by inhibiting GSK-3β by the PI3K/PKB pathway, whereas adrenalin inhibits glycogen synthase by the cAMP/PKA pathway.

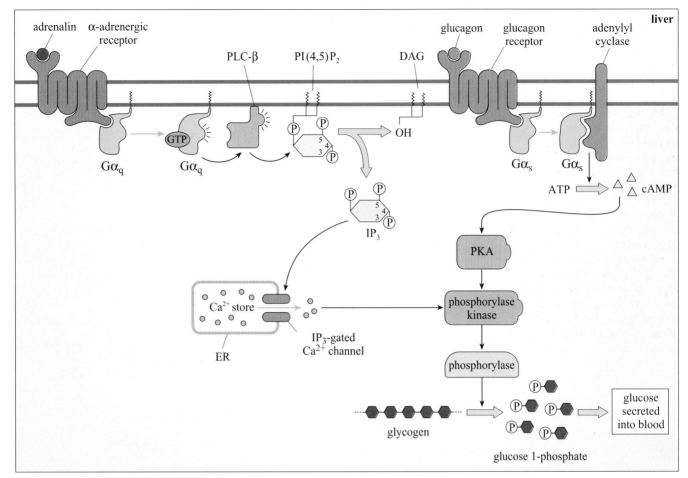

Figure 13.49   The control of glycogen breakdown in liver by adrenalin and glucagon. In liver cells, adrenalin activates a different pathway than in skeletal muscle, but the outcome is the same, namely an increase in glycogen breakdown. The receptors in liver are mainly α- rather than the β-adrenergic receptors in muscle. These are linked to $G\alpha_q$ proteins, which activate PLC to produce DAG and IP_3. The latter releases Ca^{2+} via IP_3-gated ion channels in the ER. Ca^{2+} then activates phosphorylase kinase in the same way that it does in muscle cells, promoting glycogen breakdown. So adrenalin is inducing Ca^{2+} release in liver in the same way as ACh release from nerve endings but using different pathways. Ca^{2+} release in both organs promotes glycogen breakdown. Glucagon activates the glucagon receptor coupled to $G\alpha_s$ and, subsequently, the PKA pathway in liver, promoting glycogen breakdown as adrenalin does in skeletal muscle.

4   Three pathways converge in the activation of phosphorylase by phosphorylase kinase: Ca^{2+} and PKA activate phosphorylase kinase, whereas PP1 is a negative regulator.

5   Acetylcholine, adrenalin and glucagon promote glycogen breakdown, whereas insulin inhibits it.

6   Acetylcholine in skeletal muscle and adrenalin in liver activate phosphorylase kinase by a common mechanism, an increase in cytosolic Ca^{2+}, although the effect of ACh is by voltage-dependent channels and that of adrenalin by IP_3-gated Ca^{2+} channels.

7   Adrenalin in muscle and glucagon in liver activate phosphorylase kinase by a common mechanism, namely an increase in cytosolic cAMP and subsequent activation of PKA. In addition, PKA further activates phosphorylase kinase in skeletal muscle by inhibition of PP1 either directly or indirectly.

8   Insulin has an opposite effect to adrenalin on glycogen breakdown, namely the inhibition of glycogen breakdown by activation of the phosphorylase kinase inhibitor, PP1.

Experimental investigation 3

Go to the Study Skills file: *Experimental investigation 3.* This activity will familiarize you with two assays used to study activation of signalling proteins, namely (a) SDS–PAGE and Western blotting with antibodies specific for phosphorylated forms of proteins (Box 13.1), and (b) pull-down assays using fusion proteins (Box 13.2). From your understanding of these principles, you will first design, and then carry out and interpret a series of experiments that investigate the sequence of signalling events that mediate the mitogenic response of cells to an extracellular signal, PDGF.

Learning outcomes for Chapter 13

When you have studied this chapter, you should be able to:

13.1   Define and use each of the terms printed in **bold** in the text.

13.2   Understand the basic principles of signal transduction mechanisms, in particular the concepts of response specificity, signal amplitude and duration, signal integration and intracellular location.

13.3   Give examples of different types of extracellular signals and receptors, and explain their functional significance.

13.4   Describe the mechanisms by which different receptors may be activated by their respective ligands.

13.5   Describe and give examples of the structure and properties of the major components of signal transduction pathways.

13.6   Understand and give examples of the role of protein binding domains in the specific interactions between signalling molecules.

13.7   Understand and give examples of how signalling pathways triggered by different ligands are integrated within a cell to give a specific functional response.

Questions for Chapter 13

Question 13.1

What are the general features of second messengers?

Question 13.2

What properties of proteins are particularly used by signalling proteins?

Question 13.3

Explain the difference between the ligands of transmembrane and intracellular signalling receptors.

Question 13.4

Describe how acetylcholine activates two completely different classes of receptor.

Question 13.5

'An extracellular signal that binds to a receptor without intrinsic enzymatic activity signals through a receptor tyrosine kinase.'

How can this statement be true?

Question 13.6

Explain how calmodulin is allosterically regulated.

Question 13.7

Give examples of signalling proteins that can be temporarily recruited to the vicinity of the cytosolic side of the plasma membrane following receptor activation.

Question 13.8

What would be the likely role of a signalling protein that consisted only of one SH2 domain and one SH3 domain?

Question 13.9

Draw a simple diagram to show how insulin and adrenalin affect glycogen synthase activity in skeletal muscle.

References

Cowley, S., Paterson, H., Kemp, P. and Marshall, C. J. (1994) Activation of MAP kinase is necessary and sufficient for PC12 differentiation and for transformation of NIH 3T3 cells, *Cell*, **77** (6), pp. 841–852.

Jhun, B. H., Rivnay, B., Price, D. and Abraham, H. (1995) The MATK tyrosine kinase interacts in a specific and SH2-dependent manner with c-Kit, *Journal of Biological Chemistry*, **270**, pp. 9661–9666.

Further sources

Alberts, B., Johnson, A., Lewis, J., Raff, M., Roberts, K. and Walter, P. (2002) *Molecular Biology of the Cell* (4th edn), Garland Science, New York.

Gomperts, B. D., Tatham, P. E. R. and Kramer, I. M. (2002) *Signal Transduction*, Academic Press, London.

Stryer, L. (1995). *Biochemistry* (4th edn), W. H. Freeman and Company, New York.

Pawson, T., Gish, G. D. and Nash, P. (2001) SH2 domains, interaction modules and cellular wiring, *Trends in Cell Biology*, **11** (12), pp. 504–511.

Ridley, A. J. (2001) Rho family proteins: coordinating cell responses, *Trends in Cell Biology*, **11** (12), pp. 470–477.

Leevers, S. J., Paterson, H. F. and Marshall, C. J. (1994) Requirement for Ras in Raf activation is overcome by targeting Raf to the plasma membrane, *Nature*, **369** (6479), pp. 411–414.

Ostman, A. and Bohmer, F-D. (2001) Regulation of receptor tyrosine kinase signalling by protein tyrosine phosphatases, *Trends in Cell Biology*, **11** (6), pp. 258–266.

Saltiel, A. R. and Pessin J. E. (2002) Insulin signalling pathways in time and space, *Trends in Cell Biology*, **12** (2) 65–71.

Murphy, L. O., Smith, S., Chen, R. H., Fingar, D. C. and Blenis, J. (2002) Molecular interpretation of ERK signal duration by immediate early gene products, *Nature Cell Biology*, **4** (8), pp. 556–564.

Manning, G., Whyte, D. B., Martinez, R., Hunter, T. and Sudarsanam, S. (2002) The protein kinase complement of the human genome, *Science*, **298**, pp. 1912–1934.

Smith, D. B. and Johnson, K. S. (1988) Single-step purification of polypeptides expressed in *E. coli* as fusions with glutathione *S*-transferase, *Gene*, **67**, pp. 31–40.

14 CELL DEATH

14.1 Introduction

Most of the cellular and molecular processes that have been described so far in this course could be considered to involve *generation* – of energy, new molecules, and new cells. In this chapter, we turn to the molecular and cellular processes that are involved in the *destruction* of cells and removal of their components. There are many situations in which it is advantageous, or even essential, that certain cells are removed. It is also important that these cells are eliminated in a regulated way, and that nearby cells are not damaged by the process. This regulated cell death is very different from the 'accidental' death of cells, as you shall see.

Regulated cell death is of fundamental importance during the development of multicellular organisms, in metamorphosis (Figure 14.1) and in tissue homeostasis. It sculpts developing organs and ensures the correct number and balance of different cell types in mature tissues and organs. It also enables the removal of stressed or infected cells and cells damaged by exposure to toxic agents such as radiation and some types of drugs. Change in normal regulation (dysregulation) of cell death processes occurs in some diseases; for example, too little cell death contributes to autoimmune syndromes and cancer (Chapter 19), whereas degenerative diseases can be, in part, the result of too much cell death.

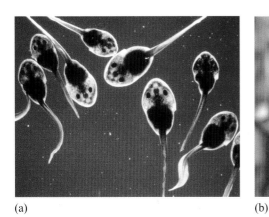
(a)

(b)

Figure 14.1
(a) Tadpoles (*Rana esculenta*, Europe) and (b) a red-eyed tree frog (*Agalychnis callidryas*, Panama). During metamorphosis, cells of the tadpole tail die by regulated cell death or apoptosis.

Cell death (including the role of caspases) was introduced in S204, Book 3 *The Core of Life, Vol. II*, Section 10.4, which provides the background for this chapter.

During the last 20 or so years, research to elucidate the molecular mechanisms by which cell death is controlled and the details of how it happens has become a major focus for cell biologists. We now know that cells can die in different ways and that the molecular events that result in cell death are complex. Regulated cell death is the culmination of the action of, and interactions between, a range of signalling, regulatory and effector proteins, of the types that you are now familiar with.

These include cell surface molecules, transmembrane receptors, adaptor proteins and perhaps most dramatic, the so-called 'executioner' enzymes, known as **caspases** (cysteine-dependent aspartate proteases or cysteine aspases), which mediate many, but not all, types of regulated cell death. These enzymes are present in all animal cells as *pro*caspases, inactive precursor proteins known as **zymogens** (or proenzymes). When activated, caspases degrade a range of cellular proteins, thereby destroying the cell.

The molecular signals that determine whether a cell will live or die are of two types: survival signals and death signals. Some of these signals originate outside the cell – for example, signals that a cell receives from its neighbours. Many others originate inside the cell – for example, changes in regulatory proteins that occur in response to DNA damage. This changing balance of death and survival signals that occurs in response to changes in the cell's external and internal environment determines the fate of the cell. Regulated cell death thus occurs as the result of a shift in the balance in favour of cell death. In many cases, this death is mediated by activated caspases.

Many of the molecules that play a role in regulated cell death are evolutionarily conserved between organisms, including *C. elegans*, *D. melanogaster*, the mouse (*M. musculus*) and humans (*H. sapiens*). Activation of the death 'programme' is a crucial event, so it is perhaps not surprising that, in complex animals such as mammals, a myriad of regulatory and effector molecules have evolved, enabling tight regulation, the result of which is that cell death normally only takes place when needed.

The evolutionary conservation of the molecules involved in the regulation of cell death between diverse animal phyla has raised the question of whether a death programme exists in other eukaryotes, particularly plants and fungi, or even in prokaryotes. Recent evidence suggests that some form of regulated cell death can occur in all eukaryotes, even in unicellular organisms such as yeasts.

We begin by outlining the main types of cell death and introducing some examples of the importance of cell death during development and homeostasis. Then we go on to summarize the main cell death pathways before looking in more detail at some of the proteins involved. Finally, we consider some specific examples, focusing on the nervous and immune systems.

14.1.1 Different types of cell death

Rapid developments in cell and molecular biology have forced biologists to rethink their classification of organisms, cell organelles, cellular processes and the functions of molecules. Cell death is no exception; as our appreciation of the diversity and versatility of the molecules involved has grown, there has been a debate about how different types of cell death should be categorized, or even if cell death should be categorized at all.

Appearance of dying cells

For many years, because microscopy was the main technique used to study dying cells, cellular morphology was used as the means of classifying cell death. A major distinction was made between cells dying by 'accident', in other words after exposure to an acute toxic insult, such as strong detergents, oxidants or ionophores (small organic molecules that allow passage of ions, and sometimes also water, across cell membranes), and those cells that die predictably – for example, as part of the process of development.

Acute toxic insults cause cells to swell and lyse (burst). This type of death was termed **necrosis**. Strictly speaking, the term necrosis describes what happens in a tissue *after* cells have died. So, we define **necrotic cell death** as the uncontrolled death of a cell that occurs as a result of the *direct* toxic action of exogenous agents and does not depend upon the actions of the cell's own proteins (Figure 14.2a).

The appearance of cells dying during normal tissue development and tissue turnover is very different from that of cells undergoing necrosis. In 1972, a landmark review of the literature on the ultrastructural appearance of dying cells was published by Kerr *et al.* These authors and others had studied cell death in a range of tissues and circumstances – for example, in epithelia (where there is a rapid turnover of cells), in the adrenal cortex after depletion of ACTH (adrenocorticotropic hormone), in cancerous tissue and during development. In all these cases, the appearance of the dying cells was characteristic (Figure 14.2b). To emphasize that this process is, in terms of tissue homeostasis, the opposite of mitosis, by which new cells are generated, Kerr *et al.* coined the term 'apoptosis' (from the Greek, meaning 'falling of leaves'). These authors also suggested that, since apoptosis seemed to be an integral part of tissue homeostasis, it should be considered a basic cellular process, alongside cell division.

So, **apoptosis** (sometimes called **programmed cell death** or **PCD**, and, by some authors, **PCD type I**) can be defined as the controlled 'suicide' of a cell, which we now know is mediated by the cell's own proteins. An important feature of apoptosis is that the cellular components are removed in a controlled fashion (usually by phagocytosis), no surrounding tissue damage ensues and, in vertebrates, no inflammatory reaction is triggered. In some tissues, apoptotic cells are not removed by phagocytosis but in other ways. For example, dead cells of the skin and gut epithelium are shed from the epithelial surface, which in both cases is an interface with the external environment; thus no active removal of the remains of these cells is required. (The removal of the remains of dead and dying cells is an important process, but we do not have space to describe it in this chapter.)

Because cell death occurs predictably during animal development, biologists believed the process to be part of the developmental 'programme', and so the term, programmed cell death was coined (see Kerr *et al.*, 1972).

After the concept of apoptosis was introduced, for many years the popular view among cell biologists was that cells die either by apoptosis or by necrotic cell death. However, it had long been known that some dying cells have an appearance that could not be so conveniently classified, and more detailed classifications involving additional, intermediate types of death have been proposed. One such is known as **autophagic cell death** (sometimes referred to as **PCD type II**), in which organelles do not swell, or get degraded by cytosolic enzymes, but rather become engulfed by lysosomes.

▢ What are lysosomes, and what is their function?

● Lysosomes are membrane-bound organelles responsible for digestion of intracellular debris. Their interior is acidic and contains hydrolases, which break down proteins, lipids, carbohydrates and nucleic acids and also defective organelles and macromolecules (Chapter 12).

In autophagic cell death (Figure 14.2c), cytoplasmic components are degraded *before* nuclear changes are detected. The first and most obvious feature of cells undergoing autophagic cell death is an abundance of lysosomes and also of cytoplasmic vacuoles that have double membranes. These vacuoles are known as **autophagic vacuoles**, and contain fragments of organelles and other cellular 'debris'. The autophagic vacuoles fuse with lysosomes, resulting in the breakdown of cellular debris. Nuclear changes, which resemble those seen during apoptosis, only become apparent after most of the cytoplasm has been digested. Any remnants of the cell that remain are removed by phagocytosis, but often the cell completely 'self-destructs', and autophagy is sometimes regarded as a clearance mechanism. Autophagic cell death occurs in yeast, in insect metamorphosis and in some types of neurons. The molecular mechanisms that underlie the process are at present unclear.

Now that much more is known about the molecular mediators of cell death and their regulators, it is appreciated that, in molecular terms, there are many ways in which cells can die. What is considered to be 'classical' apoptosis or programmed cell death primarily involves the action of the caspases. In some cases, if caspases are inhibited, cell death can proceed, in a non-necrotic manner, by the action of other proteolytic systems in the cell. Thus it has been suggested that a more realistic view is that there is a continuum between the different types of cell death (Lockshin and Zakeri, 2002). Nevertheless, classical apoptosis is very clearly a fascinating and important process and it has been studied extensively; it is the process that we focus on here.

14.1.2 Apoptosis in development and normal tissue maintenance

Apoptosis was first recognized by developmental biologists in the 19th century. Examples of apoptosis during animal development are numerous; perhaps the best-known are the formation of the digits (e.g. fingers) by the death of intervening cells and the loss of the tadpole tail during amphibian development.

Other well-studied examples of apoptosis are in the development of the nervous and immune systems, during which the appropriate numbers and types of cell must be generated. During nervous system development, sufficient neurons must be generated to innervate their target tissue (e.g. skeletal muscle). This balance is

Figure 14.2   Schematic diagrams and electron micrographs illustrating the main types of cell death: necrotic cell death, apoptosis and autophagic cell death. (a) During necrotic cell death, the first events are the irregular condensation of chromatin, swelling of mitochondria and breakdown of membranes and ribosomes (i). The plasma membrane ruptures – shown diagrammatically (ii) and in an electron micrograph (iii). The released cell contents may damage surrounding cells and, in vertebrates, cause an inflammatory reaction (inflammatory reactions never occur in invertebrates). (b) In apoptosis, the plasma membrane 'blebs', the cell shrinks, the nucleus involutes and the chromatin condenses into large aggregates, but the organelles appear normal (iv and v). The cell then breaks up into apoptotic bodies (vi), which are phagocytosed by nearby cells (vii). (c) During autophagic cell death, the nucleus initially appears normal, while a large number of autophagic vacuoles and lysosomes begin to digest cellular components (viii and ix). Large autophagic bodies form and the chromatin begins to condense (x). As in apoptosis, the remains of the cell are phagocytosed (xi).

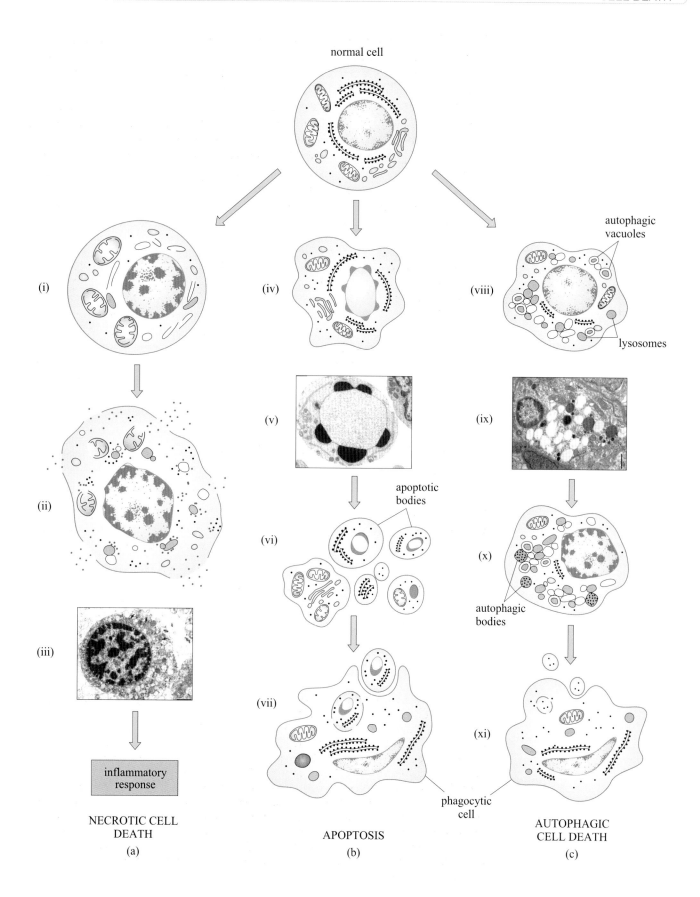

normal cell

(i)

(ii)

(iii)

inflammatory
response

NECROTIC CELL
DEATH

(a)

(iv)

(v)

apoptotic
bodies

(vi)

(vii)

phagocytic
cell

APOPTOSIS

(b)

autophagic
vacuoles

(viii)

lysosomes

(ix)

(x)

autophagic
bodies

(xi)

AUTOPHAGIC
CELL DEATH

(c)

ensured by the production of excess neurons during early development, and the later destruction of some of these cells by apoptosis. In the vertebrate immune system, many millions of different lymphocytes with specificity for different antigens are generated. Some of these lymphocytes are ineffective, and others have an inappropriate specificity, which gives them the potential to generate an autoimmune response and so cause damage to cells and tissues. These lymphocytes are destroyed by apoptosis.

> The immune system and its component cells and their functions were described in S204, Book 2 *Generating Diversity*, Chapter 5.

Apoptosis also plays a crucial role in the immune response itself. In addition to the removal of pathogens by phagocytosis, which occurs across the animal kingdom as part of the innate immune response, the selective killing of infected cells is fundamental to the adaptive immune response of vertebrates, which targets *specific* pathogens and the cells that are infected by these pathogens. This killing is mediated, in part, by lymphocytes known as cytotoxic T cells; we will consider how these lymphocytes kill their target cells later in this chapter.

During the adaptive immune response, there is a massive proliferation of the specific types of lymphocytes needed to overcome the infection, but once the infectious agents have been destroyed, these cells are no longer needed. Some of these lymphocytes differentiate into memory cells, but the majority are destroyed – again, by apoptosis.

Programmed cell death is also essential in normal tissue homeostasis; for example, there is a natural turnover of the short-lived epithelial cells that line the gut and skin. These cells die, in a consistent way, by a form of apoptosis. Apoptosis is also vital for the removal of damaged cells, some of which may be potentially tumorigenic (Chapter 19). Cells in which irreparable DNA damage occurs, and cells damaged by stress, such as oxidative stress caused by high levels of reactive oxygen species (ROS; see Book 1, p. 216), die by apoptosis. Note, however, that an *extreme* elevation of ROS in a cell may lead to its accidental, unregulated death

Finally, we should point out that damaged cells are not always removed by regulated cell death. For example, cell ageing – or senescence – is associated with a number of cellular and molecular changes that can have detrimental effects on cell function, but are not sufficient to trigger the so-called 'death programme'. Cell senescence is described in Chapter 18.

14.1.3 Studying cell death

The mechanisms of cell death, like many other cellular processes, have been widely studied using cell culture. Although cell death was initially classified by the morphological appearance of the dying cells, biochemical criteria are now more widely used to identify cells that are undergoing classical apoptosis. Some commonly used methods are outlined in Box 14.1.

Box 14.1   Methods used to identify apoptotic cells

DNA fragmentation

Nucleosomal ladder:

The enzymatic degradation of DNA by nucleases is characteristic of programmed cell death. This degradation results in fragmentation of DNA into different-sized fragments and the formation of a 'nucleosomal ladder' upon gel electrophoresis (a nucleosomal ladder is shown in Book 1, Figure 5.29c).

○ What is a nucleosomal 'ladder' and why is it formed by the action of nucleases?

● It is the result of the separation of nucleosomal DNA fragments that differ in size by one nucleosome repeat length (146 bp, Figure 5.29c). These fragments are formed because the nucleases cleave DNA between the nucleosomes.

Note that DNA fragmentation also occurs during autophagic cell death, so this method cannot be used to distinguish between PCD types I and II.

End labelling:

Another technique that has been widely used to visually identify apoptotic cells, either in cell culture or in tissue sections, also involves demonstration of DNA fragmentation, and is known as TUNEL (terminal deoxynucleotidyl transferase-mediated dUTP nick end labelling). This method employs the enzyme terminal deoxynucleotidyl transferase to add deoxyuridine monophosphate (dUMP), from the precursor dUTP, to the 3′-OH ends of the DNA fragments that result from nuclease action. The cells 'tagged' in this way are then visualized immunohistochemically (Figure 14.3).

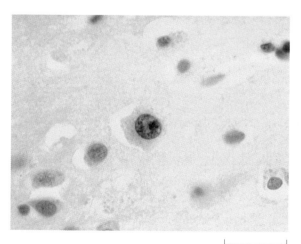

100 μm

Figure 14.3
TUNEL immunoreactivity in a neuron in post-mortem tissue from the brain of an individual with motor neuron disease. The section has been counterstained with haematoxylin. One TUNEL-positive cell (near centre) and several TUNEL-negative cells are visible. (Courtesy of Payam Rezaie, Biological Sciences, Open University)

Plasma membrane changes

One of the more recently described events that has been used to identify apoptotic cells is the movement of phosphatidylserine from the cytosolic side of the plasma membrane to the extracellular side, which occurs as a result of the breakdown of components of the plasma membrane of dying cells. This event can be detected using the protein annexin V, which binds specifically to the exposed phosphatidylserine, and can subsequently be visualized by immunocytochemical labelling using an antibody that recognizes annexin V. This externalization of plasma membrane components is functionally important, as it serves to 'mark' dying cells, allowing their identification and subsequent engulfment by phagocytic cells.

Caspase activation

Caspase activation is now widely used as another marker of cells undergoing apoptotic death. Cells in which apoptosis has been initiated can be visualized using specific antibodies raised against active caspases (Figure 14.4).

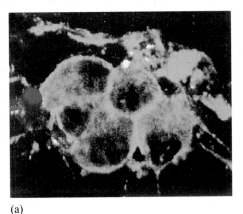
(a)

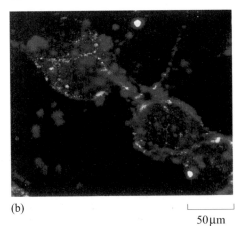
(b)

50 µm

Figure 14.4
Sympathetic neurons from mice grown in cell culture and immunolabelled with antisera raised against actin (green) and an active caspase (red). (a) Neurons grown in culture medium supplemented with nerve growth factor; no active caspase is detected within the cells. (b) Neurons grown in the absence of nerve growth factor; the caspase is activated. The reduction in actin immunolabelling in (b) is likely to be the result of degradation by the activated caspase. (Source: Troy *et al.*, 2001)

The common feature of all the methods described in Box 14.1 is that they identify cellular and molecular events that are *secondary* to the initiation of the cell death programme. In the next section, we turn to the events that take place *before* the cell death programme is initiated, and to the enzymatic mediators of cell death.

14.1.4 Conserved pathways of programmed cell death

The molecular mechanisms that result in programmed cell death began to be unravelled during the 1980s, by genetic analysis of the development of the nematode worm, *C. elegans*.

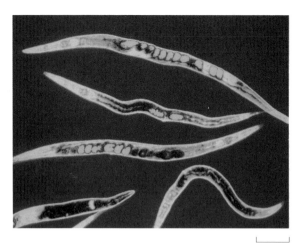

These nematodes have been an invaluable model organism in the study of developmental processes because they are small, have a short life cycle, and importantly, they are translucent – a property that allows the fate of individual cells during development to be followed by microscopical analysis of living worms (Figure 14.5). Such studies showed that each individual (of the same sex) has the same number of cells, and that development proceeds in a completely reproducible way in normal worms. Hence the lineage of each cell in a normal adult worm is known, as illustrated in

Figure 14.5   False colour image of *C. elegans*.

Book 1, Figure 1.10. Genetic analysis of mutants in which normal development is disrupted thus provides information about the roles of the products of the affected genes. As in other animals, the development of *C. elegans* involves cell death. Each adult hermaphrodite worm has exactly 959 cells. During development, however, 1090 cells are formed, but 131 die. In 1986, Ellis and Horvitz published groundbreaking work on mutant worms in which this predictable cell death did not take place, or in which extra cells died. Many of the genes identified by study of these mutants were given the name *ced* genes, for *cell death defective*. Analysis of these mutants revealed a pathway for cell death that involved several proteins (Figure 14.6, left).

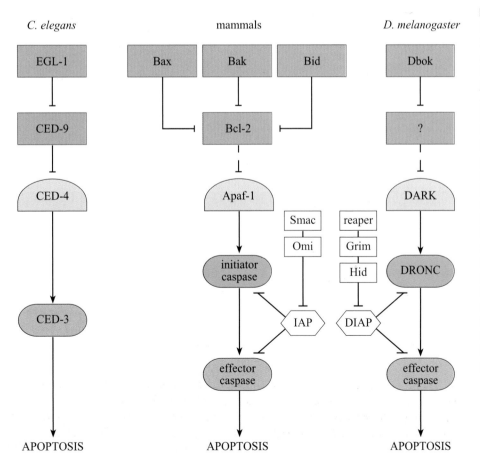

Figure 14.6
Simplified diagram showing how homologous proteins regulate apoptosis via similar pathways in *C. elegans*, mammals and *D. melanogaster*. (Details of these proteins are given later in the chapter.) Effector caspases are shown in purple, initiator caspases are shown in orange. Caspase activation involves adaptor proteins, shown in blue, and regulatory proteins of the Bcl-2 family (which can be either pro- or anti-apoptotic – see text), shown in pink. Other regulatory molecules are shown in white. Note that although there is structural and some functional homology between the proteins, as shown, there may not always be exact homology between their *mechanisms* of action. Gaps in lines indicate that there are intermediate steps which are not shown; the '?' indicates the involvement of an as yet unidentified protein.

The proteins that regulate cell death in *C. elegans* were found to have homologues in other species, such as *Drosophila*, mice and humans. The first mammalian homologue to be identified was a protease known as interleukin-1β converting enzyme, or ICE, which is a homologue of the CED-3 protein, encoded by the *C. elegans* gene *ced-3*. ICE and CED-3 are both caspases, many of which, as you have seen, are key players in apoptosis. Shortly thereafter, homologues of other members of the *C. elegans* apoptosis pathway were discovered in flies and mammals (Figure 14.6), and the mechanisms by which they act began to be elucidated. These molecules are regulatory molecules, which stimulate or inhibit caspase activation and hence apoptosis. The proteins that stimulate apoptosis are described as **pro-apoptotic**; those that inhibit it are described as **anti-apoptotic**. The balance of pro- and anti-apoptotic proteins within the cell determines whether it will live or die.

In mammals, there are further routes to caspase activation, in addition to these cell death pathways, as you will see in the following section. It is also clear, and important to remember, that caspase-*independent* programmed cell death can occur; that is, other enzymes can play a role in some types of cell death.

14.1.5 Overview of caspase-mediated PCD in mammalian cells

The current generalized view is that in mammals there are two main signalling pathways by which caspases can be activated, known as the *extrinsic* and *intrinsic* pathways. Inevitably, this is something of a simplification, because there is now good evidence that interaction between the pathways can sometimes occur, and that some regulators can influence both pathways. Moreover, caspases can be activated by alternative routes. Here we summarize the different routes to caspase activation, before focusing on the details of the two best-studied mechanisms in Sections 14.3 and 14.4. Both routes trigger apoptosis by activating so-called **initiator caspases**, which in turn activate downstream **effector caspases** (see Figure 14.6), which digest cellular components.

Extrinsic pathway

Activation of death receptors
Activation of the extrinsic pathway begins with binding of ligands to cell surface receptors, often known as **death receptors**. The ligands that activate the extrinsic pathways may be secreted factors or molecules expressed on the surface of other cells. Activation of this pathway is one mechanism by which cytotoxic (or killer) T lymphocytes induce apoptosis in selected target cells such as virally infected cells and also in lymphocytes at the end of an immune response (Figure 14.7). Upon receptor activation, adaptor molecules are recruited, to form a multiprotein complex known as the **death-inducing signalling complex (DISC)**, which in turn recruits an initiator procaspase (the inactive precursor of an initiator caspase). As a result of the close proximity of the procaspase molecules, they self-activate (this process of autoactivation is described in Section 14.2.2). The active initiator caspase then goes on to activate downstream effector caspases, as illustrated in Figure 14.7. This type of death induction is often referred to as 'death by instruction' or 'death by design'.

○ What will determine which cells are vulnerable upon contact with the surface of cytotoxic T lymphocytes, or with secreted 'death signals'?

● The expression of the appropriate death receptors on the cell surface.

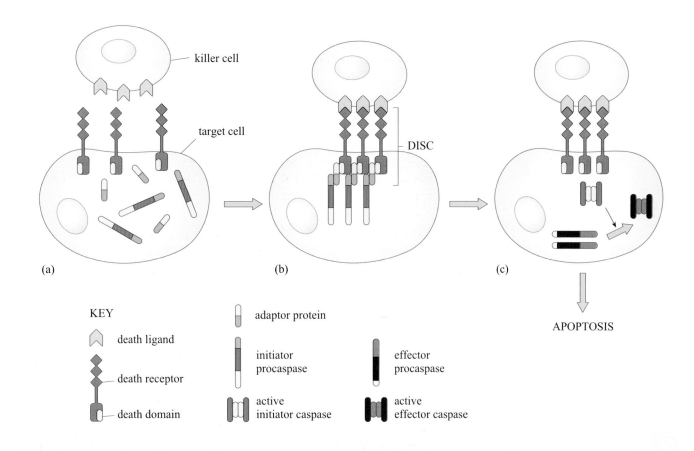

KEY

death ligand

death receptor

death domain

adaptor protein

initiator procaspase

active initiator caspase

effector procaspase

active effector caspase

Figure 14.7 Diagram summarizing the extrinsic pathway to caspase activation. The example shown involves activation by ligands on the surface of a 'killer' cell, which could be a killer lymphocyte, for example. (a) Target cells (like all other cells) contain the intracellular components of the death machinery – inactive procaspases and adaptor proteins. Death receptors are located on the surface of target cells; killer cells have ligands on their surfaces. (b) Upon ligand binding, the death receptors aggregate (three are shown) and initiator procaspase proteins are recruited via the adaptor proteins. The complex of receptors and adaptors is known as the DISC (see text). (c) The proximity of the procaspases results in their autoactivation. The active initiator caspases go on to activate downstream effector caspases, which destroy the cell.

Expression of death receptors is a regulated process that plays an important role in determining the fate of a cell.

Direct activation of caspases by cytotoxic lymphocytes
In addition to activation of death receptors, killer lymphocytes can also activate caspases in target cells *directly*. This mechanism involves the secretion, by the killer lymphocyte, of a pore-forming protein known as **perforin**, as well as proteolytic enzymes, onto the surface of the target cell. Perforin forms channels in the target cell membrane, through which the proteolytic enzymes enter. One of these enzymes, **granzyme B**, cleaves procaspases and thereby initiates apoptosis.

Intrinsic pathways

Intrinsic pathways are activated in response to *intracellular* changes, including changes in the balance of regulatory proteins within the cell, in favour of pro-apoptotic proteins, which are then able to activate the intrinsic pathways of caspase activation. A change in the balance of regulatory proteins can be triggered by the removal of protective extracellular signalling molecules (sometimes referred to as 'death by neglect'), or by intracellular stressors such as DNA damage, the build-up of unfolded or misfolded proteins, ionic changes and oxidative damage, which results from excess ROS generation. Evidence to date indicates that, in most cases, mitochondria play a pivotal role in the intrinsic pathways.

The mitochondrial pathway

If mitochondrial permeability is compromised, either by direct stress such as oxidative damage, or by the action of specific pro-apoptotic proteins (members of the Bcl-2 family, Figure 14.6, described more fully in Section 14.4), then cytochrome *c* (a component of the electron tranport chain) is released and binds to cytosolic adaptor proteins. The resulting complex recruits an initiator procaspase, to form a multiprotein structure known as the **apoptosome**. The close proximity of the initiator procaspase proteins in the apoptosome allows autoactivation and the active initiator caspase subsequently activates downstream effectorprocaspases. The intrinsic mitochondrial pathway to caspase activation is summarized in Figure 14.8.

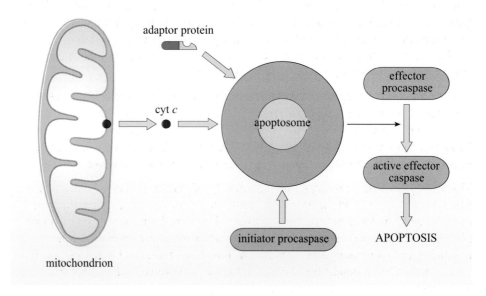

Figure 14.8
Summary diagram of the mitochondrial pathway to caspase activation. Cytochrome *c* released from mitochondria forms a large multiprotein complex (the apoptosome) with adaptor proteins and initiator procaspases. Active initiator caspase goes on to activate downstream effector caspases, which destroy the cell.

○ In addition to removal of extracellular protective molecules, suggest two other types of stimuli originating *outside* the cell that could cause apoptosis by activating the intrinsic pathways for caspase activation, and state why they would do so.

● Two that you may have thought of are exposure to some toxic substances, and to UV or ionizing radiation, both of which cause DNA damage which, if not repaired, can cause apoptosis via the intrinsic pathways.

In addition to the effects of UV and ionizing radiation on DNA, which were described in Chapter 9, a number of chemicals and drugs also cause DNA damage. If the damage is not repaired, it leads to apoptosis, in part by activation of the intrinsic apoptotic pathways. We return to this topic in Section 14.4.

Some drugs that are used in the treatment of cancer act in part by stimulating apoptosis. These and other drugs have been utilized in the study of the regulation of apoptosis, particularly in experiments using cultured cells.

The ER and Golgi apparatus
Evidence indicates that the endoplasmic reticulum (ER) and possibly the Golgi apparatus may also play a primary role in programmed cell death in mammals. These organelles must not only be effectively dismantled during apoptosis, but they are also sensitive to stress, and it has been proposed that they may be involved in the initiation of apoptosis in some situations. Other mechanisms of cell death that involve the ER are better characterized.

You will recall that the ER is the site of protein modification. It also plays an essential role in cell signalling.

○ Which ions are sequestered by the ER and play important role in cell signalling?

● Calcium ions, which act as second messengers (Chapter 13, Section 13.1.4).

Regulation of the levels of calcium ions within the cell is crucial, not only for cell signalling, but also for cell survival. While transient changes in cytosolic calcium levels are essential for normal cellular functions, more prolonged or extreme elevations in cytosolic calcium levels or dysregulation of calcium homeostasis at the ER can have disastrous effects. Depending upon its concentration, calcium may trigger either apoptosis or necrotic cell death.

The ER and mitochondria are now known to be closely apposed; calcium released from the ER is taken up rapidly by nearby mitochondria. Calcium increases mitochondrial membrane permeability, which may explain how apoptosis is induced by agents that cause the release of calcium from the ER lumen. Examples of such agents are some chemotherapeutic drugs and some types of oxidative stress.

This example serves to illustrate the complexity of mammalian cell death pathways. Much experimental evidence for these complexities has come from the study of cultured cells, and has not yet been confirmed *in vivo*. Importantly, it seems that differences exist between the molecular mechanisms that are involved in the regulation and mediation of cell death in different cell types, and in the same cell type under different conditions. For example, the involvement of particular molecules and mechanisms in the death of lymphocytes may differ from that in the regulation of the death of neurons, as we shall see.

○ Why might a diversity of molecules and mechanisms for the regulation of cell death have evolved in more complex animals?

● Cell death is an 'all-or-nothing' event, and dysregulation of cell death pathways can have serious consequences for the survival of the organism. Differential regulation of similar pathways in different cell types allows a more flexible control of the cell death process, which is needed to maintain the balance of different types of cells in complex animals.

Figure 14.9 shows the main pathways leading to caspase activation and thereby apoptosis in mammalian cells, and some of the many types of molecules involved. You need not study all the details included in the diagram now, but you should refer to it as you study later parts of the chapter.

Caspase activation is a key step in apoptosis. In the next section, we examine the caspases in more detail. Then we turn to look at some specific examples of caspase-mediated cell death.

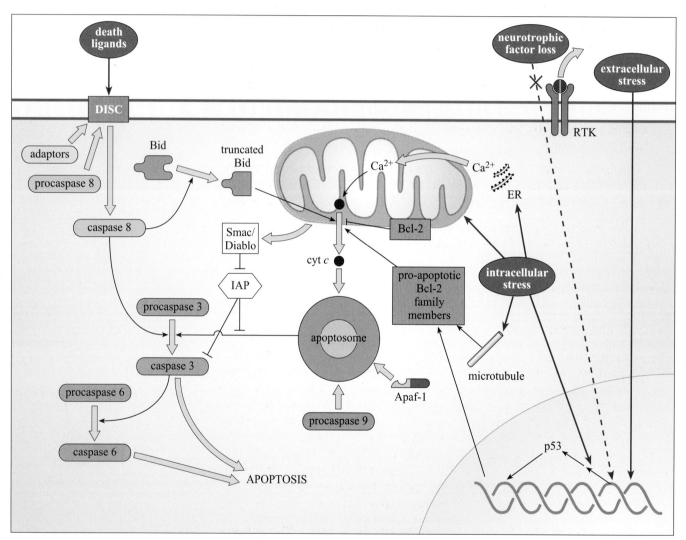

Figure 14.9   The main routes to caspase activation and apoptosis in mammalian cells. Stimuli that lead to activation of the apoptotic pathways are shown in red. The extrinsic pathway is shown on the left side of the diagram; different routes to the activation of the intrinsic pathway are shown on the right. Loss of neurotrophic factor leads to reduced signalling downstream from receptor tyrosine kinases (RTKs) (indicated by the dashed line with a cross), as described in Section 14.4.5, and thereby a reduction in the activation of proteins that affect p53. Both extrinsic and intrinsic pathways lead to activation of effector caspases, such as caspase 3 and caspase 6 (see Sections 14.2 and 14.3). Note that the diagram is simplified; not all mediators are shown.

Summary of Section 14.1

1   Cell death is an essential process in development and tissue homeostasis.

2   Cells can die by different mechanisms. Regulated cell death can be of several types, including apoptosis, which involves the action of caspases, and autophagic cell death, in which lysosomes are involved. Other forms of death have been described. Necrotic cell death is an unregulated response to severe physiological insults.

3   Dying cells can be identified not only by their appearance under the EM, but also by histochemical and biochemical methods that demonstrate DNA fragmentation, membrane disruption and caspase activation.

4   Apoptosis, or programmed cell death, involves proteins and signalling pathways that are evolutionarily conserved between animals from *C. elegans* to humans.

5   In mammals, many homologues of these proteins have been identified, and apoptosis is under complex and tight regulation, which varies between different cell types.

6   Caspases exist as zymogens, the procaspases, which can be activated by two main routes; an extrinsic pathway, which involves the activation of cell surface death receptors, and intrinsic routes, most of which involve the mitochondria.

7   Other organelles, in particular the endoplasmic reticulum, also play a role in the regulation of cell death via intrinsic pathways.

14.2 Caspases – their activation and inhibition

14.2.1 Overview

Caspases are a family of proteases that all contain cysteine at their catalytic sites, and almost always cleave their protein substrates on the carboxyl side of aspartate residues. Caspases cleave specific proteins, determined by the amino acid residues adjacent to the target aspartate residue. To date, 14 caspases have been identified in mammals, 11 of which are found in humans. Fewer caspases occur in invertebrate species; seven have been identified in *Drosophila*, but only one in *C. elegans*. Because many caspases play major roles in apoptotic cell death, they are often referred to as cell 'executioners'; however, it is important to remember that other enzymes are also involved in cell death, and that not all caspases are involved in apoptosis; for example, some play a role in cytokine processing.

There are two main caspase subfamilies in mammals, the caspase 1 and caspase 3 subfamilies. The caspase 1 subfamily includes caspase 1 (also known as ICE; Section 14.1.4) and caspases 4, 5 and 11–14; members of this family are involved in cytokine processing. It is the caspase 3 subfamily members (caspases 2, 3 and 6–10) that are involved in apoptosis. Caspases exist in cells as inactive proenzymes called procaspases. Procaspases have two domains that correspond to the large and small subunit of the activated caspase, and these are joined by a short linker region. There is also either a short or a long section known as a prodomain at the N-terminus, as shown in Figure 14.10.

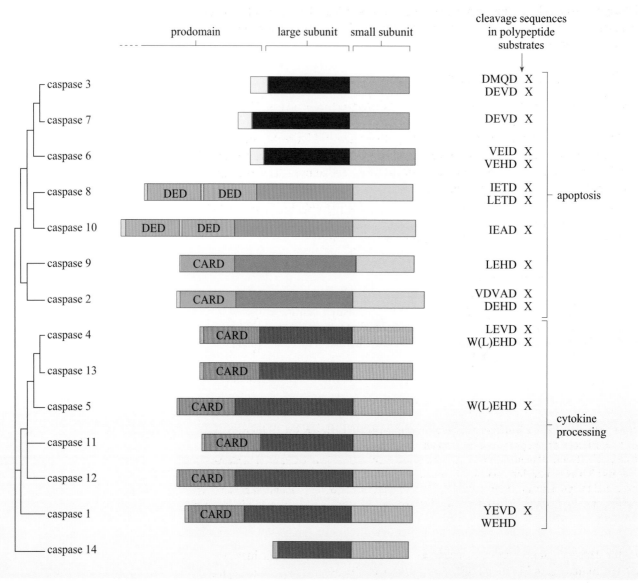

Figure 14.10 Mammalian caspases. Schematic diagram showing relative sizes, location of functional domains, phylogenetic relationships and substrate cleavage sequences. (Based on Shi, 2002; and Earnshaw *et al.*, 1999)

Apoptotic caspases that have a short prodomain (e.g. caspases 3, 6 and 7) are effector caspases, and when activated they cleave cellular substrates, directly causing cell death. The effector caspases are activated by upstream initiator caspases, which have long prodomains.

The prodomains of initiator caspases contain one or more domains that are involved in protein–protein interactions, and are of two types, the **death effector domain (DED)**, and the **caspase recruitment domain (CARD)**. These domains are also present in other proteins, enabling them to interact with the initiator caspases, with important functional consequences.

○ From Figure 14.10, which apoptotic caspases have long prodomains, and are thus likely to be initiator caspases?

● Caspases 8 and 10, which both have two DED domains, and caspases 2 and 9, which both have a CARD domain.

Although most evidence has implicated caspases 8 and 9 as the main initiators of the caspase cascade that leads to apoptosis, caspases 2 and 10 may also initiate apoptosis in some situations.

14.2.2 Caspase activation

Effector and initiator caspases are activated by different mechanisms. The activation of effector caspases is simpler, so we will describe it first. In their inactive form, effector caspases are homodimers (as already illustrated in Figure 14.7c). Activation involves cleavage of each molecule between the large and small subunits at the linker region, followed by cleavage of the short prodomain, as shown in Figure 14.11. The mature, active enzyme is a tetramer; comprising two short and two long subunits. Cleavage is predominantly mediated by initiator caspases, but other enzymes may also cleave procaspases; a notable example is granzyme B which, as you will recall, is secreted by killer lymphocytes.

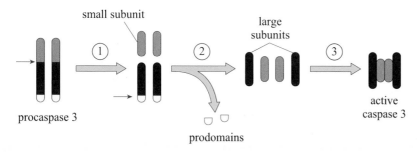

Figure 14.11   Schematic diagram showing activation of effector caspases, in this case caspase 3. Effector procaspases exist as homodimers, each of which comprises a long subunit domain, a short subunit domain and a prodomain. (1) Activated initiator caspases first cleave procaspase 3 between the long and short subunit domains, then (2) between the large subunit domain and the prodomain (red arrows). (3) The two large and two short subunits together form the active caspase 3, which is a tetramer. Each of these active effector caspase molecules has two active sites.

Initiator caspases, unlike effector caspases, exist as monomers in their inactive form (as indicated in Figure 14.7a). For a number of years, the widely accepted model for their activation was one of induced proximity (that is, the bringing together of several initiator procaspase molecules by the action of adaptor proteins) allowing autocatalytic cleavage. However, there is evidence to suggest that although induced proximity is required for initiator caspase activation, cleavage is not. Rather, the bringing together of two initiator procaspase molecules allows rearrangement that exposes the catalytic sites (Boatright and Salvesen, 2003).

Initiator caspases are brought together by assembly with adaptor and other proteins into multimolecular complexes, a process sometimes called **scaffold-mediated activation**. Assembly of the complexes involves **homotypic** protein–protein interaction, i.e. interaction between homologous sequences in the two proteins. The caspase DED or CARD domains interact with DED or CARD domains respectively on the adaptor proteins. The formation of these complexes results in several of the *same type* of procaspase molecule being brought together. We describe how these scaffolds are formed when we consider some specific examples in Sections 14.3 and 14.4.

Once activated, the initiator caspases cleave the prodomains from downstream effector caspases, which in turn degrade other effector caspases and downstream cellular substrates. The substrates that are degraded by effector caspases are varied – around 200 proteins have been identified to date, and the application of proteomic analysis (Chapter 3, Section 3.8.3) to apoptotic cells may well reveal many more. They include structural proteins, for example actin (see Figure 4.4) and nuclear lamins, regulatory proteins such as some protein kinases, and inhibitors of deoxyribonucleases. An example of the latter is activation of the nuclease known as CAD (caspase-activated deoxyribonuclease) by cleavage of the inhibitory subunit to which it is usually complexed (the complex is known as ICAD). The action of CAD results in formation of genomic DNA fragments that form the hallmark apoptotic nucleosomal ladder (Box 14.1).

In summary, caspase-mediated cell death depends upon a chain of caspase activity that begins with initiator caspases, and ends with the 'executioner' or effector caspases. Since effector procaspases are more abundant in the cell than initiator procaspases, there is a *cascade* of caspase activation.

○ Activation of caspases by cleavage is essential for many types of regulated cell death. From what you have learnt earlier in the course about methods used to identify proteins in cells, or in extracts from cells, which two techniques could you use to identify cells in which caspases have been activated. What reagents would you need to perform this investigation?

● You could use the techniques of immunofluorescence (Box 8.1) or Western blotting (*Experimental investigation 1*). You would need antibodies that specifically recognize the cleaved forms of specific caspases. You would also need labelled secondary antibodies.

Clearly, activation of the potentially lethal caspases must be kept in check in normal healthy cells, and accordingly caspase activation is controlled by a variety of regulatory proteins. Destruction of healthy cells would be an energetically wasteful process for an organism; molecular controls ensuring that apoptosis occurs only when cells are superfluous or damaged, have therefore evolved.

In addition to regulation of caspase *activation*, described in Section 14.4, transcriptional regulation of caspase *expression* also occurs. An exciting development has been the discovery of a conserved family of molecules that inhibit activated caspases and the recent elucidation of their modes of action.

14.2.3 Inhibition of activated caspases

Baculoviruses are DNA viruses that infect insect cells. Modified baculoviruses are widely used as expression vectors.

Proteins that inhibit the action of activated caspases were first discovered in virally-infected cells. Genes encoding at least three different types of protein that inhibit the activity of caspases have been found in viral genomes. These include a family of proteins known as the **inhibitors of apoptosis (IAPs)**, which were first discovered as a product of the baculovirus genome.

○ Why would it be advantageous for viruses to express an inhibitor of apoptosis in the cells that they infect?

● Virally-infected cells express surface markers that trigger apoptosis via the extrinsic pathway. Viruses are dependent upon the host cell for replication of their genomes. So if the host cell dies, the virus is unable to reproduce.

Members of the IAP family have been found in organisms from yeasts to humans, and their sequences are highly conserved. In mammals, eight IAPs have been identified, one of which specifically inhibits caspases 3, 7 and 9, but not caspase 6 or 8 (Figure 14.9).

The IAPs have from one to three BIR domains (for baculovirus IAP repeat). The BIR domains and the linker regions between them interact with activated caspases. The specificity of action of the different IAPs therefore depends upon both the number of BIR domains and adjacent regions. Some IAPs also possess a 'RING' domain that is characteristic of some types of ubiquitin ligases (the action of ubiquitin ligases was described in Chapter 11).

The IAPs are cytosolic proteins, and it is now thought that they may have several different modes of action:

▶ They bind to activated caspases, thereby inhibiting caspase activity.

▶ Those that are ubiquitin ligases transfer ubiquitin residues to bound caspases, thereby targeting caspases for degradation via the proteasome (see Chapter 11, Section 11.7.1).

▶ The *Drosophila* IAP, DIAP (shown in Figure 14.6), has been found to be cleaved by activated caspases to a form that has a rapidly degraded N-terminal amino acid. The cleavage of DIAP by activated caspases would at first sight seem to be a *pro*-apoptotic event, but it has been suggested that it is *anti*-apoptotic because associated caspases would also be degraded along with the cleaved DIAP.

An unexpected finding is that IAPs with ubiquitin ligase activity can also transfer ubiquitin to themselves. This discovery indicates that the IAPs may be relatively unstable, and has aroused much interest about the modes of action of this interesting family of proteins (Ditzel and Meier, 2002).

Box 14.2	Synthetic caspase inhibitors in the study of apoptosis

We have seen that, in almost all cases, caspases cleave their target proteins at aspartate residues, and that the substrate specificity of the different caspases is determined by the sequence of amino acids adjacent to Asp residues in their substrates. This property has enabled inhibitors of caspases to be developed. Most of these inhibitors are tetrapeptides that correspond with the different recognition sequences, coupled to groups such as fluoromethylketone (FMK), which results in irreversible binding to the enzyme, or aldehyde (CHO), which results in reversible binding.

Synthetic caspase inhibitors are often used in cell culture systems to determine, for example, which caspases are activated by particular apoptotic stimuli.

☐ From Figure 14.10, which caspases will be inhibited by the FMK-coupled tetrapeptide DEVD-FMK?

● Caspases 3 and 7, which cleave their substrates at DEVD sequences.

Summary of Section 14.2

1   Caspases are a family of proteases that cleave substrates at aspartate residues.

2   There are two subfamilies of caspases, one involved predominantly in cell death and the other in cytokine processing.

3   Inactive caspases (i.e. procaspases) consist of a large and a small subunit and a prodomain of variable length.

4   Two types of caspase, initiator caspases and effector caspases, are involved in cell death. Initiator caspases, when activated, go on to activate effector caspases, which in turn go on to cleave downstream cellular proteins.

5   Initiator procaspases exist as monomers and possess a long prodomain, which include either CARD or DED domains. They are self-activated, a process made possible by assembly into large multimolecular aggregates.

6   Effector procaspases exist as dimers. They have a short prodomain and are activated upon cleavage by initiator caspases. Activation takes place by cleavage between the subunit domains, and removal of the prodomain; activated effector caspases are tetramers.

7   Certain activated caspases are inhibited by IAPs, a family of proteins some of which are ubiquitin ligases. IAPs act by binding activated caspases, thereby inactivating them directly, and also targeting them for degradation at the proteosome. (They may also act by a mechanism that involves their N-terminal amino acid.)

8   Caspases may be inhibited by synthetic peptides that have the same sequence of amino acids as that of the cleavage sites of their substrates.

14.3 The extrinsic apoptotic pathway – 'death by design'

14.3.1 Overview

The extrinsic apoptotic pathway allows the *targeted* killing of cells to take place. Most of what we currently know about this pathway has come from the study of cells of the immune system, where it is essential that elimination of certain cell populations takes place in a temporally appropriate manner, but there is also evidence that the pathway may be activated in some other cell types, such as neurons. We have already outlined how the extrinsic apoptotic pathway is activated – by binding of ligands to the death receptors (Section 14.1.5). Now we consider in more detail how activation takes place. To illustrate this process, we have chosen as an example the Fas signalling pathway, which is involved in the regulation of lymphocyte numbers both during development and after an immune response.

14.3.2 The Fas pathway and apoptosis in the immune system

Fas (also known as CD95) is a member of the family of receptors known as the **tumour necrosis factor α receptor (TNFαR)** family, and plays an important role in the removal of autoreactive lymphocytes (i.e. those that could generate an autoimmune response) during development, and in the removal of mature lymphocytes after an immune response has occurred.

The TNFαR family is large (in mammals, 29 members had been reported at the time of writing, Spring 2004) and not all of its members are death receptors; some convey survival signals. The ligands for these receptors are members of the TNFα protein family.

Fas is a death receptor. You will recall from Figure 14.7 that the common feature of the death receptors is a so-called **death domain (DD)** in the intracellular part of the molecule (also shown in Figure 14.12). Fas receptors are activated by the Fas **death ligand**, which is expressed on the surface of killer T lymphocytes. Ligand binding results in clustering of the receptors, which brings together their intracellular domains (Figure 14.12, step 1). The next stage is the recruitment, to the activated complex of death receptors, of intracellular adaptor proteins (Figure 14.12, step 2). These adaptors have homologous DD domains to the death receptors, so their recruitment to the activated receptors occurs because of homotypic interactions. The adaptor that binds to activated Fas is known as FADD (fas-associated protein with death domain). The resulting complex of receptors and adaptors is the death-inducing signalling complex (DISC).

The adaptor proteins have another domain, the death effector domain (DED) which, as you have seen, is also present in the long prodomain of procaspases 8 and 10 (Figure 14.10).

- ☐ What is the functional significance of the fact that both the adaptors present in the DISC and caspases 8 and 10 possess DED domains?

- ⬤ Caspase 8 and 10 will be recruited to the DISC, by homotypic DED–DED interactions between their DEDs and those of the adaptors.

- ☐ What will be the result of the induced proximity of procaspase 8 (or procaspase 10) molecules?

- ⬤ The induced proximity will allow their autoactivation (Section 14.2.2).

Most evidence has implicated procaspase 8 as the initiator caspase activated in the extrinsic pathways in most mammalian cell types studied, so that is what we focus on here. Other evidence, however, indicates that in a few cell types, procaspase 10 may be the initiator caspase, activated by a similar mechanism.

The procaspases are recruited to the DISC by homotypic binding of their DED domain with that of the adaptor molecules that have been recruited to the DISC (Figure 14.12, step 3). The close proximity of several procaspase 8 molecules recruited to the DISC results in their autoactivation (step 4). What occurs next seems to depend on cell type; in some cells ('type I' cells, such as some lymphoid cell lines) the active caspase 8 then activates the effector caspase, caspase 3 (step 5), which in turn cleaves a number of cellular substrates, including other effector caspases such as caspase 6 (not shown), leading to apoptosis.

In most other cells, however ('type II' cells), caspase 8 activation of caspase 3 is weak. In these cells, caspase 8 also cleaves another cytosolic protein, known as **Bid** (step 6). Bid is a pro-apoptotic member of an important group of apoptotic regulators known as the Bcl-2 family (discussed in Section 14.4), and its activation results in stimulation of the intrinsic apoptotic pathway. We consider this pathway, and the role of Bid, in Section 14.4.

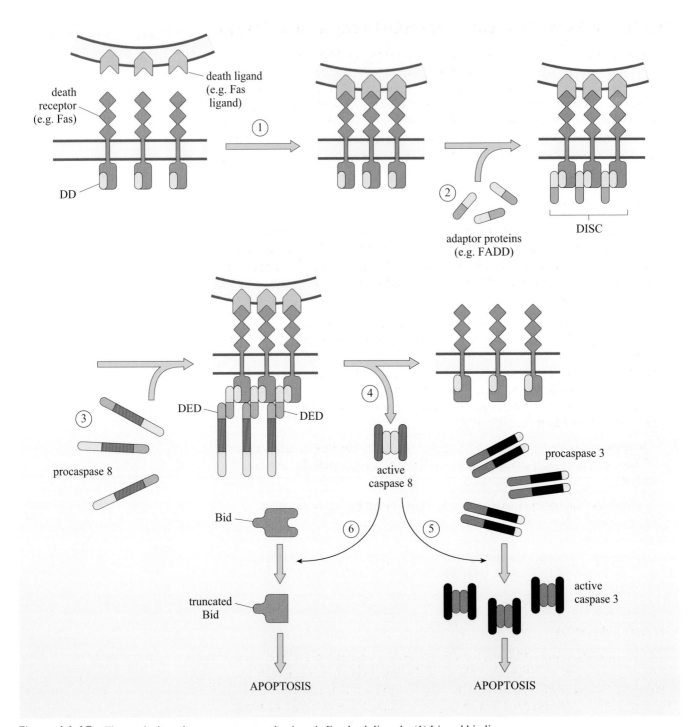

Figure 14.12   The extrinsic pathway to caspase activation via Fas death ligands: (1) Ligand binding causes receptors with death domains (DD) to come together. (2) Adaptor proteins are recruited by homotypic interactions of their death domains with those of the receptors, thereby forming the death-inducing signalling complex (DISC). (3) Procaspase 8 is recruited by homotypic interaction between the death effector domains (DED) and those of the adaptors. (4) Procaspase 8 is activated. (5) Active caspase 8 cleaves and thereby activates procaspase 3, and, in some cells, also cleaves Bid (6). These events lead to cell death.

14.3.3 Inhibitors of the extrinsic route to caspase activation

As with other parts of the apoptotic signalling pathways, inhibitory proteins that act in the extrinsic route to caspase activation have been found. These are of two types: so-called **decoy receptors**, which lack a functional intracellular domain and may be anchored to the cell membrane or free in the cytosol; and **decoy adaptors/ caspases** (e.g. FLIP, also known as casper), which are cytosolic proteins that have DED domains. Decoy receptors act by binding death ligands, and decoy adaptors/ caspases become incorporated into the DISC, thereby preventing induced proximity of the procaspases.

Summary of Section 14.3

1   The extrinsic apoptotic pathway involves activation of cell surface receptors by ligands that may be soluble or on the surface of other cells. The extrinsic pathway is involved in targeted killing and is essential, among other things, for lymphocyte development and regulation of lymphocyte numbers following an immune response.

2   Death receptors (e.g. Fas) on the target cells cluster upon binding of ligand (e.g. Fas ligand). The intracellular part of each death receptor includes a death domain that is also present in adaptor proteins, which are hence recruited to the activated receptor to form a complex known as the DISC. The adaptors also possess a death effector domain, shared by some initiator procaspases (e.g. procaspase 8). Thus initiator procaspases are recruited to the DISC and this proximity allows their autoactivation.

3   The activated initiator caspases may go on to directly cleave downstream effector caspases (e.g. procaspase 3) or Bid, which stimulates the intrinsic pathway.

4   Activation of the extrinsic pathway may be inhibited by decoy receptors, or decoy adaptors/caspases, which lack functional domains.

14.4 The intrinsic apoptotic pathway – 'stress and neglect'

14.4.1 Overview

The key organelles in the intrinsic apoptotic pathway are mitochondria (see Figure 14.8). Alterations in the permeability of the outer mitochondrial membrane result in the release of molecules from the mitochondrion into the cytosol. These molecules include cytochrome c, which plays an essential role in the formation of the second type of multimolecular scaffold needed for initiator caspase activation. (The first type, which is part of the extrinsic pathway, you will recall, is the DISC.) The other pro-apoptotic molecules that are released from mitochondria are described later in this section.

Activation of the intrinsic apoptotic pathway is crucially dependent upon the induction of a change in the permeability of the outer mitochondrial membrane. How this permeability change occurs is currently a controversial subject, which we cannot review in detail here. Some apoptotic agents, such as oxidative stress and calcium influx, are thought to directly induce formation of the so-called mitochondrial **permeability transition pore (PTP)**, a large, non-specific channel formed when transmembrane proteins from the inner and outer mitochondrial membrane come together. The exact composition of the PTP is currently uncertain.

Other mediators of a change in mitochondrial permeability are members of the **Bcl-2 family** (for B cell lymphoma 2, a type of cancer in which the expression of Bcl proteins is dysregulated), all of which play pivotal roles in the regulation of the intrinsic pathway of programmed cell death. There are both pro- and anti-apoptotic members of the Bcl-2 family of proteins. A change in the balance of these regulatory proteins in the outer mitochondrial membrane in favour of the pro-apoptotic proteins increases permeability by an as yet unconfirmed mechanism, which may or may not involve the PTP. This change in the proteins of the mitochondrial membrane occurs as a direct result of changes in the balance of these proteins in the cytosol, which can in turn be caused by many factors.

An event that changes the balance of pro- and anti-apoptotic proteins within the cell occurs as a result of a failure to repair DNA damage – which you first encountered in Chapters 8 and 9.

○ Which proteins are activated in response to different types of DNA damage?

● ATM is activated in response to double-strand breaks caused by radiation damage or occurring during replication. ATR is activated by UV damage or stalled replication forks (Section 9.8.7).

○ What is the result of the activation of the ATM and ATR proteins?

● ATM and ATR activate the downstream proteins Chk1 and Chk2. All four proteins influence the phosphorylation and stabilization of the p53 protein (Section 8.3.4).

Activated p53 goes on to have vital effects on the fate of the cell; it has been shown to affect transcription of a range of genes encoding regulators of apoptosis (see Figure 14.9). Results to date do not support the notion that p53 has a single mechanism of action common to all cells, but rather that the role of p53 in the regulation of apoptosis may vary according to cell type (Hickman *et al.*, 2002). Nevertheless, p53 function is of fundamental importance in determining whether a cell will die in response to signals indicating DNA damage. If apoptosis is not triggered, and the cell continues to divide, it is susceptible to further damage, which could lead to cancer (Chapter 19). We shall refer to the example of p53 during our description of the regulators of the intrinsic apoptotic pathway.

14.4.2 Mitochondrial release of cytochrome *c* triggers apoptosis

The change in mitochondrial membrane permeability induced by the pro-apoptotic Bcl-2 family members results in the release of several proteins, including cytochrome *c*, as you saw in Figure 14.8. Once released, cytochrome *c* interacts with a protein present in the cytosol, known as **Apaf-1** (apoptotic protease activating factor-1). Apaf-1 has a nucleotide binding domain and a CARD domain, but usually exists in an inactive or 'closed' form. Binding of cytochrome *c* and subsequent binding of ATP to the nucleotide binding domain changes the conformation of the protein to an 'open' form, exposing the CARD domain.

○ Which apoptotic procaspases could be recruited to the 'open' form of Apaf-1?

● Procaspase 9 and procaspase 2, both of which also possess a CARD domain (see Figure 14.10).

Procaspase 9 is recruited by homotypic interactions between its CARD domain and that of Apaf-1, forming a multiprotein complex, the apoptosome. Recent evidence from electron cryomicrography has shown that the apoptosome has a seven-spoked, wheel-shaped structure (as shown in Figure 14.13) comprising heptamers of activated Apaf-1 and procaspase 9.

Electron cryomicrography is a technique that allows the structural analysis of large molecules under the electron microscope.

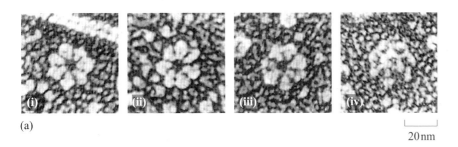

(a)

20 nm

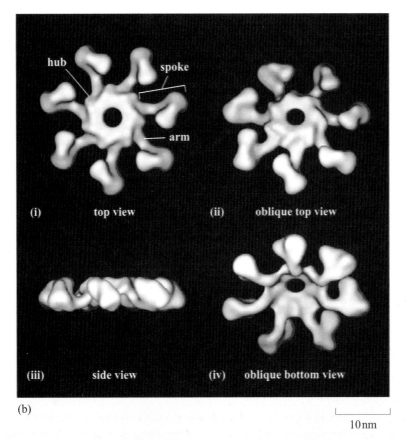

(b)

10 nm

Figure 14.13   (a) Images of the apoptosome obtained by electron cryomicrography. Three bottom views, (i)–(iii), and one top view (iv) are shown. (In (i), actin filaments – visible at the top of the image – were added as a control.) (b) Model for the structure of the apoptosome produced from analysis of electron cryomicrographs. The 3-D structure of the apoptosome is shown as a series of surface views, (i)–(iv). Features of interest are labelled – the central hub, the spoke, and the arm. (Source: Acehan et al., 2002)

Some enzymes only act when they are part of a multiprotein complex, or when complexed with cofactor(s); 'holoenzyme' is the term that is sometimes used to describe these active complexes. (Another example of a holoenzyme is RNA polymerase.)

Procaspase 9 is autoactivated. Cleavage is not necessary for its activation; rather its activity seems to be increased upon binding to Apaf-1, and it has been suggested that the complex effectively acts as a *holoenzyme*. The holoenzyme, in turn, cleaves and activates the effector caspase, caspase 3, leading to cleavage of cellular substrates and hence cell death, as shown in Figure 14.14.

The p53 protein has also been implicated in influencing this part of the intrinsic apoptotic pathway, as it stimulates transcription of the gene encoding Apaf-1.

◯ From Figure 14.6, which proteins in *C. elegans* and *D. melanogaster* are homologous to Apaf-1?

⬤ CED-4 in *C. elegans*, and DARK in *Drosophila*.

In mammals, additional homologues of Apaf–1 have been identified, which have CARD domains.

◯ What might be inferred from the discovery of these proteins?

⬤ There may be other, as yet unidentified, mechanisms for activation of initiator caspases.

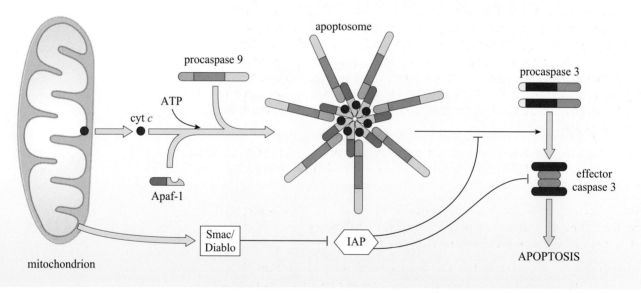

Figure 14.14   The intrinsic pathway of caspase activation involves the release of mitochondrial proteins, including cytochrome *c*, binding of cytochrome *c* and ATP to Apaf-1, which is thereby activated and recruits procaspase 9. Formation of the apoptosome results in autoactivation of procaspase 9, which activates caspase 3. In addition, Smac/Diablo is released from the mitochondrion and interacts with IAPs to relieve their inhibition of activated caspases 9 and 3 (discussed below).

14.4.3 The roles of other mitochondrial pro-apoptotic proteins

In addition to cytochrome *c*, damaged mitochondria release other pro-apoptotic proteins, which have a range of roles in promoting cell death. These are of two types; those that act downstream, to facilitate activation of the caspase cascade, and those that act independently of caspases.

An example of a protein that has a downstream action is **Smac** (second mitochondrial-derived activator of caspases) which is also known as **Diablo** (direct IAP-binding protein with low pI; you met the parameter pI in Figure 2.27). Smac/Diablo is normally located in the mitochondrial intermembrane space. Upon release, it acts to promote apoptosis by inhibiting the action of the IAP family. Smac/Diablo interacts with IAPs, and relieves their inhibition of caspase activity, as illustrated in Figure 14.14.

Two molecules that act independently of caspases are also released from mitochondria, but are not shown in Figure 14.14. One is **endonuclease G**, which translocates to the nucleus, where, as its name implies, it causes DNA degradation. Another is a protein named **apoptosis initiating factor (AIF)**. Evidence suggests that AIF may have several pro-apoptotic functions. In addition to translocating to the nucleus, where it induces DNA condensation and degradation in a caspase-independent manner, it has also been found to cause a dissipation of the mitochondrial membrane potential when injected into normal cells in culture. This effect on mitochondria is independent of Bcl-2 and caspase activity, suggesting that it may provide positive feedback in the intrinsic mitochondrial pathway.

Another protein that is also released from damaged mitochondria and acts in a similar way to Smac/Diablo is OMI (see Figure 14.6). Non-homologous proteins that have similar functions in *D. melanogaster*, and are also shown in Figure 14.6, are reaper, grim and Hid (see S204 Book 3, p. 472).

14.4.4 Bcl-2 proteins affect mitochondrial permeability

The pro-apoptotic protein Bid was introduced in Section 14.3.2. Bid is a member of the Bcl-2 family. In mammals, the Bcl-2 proteins are involved in regulating the release of pro-apoptotic proteins from mitochondria. At least 20 Bcl-2 family members are known in mammals. An anti-apoptotic member of this family is the Bcl-2 protein itself; pro-apoptotic family members include Bax, Bak and Bid (see Figures 14.6 and 14.15). It is the *balance* between the anti- and pro-apoptotic Bcl-2 family members within the cell that determines if the mitochondrial death pathway is activated.

Structurally, the Bcl-2 family can be divided into three groups, depending upon the number and type of Bcl-2 homology (BH) domains that they possess, as illustrated in Figure 14.15.

Anti-apoptotic family members have four BH domains, whereas pro-apoptotic members either have three BH domains (the **Bax family**) or a single BH3 domain (**BH3-only family**, e.g. Bid, Bim and Bad).

In 'normal' circumstances, Bcl-2 itself is an integral membrane protein; it associates with the cytosolic surface of the outer mitochondrial membrane, and also with the cytosolic surfaces of the nuclear membrane and the endoplasmic reticulum.

The pro-apoptotic Bax family and BH3-only proteins are usually cytosolic in 'normal' conditions; they are present at different sites within the cell (Figure 14.16) and exert their pro-apoptotic effects only after translocation to the mitochondrial membrane. Evidence suggests that, at the mitochondrion, the Bax family members form a complex and insert into the membrane. This insertion causes increased membrane permeability, which results in the release of cytochrome *c* and other pro-apoptotic proteins. The mechanism by which this change in membrane permeability occurs is currently the subject of intense study and remains controversial.

Figure 14.15
The Bcl-2 family of regulatory proteins. There are three subgroups of this family, some members of which are shown: (a) the anti-apoptotic Bcl-2 group, which includes the Bcl-2 protein itself; (b) the pro-apoptotic multidomain Bax group and (c) the pro-apoptotic BH3-only group. The grey bars show the hydrophobic domain present at the C-terminus of some of the family members. (Source: Kuwana and Newmeyer, 2003)

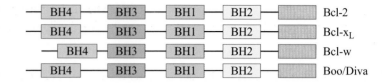

(a) anti-apoptotic

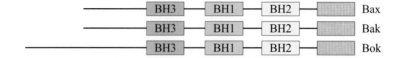

(b) pro-apoptotic multidomain – Bax family

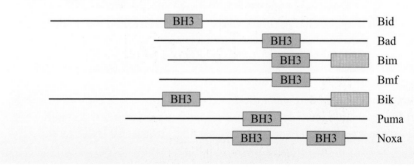

(c) pro-apoptotic BH3-only

Figure 14.16
BH3-only proteins are kept 'in check' by diverse means in normal cells. (a) Bim is 'tethered' by a dynein motor complex to microtubules. (b) Bmf is 'tethered' by a myosin V motor complex to the actin cytoskeleton. (c) Bid requires cleavage for its activation.

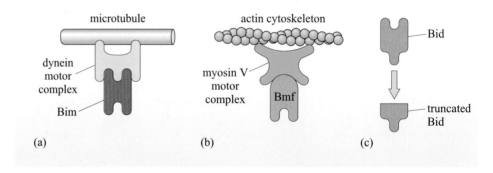

Similarly, the actions of the anti-apoptotic Bcl-2 proteins are not yet fully understood. Bcl-2 itself may act by binding to activated Bax, thereby preventing its action at the mitochondrial membrane. The BH3-only proteins appear to *facilitate* the action of the Bax proteins, but cannot initiate death if Bax proteins are absent – for example, in cells taken from knock-out mice that do not express Bak or Bax (see Chapter 9, Box 9.3; Joza *et al.*, 2002).

Interestingly, it seems as if the *C. elegans* homologue of Bcl-2, CED-9 (shown in Figure 14.6) acts in a different way, by sequestering the Apaf-1 homologue CED-4. In other words, CED-9 segregates CED-4 from the surrounding molecules (by binding to it), thus preventing its action. The BH3-only homologue EGL-1 is thought to displace CED-4 from CED-9, thereby freeing CED-4 to activate the caspase CED-3.

These two proposed modes of action of Bcl-2 family members are outlined in Figure 14.17.

Additional roles for Bcl-2 family members in mammals have also been presented. Clearly, much remains to be learnt about the actions of this family of regulatory proteins.

◯ Why might so many forms of the Bcl-2 family have evolved in mammals?

◼ Because they allow differential control of cell death in different cells, or in response to different stresses.

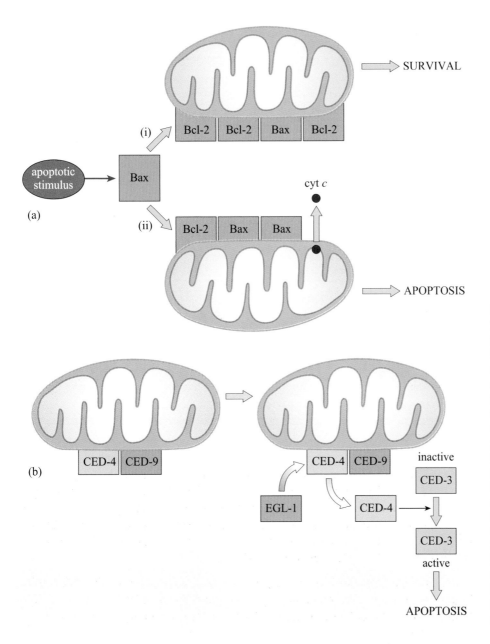

Figure 14.17
Two models for the actions of Bcl-2 family members. (a) In mammals, Bcl-2 itself may act by preventing Bax action at the mitochondrial membrane. Apoptotic signals stimulate translocation of Bax family members to the mitochondria. (i) If Bcl-2 family members predominate, membrane permeability is not compromised. (ii) If Bax family members predominate, membrane permeability is compromised, leading to loss of cytochrome *c* and other soluble mitochondrial proteins, and apoptosis results. (b) In *C. elegans*, the Bcl-2 homologue CED-9 binds the Apaf-1 homologue CED-4. Apoptosis is triggered by the BH3-only protein EGL-1, which displaces CED-4, which is in turn then able to activate the caspase CED-3.

○ From the description of Bcl-2 proteins in this chapter, is there any evidence that different proteins might be involved in the response to different stresses?

● The fact that some different Bcl-2 proteins are located in different places within the cell suggests that they may be in a position to respond to the different apoptotic triggers that occur at these sites.

There is also *direct* evidence for different pro-apoptotic Bcl-2 proteins being involved in triggering apoptosis following different pro-apoptotic stimuli. For example, Bid is activated following death receptor activation (Figure 14.12, step 6), Bmf has been shown to be activated after cells detach from their substratum (the surface upon which they are growing), while evidence suggests that Bim plays a role in apoptosis in response to UV irradiation, in the death of cells in the developing immune system, and also in the death of cells of the nervous system that are deprived of trophic support (Section 14.4.5 below).

The availability of Bcl-2 proteins is also regulated at the transcriptional level. One stimulus that results in altered transcription of Bcl-2 proteins is DNA damage, leading to p53 activation. Activated p53 has been shown to affect transcription of several Bcl-2 family members (see Figure 14.9). For example, it activates transcription of Bax, and represses transcription of the anti-apoptotic Bcl-2 protein itself.

○ How would the balance of pro and anti-apoptotic regulators in the cell be affected by increased transcription of Bax and reduced transcription of Bcl-2?

● These transcriptional changes would result in a shift in the balance in favour of apoptosis.

In some cells, it has been shown that p53 also activates transcription of the BH3-only proteins Puma and Noxa (Figure 14.15). So, p53 activation in response to DNA damage stimulates apoptosis via several routes, thereby facilitating removal of potentially tumorigenic cells.

The importance of the Bcl-2 family of proteins is clearly demonstrated by the observation that Bcl-2 itself, which is anti-apoptotic, is over-expressed in around 80% of B cell lymphomas, 90% of colorectal cancers and in many other cancers, too. This over-expression is associated with resistance of the tumour cells to chemotherapy and radiation treatment. Establishing how Bcl-2 family members function in different cell types is therefore of major importance, and the development of novel ligands that interact with different members of this family of regulatory proteins is a promising avenue for the therapeutic control of tumorigenesis.

We have described some of the stresses that result in activation of the intracellular apoptotic pathways; next we turn to how the shift in the balance between the life and death of the cell occurs because of 'neglect'.

14.4.5 Withdrawal of trophic support – 'death by neglect'

It has long been known that specific factors are needed for many types of cell to survive, and that the removal of these factors causes cell death. A well-characterized example is the developing nervous system. Developing neurons depend upon proteins known as **neurotrophic factors** for their survival.

Neurotrophic factors are small proteins that are secreted principally, but not exclusively, by target cells that the developing neurons will innervate, and they act via cell surface receptors. The first neurotrophic factor to be described was **nerve growth factor (NGF)**, but several different families of such factors have now been identified. Most neurotrophic factors act via tyrosine kinase receptors.

○ How are receptor tyrosine kinases activated following ligand binding?

● By dimerization, which leads to autophosphorylation (Chapter 13).

Binding of neurotrophic factors to receptor tyrosine kinases causes receptor dimerization and autophosphorylation, recruitment of adaptor proteins and activation of the PI 3-kinase and ERK pathways, described in Chapter 13 (Figures 13.31, 13.36 and 13.46). Signalling along these pathways activates two key downstream kinases, PKB (also known as Akt) and Rsk, respectively (Figure 14.18). These kinases have a number of anti-apoptotic effects, some of which are illustrated in Figure 14.18. Such effects include phosphorylation of the pro-apoptotic BH3-only protein, Bad, and of transcription factors of the Forkhead family, thereby inhibiting their pro-apoptotic actions. The pro-apoptotic effects of Bad have already been outlined. Forkhead proteins act by stimulating the transcription of pro-apoptotic genes, including that encoding the Fas ligand (Section 14.3.2) in the nervous system, and Bim in the immune system.

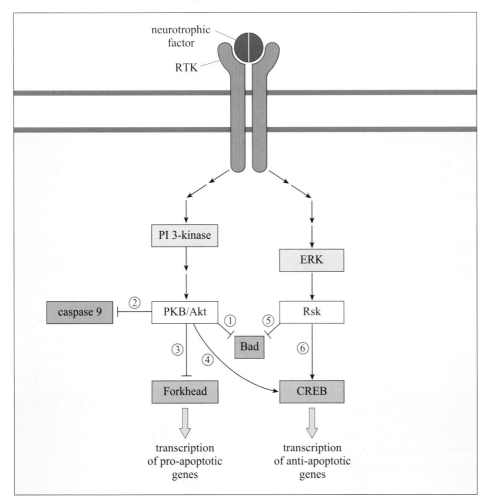

Figure 14.18
Summary of the pathways by which trophic factors promote cell survival. Binding of neurotrophic factors to receptor tyrosine kinases (RTK) results in activation of the PI 3-kinase and the ERK pathways. The small arrows denote the sequential activation of intermediates (not shown) in the two signalling pathways. Note that although some RTKs activate PI 3-kinase directly, neurotrophic factor receptors activate this kinase via adaptors (not shown). Activated PI 3-kinase activates PKB/Akt, which exerts a number of anti-apoptotic actions by phosphorylation of down-stream proteins: (1) it phosphorylates Bad, thereby promoting Bad's sequestration by an adaptor protein (not shown); (2) it phosphorylates and thereby inhibits caspase 9 (in humans); (3) it phosphorylates and thereby inhibits members of the Forkhead family of transcription factors, which stimulate transcription of pro-apoptotic genes; and (4) it phosphorylates and thereby activates the transcription factor CREB, which stimulates transcription of anti-apoptotic genes. Activated ERK activates Rsk, which has similar effects to those of Akt on Bad (5) and CREB (6).

Removal of neurotrophic factors therefore results in reduction or cessation of signal transduction along these pathways and so shifts the balance of many apoptotic regulators in favour of cell death.

Two other examples of 'death by neglect' occur in the mammalian immune system: the death of lymphocytes that do not develop appropriate antigen receptors during development, and loss of cytokine support to activated lymphocytes after an immune response.

Activation of programmed cell death by withdrawal of signals from other cells occurs when some types of cell are separated from their neighbours – for example, when cells from a tissue are dispersed and grown in culture at a low density. When grown in a culture medium containing only nutrients, the cells die, exhibiting the typical morphology of cells undergoing apoptosis. Addition of specific trophic factors to the culture medium prevents this cell death. This phenomenon, which has been described for many cell types, prompted Jacobson and colleagues (1997) to introduce the concept that there is a 'society of cells', and that most cells are dependent upon their neighbours for trophic support.

To conclude, in this chapter we have provided an overview of cell death, focusing on apoptosis. Having studied the chapter, you should be aware of some of the current issues and controversies in this exciting area.

Reading scientific literature 3

Go to the Study Skills file: *Reading scientific literature 3*. The paper provided describes recent research in an aspect of cell death.

Summary of Section 14.4

1   The intrinsic apoptotic pathway involves mitochondria. It is activated in response to cellular stresses, including DNA damage, oxidative stress and the build-up of misfolded proteins.

2   Alterations in mitochondrial membrane permeability caused either directly, by oxidative stress or influx of calcium ions, or indirectly, by a change in the balance in favour of pro-apoptotic members of the Bcl-2 family, allow release of pro-apoptotic proteins from the mitochondrion into the cytosol.

3   Released cytochrome c binds to the adaptor protein Apaf-1, which possesses a CARD domain. Subsequent binding of ATP changes the conformation of the adaptor, exposing the CARD domain, and allowing formation of a heptamer, known as the apoptosome, to which procaspase 9 (which also possesses a CARD domain) can bind.

4   Other pro-apoptotic proteins released from mitochondria include: Smac/Diablo, which removes the inhibitory action of the IAPs; and endonuclease G and apoptosis initiating factor (AIF), which act – in a caspase-independent manner – by fragmenting nuclear DNA.

5   Members of the Bcl-2 family are key regulators of mitochondrial permeability. The anti-apoptotic members include Bcl-2 protein itself, which is located in the mitochondrial (and also ER and nuclear) membrane. Pro-apoptotic members include Bax and the BH3-only proteins such as Bid and Bim, which are normally cytosolic, and are kept in check by a range of mechanisms. When the level of free pro-apoptotic family members increases, or transcription of their genes is activated, e.g. that of the BH3-only protein Noxa in response to DNA damage, they translocate to the mitochondrial membrane and cause an increase in permeability by an as yet unconfirmed mechanism.

6   Signalling along pathways stimulated by some cytokines and trophic factors such as nerve growth factor, promotes cell survival by inhibiting transcription of pro-apoptotic genes. Removal of these factors therefore leads to cell death, by 'neglect'.

Learning outcomes for Chapter 14

When you have studied this chapter, you should be able to:

14.1   Define and use each of the terms printed in **bold** in the text.

14.2   Give examples of the importance of cell death in development and in tissue homeostasis.

14.3   Outline the main structural features/changes exhibited by dying cells, and how dying cells can be identified.

14.4   Differentiate between apoptosis, necrotic cell death and autophagic cell death.

14.5   Describe the pathways that result in caspase activation, giving examples of events that trigger activation of each pathway.

14.6   Describe the structures and roles of initiator and effector caspases and outline how they are activated.

14.7   Explain the roles of mitochondrial proteins in apoptosis.

14.8   Give examples of how the pathways to apoptosis are inhibited.

14.9   Give an account of the Bcl-2 family of proteins and outline their roles in the regulation of cell death.

14.10 Critically review or summarize findings from selected primary literature on the above topics.

Questions for Chapter 14

Question 14.1

You are studying a strain of mice that appears to be developing abnormally. You suspect that cell death is abnormal in these mice; it seems that too few neurons are present in the spinal cord. As a first step in investigating the nature of the defect, you examine tissue by electron microscopy, at the time when the cell numbers undergo a rapid decline. What features would make you suspect that apoptosis rather than autophagic cell death was the primary cause of the cell loss?

Question 14.2

Transgenic animals deficient in the expression of various apoptotic proteins have been used to determine the importance of the different components of the death signalling pathways. Mice deficient in caspase 8 die at around day 12–13 of gestation (mice are normally born after 19–20 days gestation). Would you expect cells taken from these caspase-deficient early embryos (i.e. before 12–13 days gestation) and grown in cell culture to be sensitive or insensitive to (a) tumour necrosis factor (TNF), and (b) UV irradiation? Explain your answers.

Question 14.3

What caspase inhibitors could you use to determine if caspase 8 or caspase 9 were involved in initiation of apoptosis in the cells described in Question 14.1? Do you foresee any possible problems with this approach? What other method could you use to determine which initiator caspases were involved?

Question 14.4

Which mitochondrial proteins promote apoptosis directly, and which do so indirectly? How do these proteins exert their effects?

Question 14.5

A new member of the Bcl-2 family has been isolated. What sequence properties would you expect this protein to exhibit if it were a pro-apoptotic family member? How might its action be prevented in a healthy cell?

References

Acehan, D., Jiang, X., Morgan, D. G., Heuser, J. E., and Wang, X. (2002) Three-dimensional structure of the apoptosome: implications for assembly, procaspase-9 binding, and activation, *Molecular Cell*, **9**, pp. 423–432.

Boatright, K. M. and Salvesen, G. S (2003) Mechanisms of caspase activation, *Current Opinion in Cell Biology*, **15**, pp. 1–7.

Ditzel, M. and Meier, P. (2002) IAP degradation: decisive blow or altruistic sacrifice?, *Trends in Cell Biology*, **10**, pp. 449–452.

Earnshaw, W. C., Martins, L. M. and Kaufmann, S. H. (1999) Mammalian caspases: structure, activation, substrates, and functions during apoptosis, *Annual Review of Biochemistry*, **68**, pp. 383–424.

Ellis, H. M. and Horvitz, H. R. (1986) Genetic control of programmed cell death in the nematode *C. elegans*, *Cell*, **44**, pp. 817–829.

Hickman, E. S., Moroni, M. C. and Helin, K. (2002) The role of p53 and pRb in apoptosis and cancer, *Current Opinion in Genetics and Development*, **12**, pp. 60–66.

Jacobson, M. D., Wei, M. and Raff, M. C. (1997) Programmed cell death in animal development, *Cell*, **88**(3), pp. 347–354.

Joza, N., Kroemer, G. and Penninger, J. M. (2002) Genetic analysis of the mammalian cell death machinery, *Trends in Genetics*, **18**(3), pp. 142–149.

Kerr, J. F. R., Wyllie, A. H. and Currie, A. R. (1972) Apoptosis: a basic biological phenomenon with wide-ranging implications in tissue kinetics, *British Journal of Cancer*, **26**, pp. 239–257.

Kuwana, T. and Newmeyer, D. (2003) Bcl-2-family proteins and the role of mitochondria in apoptosis, *Current Opinion in Cell Biology*, **15**, pp. 1–9.

Lockshin, R. A. and Zakeri, Z. (2002) Caspase-independent cell deaths, *Current Opinion in Cell Biology*, **14**, pp. 727–733.

Shi, Y. (2002) Mechanisms of caspase activation and inhibition during apoptosis, *Molecular Cell*, **9**, pp. 459–470.

Troy, C. M., Rabacchi, S. A., Hohl, J. B., Angelastro, J. M., Greene, L. A. and Shelanski, M. L. (2001) Death in the balance: alternative participation of the caspase-2 and -9 pathways in neuronal death induced by nerve growth factor deprivation, *Journal of Neuroscience*, **21**, pp. 5007–5016.

Further sources

Adams, J. M. and Cory, S. (2002) Apoptosomes: engines for caspase activation, *Current Opinion in Cell Biology*, **14**, pp. 715–720.

Cory, S. and Adams, J. M. (2002) The Bcl-2 family: regulators of the cellular life-or-death switch, *Nature Reviews: Cancer*, **2**, pp. 647–656.

ANSWERS TO QUESTIONS

Question 12.1

1   Binding of transferrin to the transferrin receptor.

2   Deformation of the membrane to form a pit (epsin).

3   Clustering of the receptor and other membrane components to the pit (v-SNARE, ARF, Rab5a).

4   Assembly of the coat components of a vesicle (clathrin, AP2, GGA-protein).

5   Scission of the vesicle (dynamin).

6   Recruitment of a molecular motor and movement of the coated vesicle towards the endosome and its uncoating (kinesin, tubulin, Rab5A).

7   Capture of the vesicle by the endosomal membrane and membrane fusion (v-SNARE, t-SNARE).

8   Release of transferrin from its receptor in the acidic endosome.

Question 12.2

Proteins are synthesized in the ER, and transferred to the Golgi network for post-translational modification (glycosylation, cleavage, etc.). Transport vesicles leave the *trans* Golgi to assemble as immature secretory vesicles, which then mature into secretory vesicles.

Release of the vesicles is typically triggered by a rise in intracellular $[Ca^{2+}]$, caused by the opening of voltage-gated or ligand-gated Ca^{2+} channels. CAM kinases activated by the rise in $[Ca^{2+}]$ phosphorylate and activate molecules in the membrane of the secretory vesicle and/or the plasma membrane, causing the membranes to fuse.

Question 12.3

If the plus end is capped with a capping protein and the concentration of actin-ATP is above the critical threshold, then polymerization at the minus end is faster than depolymerization.

Question 12.4

These drugs inhibit the assembly of new microtubules from the pool of tubulin heterodimers. Microtubule assembly is required to form mitotic spindles, so the drugs affect dividing cells. In many non-dividing cells the microtubules are capped and relatively stable, so the drug affects these cells to a lesser degree.

Question 12.5

As KDEL is the ER targeting signal peptide, one would expect the modified enzyme to be recycled to the ER, and not to be secreted.

Question 12.6

They both have motor domains, act as ATPases, and interact with microtubules.

Dyneins move to the minus end of microtubules, whereas almost all kinesins move to the plus end.

Question 13.1

Second messengers are small, water-soluble mediators, which diffuse rapidly through the cytoplasm (for example, Ca^{2+} ions) or located on the cytoplasmic leaflet of the plasma membrane via a lipid group (such as $PI(3,4,5)P_3$), serving to broadcast and amplify a signal throughout a cell.

Question 13.2

Firstly, signalling proteins often employ the specific binding capability of proteins, in order to create temporary binding sites between signalling proteins. An example of this would be SH2 domains, which bind to specific amino acid sequences containing a phosphotyrosine residue.

Secondly, signalling proteins are often able to adopt an alternative conformation when bound to a ligand or another protein, thus enabling them to switch from an inactive to an active signalling state. An example of this are the receptor tyrosine kinases.

Question 13.3

Ligands binding to intracellular receptors must be able to cross the plasma membrane, in other words be lipid-soluble, such as steroid hormones, or small and diffusible molecules such as NO, in contrast to peptide growth factors, for example, which are not lipid-soluble and have transmembrane cell-surface receptors.

Question 13.4

Acetylcholine activates ion-channel receptors at skeletal muscle motor end-plates, binding within the channel pore. Nicotine is an antagonist. In cardiac muscle, the ACh receptors are G protein-coupled receptors, whose agonists include muscarine. Acetylcholine has a flexible structure, facilitating binding to the two different receptors, whereas its more specific agonists (and antagonists) are more rigid, preventing them from binding to the alternate class of receptor.

Question 13.5

Ligand binding may induce the heterodimerization or oligomerization of some recruiter receptors with receptor tyrosine kinases, which act as co-receptors. The receptor tyrosine kinase becomes activated and initiates intracellular signal transduction cascades.

Question 13.6

Calmodulin has four EF hands (calcium-ion binding sites), and at least two of them need to be occupied by calcium for the protein to adopt an active conformation.

Question 13.7

Proteins containing SH2 domains, which bind to phosphotyrosines on activated tyrosine kinase receptors, such as PI 3-kinase, GAP, phospholipase C or Grb-2.

Proteins with PH domains that bind phosphorylated inositol phospholipids, such as PLC and PKB.

Proteins such as Sos that are brought to the membrane via adaptors. Raf is recruited to the membrane by Ras.

Question 13.8

It would be an adaptor protein, able to bring a protein with a proline-rich domain (via its SH3 domain) into the vicinity of a protein with a phosphotyrosine (via its SH2 domain).

Question 13.9

See Figure 13.50.

Question 14.1

Features of the tissue that would indicate apoptosis rather than autophagic cell death are as follows:

- very few abnormal cells;
- no cells with large numbers of lysosomes or autophagic vacuoles;
- a small number of cells with large condensations of chromatin.

Question 14.2

Caspase 8 initiates the extrinsic apoptotic pathway. Cells from mouse embryos that lack caspase 8 would therefore be expected to be defective in this pathway. Thus one would expect these cells to be (a) insensitive, and thus unaffected by death ligands such as TNF, and (b) sensitive to triggers of the intrinsic pathway, such as UV irradiation, which can activate the intrinsic pathway by its actions on DNA, for example.

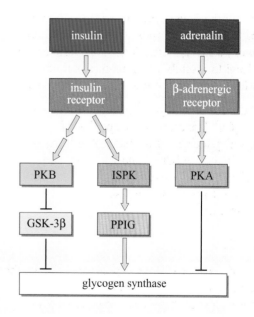

Figure 13.50   Schematic diagram of insulin and adrenalin signal transduction pathways leading to regulation of glycogen synthase activity.

Question 14.3

Caspase 8 would be inhibited by peptide inhibitors containing the sequence IETD or LETD coupled to (e.g.) FMK (see Box 14.1), but caspase 9 would not. Caspase 9 would be inhibited by a peptide with the sequence LEHD, whereas caspase 8 would not. One possible problem would be the specificity of this approach, as these sequences are very similar. An alternative or, better still, additional approach would be to determine which activated caspases could be detected, by immunohistochemical labelling and/or Western blot analysis.

Question 14.4

Cytochrome *c* promotes apoptosis directly, by binding with Apaf-1, allowing formation of the apoptosome, and thus activation of caspase 9. Endonuclease G and AIF also act directly, by causing DNA degradation; AIF also has an indirect action, increasing the permeability of mitochondria. Smac/Diablo has an indirect action, interacting with apoptotic inhibitors of the IAP family, and so removing their inhibition.

Question 14.5

Pro-apoptotic Bcl-2 family members can have either three BH domains, one each of BH1, 2 and 3 (the multidomain Bax family), or a single BH3 domain (BH3-only proteins). The translocation of Bax family pro-apoptotic proteins to the mitochondrion is often inhibited by their association with cellular structures such as the cytoskeleton or with adaptor proteins, or their expression may be transcriptionally controlled. BH3-only proteins may be present in an inactive form (zymogen), their activation requiring proteolytic cleavage.

ACKNOWLEDGEMENTS

Every effort has been made to contact copyright holders. If any have been inadvertently overlooked, the publishers will be pleased to make the necessary arrangements at the first opportunity. Grateful acknowledgement is made to the following sources for permission to reproduce material within this book.

Cover image: Science Photo Library.

Chapter 12

Figures 12.4, 12.8 Alberts, B. *et al.* (2002) *Molecular Biology of the Cell*, 4th edn, Garland Science, reproduced with permission of Routledge/Taylor and Francis Books, Inc.; *Figures 12.15, 12.16, 12.17a, b, 12.21* Taken from www.biozentrum.unibas.ch/Teaching/Lectures/Pieters/Vesicular_Transport.pdf; *Figure 12.17c* Alberts, B. *et al.* (2002) *Molecular Biology of the Cell*, 3rd edn, Garland Publishing Inc., Chapter 13, 'Vesicular traffic in the secretory and endocytic pathways', reprinted by permission of Hodder Headlines plc; *Figure 12.18* Perry, M. M. and Gilbert, A. B. (1979) 'Yolk transport in the ovarian follicle of the hen…', *Journal of Cell Science*, **39**, pp. 257–272, Company of Biologists Limited; *Figure 12.19* Boman, A. L. (2001) 'GCA proteins: new players in the sorting game', *Journal of Cell Science*, **114**, pp. 3413–3418, Company of Biologists Limited; *Figure 12.20* Reprinted from De Camilli, P. *et al.* (1995) 'The function of dynamin in endocytosis', *Current Opinion in Neurobiology*, **5**, p. 562, copyright © 1995, with permission from Elsevier; *Figure 12.22* Courtesy of Lelio Orci; *Figure 12.35* Conner, S. D. and Schmid, S. L. (2003) 'Regulated portals of entry into the cell', *Nature*, **422**, 6 March 2003, copyright © Nature Publishing Group; *Figures 12.36, 12.39* Riezman, H. (2002) 'The ubiquitin connection', Nature, **416**, 28 March 2002, copyright © Nature Publishing Group; *Figure 12.37* Reprinted from Roitt, I. M. (1993) 'Fusing granule discharges contents into the phagocytic vacuole', in *Essential Immunobiology*, 3rd edn, by permission of the publisher, Mosby; *Figure 12.41* Reprinted from Roitt, I. M. *et al.* (2001) *Immunology*, 6th edn, p. 111, Fig. 6.13, Mosby Inc., with permission from Elsevier; *Figure 12.43* Kavalali, E. T. (2002) 'SNARE interactions in membrane trafficking: a perspective from mammalian central synapses', *BioEssays*, **24**(10), copyright © 2002, used by permission of Wiley-Liss Inc., a subsidiary of John Wiley and Sons Inc.; *Figure 12.45* Roitt, I., Brostoff, J. and Male, D. (2001) *Immunobiology*, 6th edn, Mosby, an imprint of Elsevier Science Limited; *Tables 12.2, 12.5* Alberts, B. *et al.* (2002) *Molecular Biology of the Cell*, 4th edn, Garland Science, reproduced with permission of Routledge/Taylor and Francis Books, Inc.

Chapter 13

Figure 13.1 Copyright © Michael Snyder; *Figures 13.2, 13.6, 13.11, 13.12, 13.23, 13.25, 13.27, 13.30a, b, c, 13.32, 13.41, 13.44, 13.46* Alberts, B. *et al.* (2002) *Molecular Biology of the Cell*, 4th edn, Garland Science, reproduced with permission of Routledge/Taylor and Francis Books, Inc.; *Figure 13.9* Jhun, B. H. (1995) 'The MATK tyrosine kinase interacts in a specific and SH2-dependant manner with c-Kit', *Journal of Biological Chemistry*, **270**(16), The American Society for Biochemistry and Molecular Biology; *Figure 13.21b, c, d* Courtesy of Nigel Unwin, MRC Labroratory of Molecular Biology, Cambridge;

INDEX

Note: Entries in **bold** are key terms. Page numbers referring to information that is given only in a figure or caption or a table are printed in *italics*.

A

Acanthamoeba, myosin 6

acetylcholine 90–2
    binding sites *95, 96*
    degradation 102
    receptors 71, *75*
    regeneration 33

ACh receptors *see* cholinergic receptors

actin
    cross-linking *5*
    degradation in apoptosis *148*
    endocytosis 49
    polymerization and depolymerization 2–6

action potential, in vesicle release 56–7, 58

acute toxic insults 142–3

acylation 42

adaptor proteins (AP) *21,* **23**, 77
    binding domains *85*
    in the Fas pathway 161, *162*
    in vesicle recovery 32

adenylyl cyclase *108,* **114**

ADP
    in actin polymerization 3–4
    GTP binding *26*
    in kinesins *44*
    ribosylation factor *21,* 23

adrenalin 90, 91, *93, 94*
    increase in cell cAMP levels 114
    binding to 7TM receptor *96*
    in glucose metabolism 135–7

adrenergic receptors 91, *93,* 94, 135, *136, 137*

Agalychnis callidryas (red-eyed tree frog), metamorphosis *141*

agonists 90–4

Akt 110, 171
    see also protein kinase B (PKB)

allosteric regulation 77

Alzheimer's disease 7–8

annexin V 148

antagonists 90–4

anti-apoptotic proteins **150**, 167, *168*

antibodies *see* monoclonal antibodies

antigen presentation 54–5, 67
    CD45 and Lck 129

antigen processing 54–5

Apaf-1 164–6

apical domains 13–14

apolipoproteins 51

apoptosis 143
    caspase-mediated 150–5
    conserved pathways 149–50
    in development and tissue maintenance 144–6
    DNA fragmentation 147
    extrinsic pathway 160–3
    inhibitors 158–9
    intrinsic pathway 163–72
    phagocytosis of apoptotic cells 52, *53*
    see also cell death

apoptosis initiating factor (AIF) 167

apoptosome 152, *165, 166*

apotransferrin 16, *17*

ARF (ADP ribosylation factor) *21,* 23
    GTP binding *26*

arrestin 103

asparagine 39, *40*

aspartate residues 155, 159

astrocytes *8,* 9

ATP
    in actin polymerization 3–4
    hydrolysis *33*
    and kinesin motor cycle *44,* 45
    roles 70

ATP cap 4

atropine 91, *92*

autocrine signalling *68,* **69**

autophagic cell death 143–4, *145*

autophagic vacuoles 144, *145*

autophagy 53

autophosphorylation 81, *82, 99,* **100**, *101*